RESISTANCE
OF
MATERIALS

RESISTANCE

OF

MATERIALS

FRED B. SEELY *Professor of Theoretical and Applied Mechanics, Emeritus*

JAMES O. SMITH *Professor of Theoretical and Applied Mechanics*

University of Illinois

Fourth Edition

NEW YORK · JOHN WILEY & SONS, INC.

LONDON · CHAPMAN & HALL, LIMITED

Library of Congress Catalog Card Number: 56–6500

PRINTED IN THE UNITED STATES OF AMERICA

Preface

Aim in Developing Subject. During the thirty years that have elapsed since the first edition of this book appeared, many new engineering problems in the field of resistance of materials (or strength of materials or mechanics of materials, as it is often called) have arisen; likewise, much analytical and experimental research and engineering experience have brought out new and valuable information. As a result of this situation, changes in the topics treated in the subject and in the methods of presentation of the topics have been introduced over the years.

We believe, however, that there is a need at present for a more radical change in the usual approach to the subject and in the selection and organization of the topics presented in the book, with the aim of making the theory of resistance of materials more self-sufficient or self-contained and of developing more rational methods of analyses and of design that are adequate to treat a wider range of conditions met in engineering practice.

The fourth edition of the book, therefore, is essentially a new book; although, like the previous editions, it is intended for use as a first (undergraduate) course for engineering students and for the younger engineers in practice who may desire to give further study to the subject on their own initiative.

For the reader, and especially for the teacher, who examines this book it may be desirable to explain the general objectives and the approach to the subject which guided the authors in preparing this edition. In the first place, it should be realized that the subject of resistance of materials is highly important in the practice of certain phases of engineering; it deals with actual engineering conditions. Therefore, it is the purpose of this treatment of the subject to develop a rational method or theory that is readily applicable to these conditions. But the conditions in practice change as new problems arise, and hence the theories and methods used in the treatment of the subject should be expected to change also. For, in general, theory follows (rather than precedes) practice; in fact, practice usually gives rise to the need for more adequate theories and methods.

It should be clear, therefore, that the theory of resistance of materials is always in a state of flux. It is likewise evident that the theory or method used in the treatment of the subject must involve a combination of (1) a knowledge of the basic laws of mechanics (mainly statics) and (2) a knowledge, gained from experimental investigations and from experience or practice, of the deformational behavior of members of various shapes when subjected to various types of loading, and also a knowledge of the internal structural response or action of various engineering materials which accompanies the deformational behavior of the member as a whole.

The Problem Defined. The main problem or situation dealt with in the theory of resistance of materials may be described more specifically as follows. A physical body, called a member, forms part of a structure, machine, or apparatus, the main purpose of the member being to resist external forces, called loads, that act on it. The loads cause the member to deform (change its dimensions) and create internal forces (stresses) in the member. The deformation may be either elastic or permanent (inelastic or plastic) or partly each type of deformation. Either the deformation or the stress in the member may become sufficiently large to cause the member to cease to function satisfactorily in resisting the load.

The problem, therefore, consists of three main parts: namely, to derive relationships (1) between the loads and deformations, (2) between the loads and stresses, and, in addition (3) to use these relationships, in conjunction with the observed behavior of the member and the properties of the material, to introduce the student to a rational method for determining the appropriate dimensions of the member: that is, for the design of the member.

In the usual or traditional treatment of the subject of resistance of materials, the main emphasis is placed on parts 1 and 2. Furthermore, the member is assumed to act only elastically; whereas, many members, especially members made of so-called ductile material and subjected to static loads, serve their function satisfactorily as load-resisting members when subjected to some inelastic deformation. There is, therefore, a need for a broader attack on the problem which involves inelastic behavior as well as elastic behavior of a member. Especially, there is a need for a more rational approach to the concept of safety of a member or structure and of the factor of safety; this step also requires a consideration of the influence of inelastic behavior of the member. For example, the load-carrying capacity of many statically loaded members made of ductile metal lies between two limiting values: namely, the load at which inelastic strain *begins* in the most-stressed fibers (called the elastic-limit load), and that at which one (or more) whole sections of the member becomes fully plastic (called the fully plastic load).

Need for Broader Treatment of Subject. As previously noted, we believe that at present there is a real need for a treatment of the subject of resistance of materials for undergraduate engineering students that encompasses a larger, more comprehensive, and rational approach to engineering problems involving load-resisting members. This has been accomplished in the present edition by giving emphasis to all three parts of the main problem as outlined in the foregoing paragraphs, and by including inelastic behavior of the member, in addition to the elastic behavior, in the treatment of the problem in each chapter, especially in Part I. It should be understood, however, that the purpose of introducing the student to a rational approach to design is not to develop design methods (that purpose is reserved for later courses in the curricula of various branches of engineering), but merely to point out the basic concepts on which rational design procedures can be developed in the later courses.

This modern approach and forward step has been made possible by use of the information made available from practice and from theoretical and experimental investigations during recent years. The methods developed for the treatment of the general problem in resistance of materials (including the influence of inelastic behavior) make a self-contained theory with which to tackle problems that defy the processes of the mathematical theories of elasticity and plasticity. It is possible, therefore, to cover a wider range of important engineering conditions.

This result arises from the fact that, in the method or theory of resistance of materials, greater freedom of assumption and approximation is permitted, but these assumptions are not arbitrarily made; they are the outcome of experience and of careful experimental investigations in which the actual engineering conditions are simulated as nearly as feasible. This fact is one strong justification for an effective laboratory course in connection with the study of resistance of materials;

direct observation by the student of the deformational response or behavior of members subjected to loads is important in the student's understanding of the theory of resistance of materials.

The emphasis given to inelastic behavior of the member represents a rather radical change in the usual treatment of the subject, and perhaps some teachers may feel that they would prefer to treat only the elastic behavior of members mainly for two reasons: namely (1) because working values of stresses, deflections, loads, etc., are usually such that only elastic behavior of the member *as a whole* seems to be involved, and (2) because the presentation of inelastic behavior may appear to be too advanced and confusing for the beginning student, especially if the inelastic treatment is introduced in Chapter I.

The first of these reasons has resulted in the formulation and use of some design procedures that are irrational and undesirable because the safety of the member cannot be determined explicitly, whereas the use of analysis of inelastic behavior, as presented in this edition, leads to more rational design procedures because the safety of the member can be more explicitly determined.

In commenting on the second of the foregoing reasons for treating only the elastic behavior, we offer the following thoughts. First, experience indicates that ideas and procedures that are relatively new or unfamiliar to the instructor are likely to appear to him to be advanced for the student. We have found, in presenting this material to beginning students, that there has been no indication that this material is beyond their capacities. The student has no reason to feel that this part of the subject is more advanced than any other part. Moreover, none of the material in this book is any more difficult than that involved in the usual courses in the calculus which are commonly given in the sophomore year.

Likewise, experience in teaching these ideas indicates that they do not confuse the student, but, on the other hand, they help clarify certain phases of the subject which, as usually presented, are not adequately explained. Moreover, these ideas should be made a basic part of the subject and be introduced and used in the first chapter as well as in later chapters. For example, in no other way can we justify the long-standing simple approach to riveted joints in which the load is assumed to be distributed uniformly to the rivets; this assumption is shown to lead to the correct theoretical solution when inelastic action is introduced in the analysis.

Furthermore, without the development of the theory of inelastic action in Chapter I and other early chapters, the use of these ideas in subsequent chapters would not be feasible. For example, the modern treatment of buckling of columns (Chap. VI), which has done much to clarify the former confused treatment of this topic, would not be effective if the theory of inelastic behavior had not been introduced earlier in the book.

The second thought is that, in the general approach to the teaching of this subject, it should be realized that one of the conditions for effective learning and intellectual growth of the student is that he shall learn facts in their relationship to a relatively broad problem and to the over-all objectives of the study of the subject. If this condition is satisfied, the learner must continually attempt to stretch his imagination in order to grasp the broad problem and over-all objectives. Likewise, effective teaching requires that the instructor shall stimulate and encourage the student in practicing this process of learning and of intellectual growth. Under such conditions, the development of the student's capacity to comprehend and interpret the subject is not a difficult problem. We must avoid handicapping our engineering students by dealing with only the elastic aspects of this subject.

Plan of Book. The organization of the material presented in this book is such that there is a large degree of freedom in selecting topics to meet the needs for courses of different lengths and of different contents and emphases.

In this fourth edition, as in previous editions, the book is divided in two parts. Part I consists of the more basic topics that usually are included in the subject, and Part II consists of additional topics, but not necessarily more advanced ones, although several of the topics lie just beyond those discussed in Part I.

For example, in Chapter XIII in Part II is discussed the double-integration method for determining the elastic deflection of beams. And in Chapter XIV is presented the conjugate-beam method for accomplishing the same result. These two methods are no more advanced than the moment-area method used in Part I (Chap. IV) for determining the deflection of beams. But some instructors may prefer one of the two methods given in Chapters XIII and XIV to the moment-area method. To make this choice possible without increasing the size of Part I, it was thought best to place the discussion of the two additional methods in Part II.

Likewise, in Part II, Chapter XV on continuous (statically indeterminate) beams is no more advanced than Chapter VII in Part I on statically indeterminate members in general. The whole treatment of statically indeterminate members, perhaps, might well have been located in Part II, since this topic is more akin to structural analysis than to resistance of materials, although it drives home to the student's mind one important use of the deflection of beams. But, since the treatment of continuous beams is frequently given in a course on resistance of materials, it was made available in a short chapter in Part II. This chapter may be assigned after the student has completed Chapter IV on deflections of beams, whether or not Chapter VII (in Part I) on the general method of handling statically indeterminate members is assigned in the course.

Flexibility in selecting topics is also provided by virtue of the fact that in each of the early chapters the discussion is presented in three rather distinct sections: namely, (1) analysis of the elastic behavior of the member, (2) analysis of inelastic behavior, and (3) introduction to the method used in the design of the member. For example, after Chapter I has been carefully studied, the design sections of later chapters could be omitted if time did not permit the full treatment in each chapter. Other adjustments may readily be made to fit special circumstances without the continuity of thought being destroyed.

A large number of new problems and new figures have been added, many of which emphasize actual physical conditions met in engineering practice.

Acknowledgments. A textbook is not likely to fill satisfactorily a real need unless the author receives the constructive criticisms of the users of the book, including students, instructors, and practicing engineers. Such constructive criticisms and comments on the previous editions of this book have been very valuable in the preparation of this fourth edition. For this help we are deeply grateful. Likewise, we are especially indebted to a number of our colleagues whose interest and valuable suggestions have contributed greatly to the development of the subject as presented in this fourth edition.

FRED B. SEELY
JAMES O. SMITH

February 1956

Contents

§ 3   Inelastic Stresses in Beams

§ 4   Design of Beam for Static Strength

Chapter IV.   Deflection of Beams

Chapter V.   Combined Axial Tensile and Bending Loads

§ 1   Elastic Behavior

§ 2   Inelastic Behavior

Chapter VI.   Buckling Load.   Instability.   Columns.

§ 1   Elastic Buckling

§ 2   Inelastic Buckling

CONTENTS

Part I

ELEMENTARY TOPICS

Chapter I

RELATION AMONG LOADS, STRESSES, AND DEFORMATIONS

PRELIMINARY CONCEPTS

1. Introduction. Engineering machines or structures, such as automobiles, airplanes, bridges, buildings, electric generators, and steam turbines, are usually constructed by connecting or assembling various bodies, called parts or members, so that the structure, assemblage, or machine performs a given function. In many such structures the main function of a member is to resist the external forces, called loads, that are applied to it. Such members are frequently called load-resisting members, for, although they may have other purposes in the structure, the main requirement that they must satisfy is that they shall resist the loads without causing the structure to cease to function satisfactorily.

The behavior or response that is most likely to cause the member to cease to function satisfactorily as it resists the loads consists either of (a) the development of large internal forces required to hold in equilibrium the loads often leading to fracture of the member, or (b) excessive deformation, leading to permanent distortion of the member. If the intensity of the internal forces (meaning the forces per unit area,

1

called stresses) in the member caused by the loads becomes sufficiently large, the member will fracture (break in two), especially if it is made of so-called brittle material; this behavior would of course cause the member to cease to function satisfactorily and hence would limit its load-carrying capacity.   On the other hand, the load-resisting capacity of the member may be limited by the change in shape of the member (deformation or deflection) in response to the loads, even though much larger loads could be applied before it would fracture or collapse. These situations lead to the following general problem.

The Problem Defined.   In the study of the subject of resistance of materials (or strength of materials or mechanics of materials as it is also called) we deal primarily with a body or member acted on by loads that hold the member in stable equilibrium.   The main objective or problem in the study is

(a) To determine the relation of the loads acting on the member and the resulting stresses (usually maximum values) on a cross section of the member; this relationship will also involve the dimensions of the cross section; and

(b) To determine the relation of the loads acting on the member and the deformation or deflection of the member; this relationship will include the dimensions of the member and also a certain property indicating the stiffness of the material from which the member is made.

There is, however, a third part to the problem: namely, that of determining the maximum load-carrying capacity of a (slender) member when in response to a compressive load it suddenly passes from a condition of stable equilibrium and small deflection through neutral equilibrium to unstable equilibrium and large deflections leading to total collapse.   The load at which this response of instability occurs is called the critical or buckling load.   It will be dealt with in Chapter VI after parts (a) and (b) of the foregoing statement of the problem have been considered.

Since a knowledge of the deformational response of materials to loads is very important in obtaining the desired relationships and also in applying the relationships to engineering problems, it is highly desirable that the reader have laboratory experience in observing the deformational response of material to loads and in determining the properties of materials.   This experience is also valuable in understanding the problems of forming or fabricating the material to give the desired original shape to the member.

2. Types of loads.   The response of a member to loads, and the load-carrying capacity of a member, depends on the type of the loading.   Loads may be classified as follows:

1. *Static or Steady* loads are forces that are applied slowly and not repeated, and remain nearly constant after being applied to the member, or are repeated relatively few times, such as the loads on the members of most buildings or the load applied to a bar in a testing machine. Sometimes it is convenient to consider a so-called static load to be composed of two parts: namely, a *dead* load and a *live* load. For example: The weight of a bridge is a dead load on the bridge, and the weight of a train moving on the bridge and the wind pressure on the bridge are *live* loads.

2. *Repeated* loads are forces that are applied a very large number of times, causing a stress in the material that is continually changing, often through some definite cycle or range. The loads applied to the crankshaft of an engine that is running, and the bending loads that are applied to the axle of a moving locomotive, and to many parts of airplanes in flight, are repeated loads. Repeated loads are discussed in Chapter IX.

3. *Impact* loads are forces that are applied in a relatively short period of time. An impact load is usually applied by a body that is in motion when it comes in contact with the resisting member, and the force exerted by the moving body and the period during which it acts usually cannot be determined. For this reason, in some problems it is more satisfactory to calculate the stresses and deformations produced by an impact load from the energy delivered to the resisting member by the moving body. When this is done, the energy delivered to the resisting member is frequently called an *energy load* and is expressed in foot-pounds (not in pounds). Impact and energy loads are considered in Chapter X.

Other Classifications of Loads. Loads may be classified as *distributed* loads and *concentrated* loads. A distributed load may be uniformly distributed or nonuniformly distributed. Thus, if grain of uniform texture is spread on a floor so that its depth is constant, the floor will be subjected to a uniformly distributed load; whereas, if the grain is distributed so that its depth is not constant, the floor is said to carry a nonuniformly distributed load.

A concentrated load is a force distributed on an area that is negligibly small compared to the surface of the resisting member.

Another useful classification of loads may be made in terms of the simpler types of deformational response of the resisting member. Thus a given member may be subjected to *central* (axial) loads, or to *torsional* (twisting) loads, or to *bending* loads. A member, however, may be subjected simultaneously to any two or to all three of these types of loads. Members subjected to combined loads are treated in Chapters VI and VIII.

3. Influence of temperature and time. The response of a member to any given type of load may depend on the temperature of the resisting member and on the length of time the load acts. For example, at so-called *elevated* temperatures, metals may continue to deform (called creep) in service under a constant load for a long period of time (years), and ultimately may fracture at some section whose dimensions have been reduced by the deformation. Steel pipe lines for high-pressure steam sometimes fail in this way. Likewise, the elevated temperature of the aluminum surface of airplanes caused by the air friction at high speeds changes the properties of the aluminum, causing the material to creep.

Fortunately, in many service conditions involving so-called *ordinary* temperatures, we may use most metals and other engineering materials for load-carrying members without making allowance for the effects of temperature or of time, especially for commonly used operating stresses and strains; unless otherwise stated, the effects of temperature and time will be neglected in subsequent discussions involving static loads. However, the ever-changing conditions in engineering applications of load-resisting members are increasing the importance of both temperature and time in the study of resistance of materials.

4. Internal forces. Method of sections. The first step in the solution of the general problem outlined in Art. 1 is to express, by use of the equations of equilibrium, the internal forces at a section of the member in terms of the loads acting on the member. But the forces that hold a body in equilibrium are applied by bodies external to the member considered. However, the forces at a section of a member, which are internal forces with respect to the whole member, may be considered to be external to a *portion* of the member, in order that these forces can be used in equations of equilibrium.

The method of creating this situation is called the *method of sections*, and it is of great importance in the study of resistance of materials. We shall assume that the student has been introduced to the method in his study of statics, but the method will be reviewed here for convenience and emphasis. The method consists first of imagining or assuming that the member is severed at a section (usually, but not always, a plane section), and a free-body diagram is drawn of the portion of the member that lies to one side of the cut section. The forces acting on this portion are external to the portion and hold it in equilibrium; and hence the equations of equilibrium may be applied to the forces acting on it; these forces consist of the original external forces (loads) that act on this portion of the member and the forces that act at the cut section. The method is discussed in greater detail as follows:

First it will be assumed that the member is a rigid body; this means that the deformations of the member are considered to be small, and hence the change in dimensions of the member caused by the loads may be neglected.

In Fig. 1a let a body B be acted on by several *coplanar* loads P_1, P_2, P_3, P_4, P_5, and let it be required to obtain the internal forces on a section mm of the body. The portion of the body to the right of section mm has been removed in Fig. 1b, and a free-body diagram of the remaining (left-hand) portion is shown.

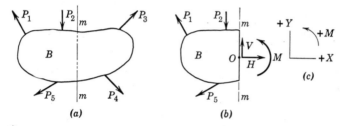

Fig. 1. Method of determining the internal forces on a cross section.

The forces on the cut section will be distributed over the area, and their resultant may be a single force or a force and a couple. However, for a coplanar system of loads, it is usually desirable to consider the forces on the cut section to consist, in general, of a normal force H, a tangential (shearing) force V, and a couple whose moment is M. The desirability of using these three components of the resultant force on the cut section lies in the fact that the stress (force per unit area) at any point in the section is conveniently expressed in terms of these components, which in turn are expressed in terms of the external forces acting on the body. For a noncoplanar system of loads, the forces on the cut section would, in general, have more than three components, including a twisting moment.

The forces H and V, the moment (couple) M, and the original forces P_1, P_5 and P_2 shown in Fig. 1b hold this portion of the body in equilibrium, and hence three equations of equilibrium may be applied to the coplanar-force system. For convenience, the point O in Fig. 1b is usually selected so that it is coincident with the centroid of the cut cross section. If then the external forces P_1, P_2, P_5 and the dimensions of the body are known, the internal forces H, V, and M at the section mm may be found from the equations $\Sigma F_x = 0$, $\Sigma F_y = 0$, and $\Sigma M = 0$, in which M here represents the moment of any force about any axis perpendicular to the plane of the forces (not the moment or couple M in Fig. 1b).

Illustrative Problem

Problem 1.   In Fig. 2a is shown a crane that carries a load of 1000 lb.   Determine the internal forces at section mm of member DG.

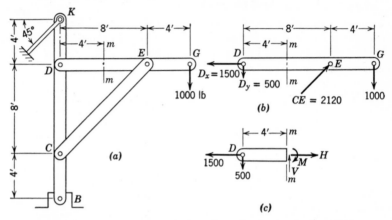

Fig. 2.   Internal forces on section of member in simple structure.

Solution.   First, the forces acting on the member DG must be found.   A free-body diagram of DG is shown in Fig. 2b.   The three equations of equilibrium applied to the forces in this diagram give the values of the unknown forces as follows:

$$\Sigma M_D = 0.707CE \times 8 - 1000 \times 12 = 0, \qquad CE = 2120 \text{ lb}$$
$$\Sigma F_x = 0.707CE - D_x = 0, \qquad D_x = 1500 \text{ lb}$$
$$\Sigma F_y = 0.707CE - 1000 - D_y = 0, \qquad D_y = 500 \text{ lb}$$

Next, the internal forces on section mm must be made external to a portion of the member DG (the left-hand portion will be used).   A free-body diagram of the left-hand portion is shown in Fig. 2c.   The equations of equilibrium applied to this coplanar-force system give

$$\Sigma F_x = H - 1500 = 0, \qquad H = 1500 \text{ lb}$$
$$\Sigma F_y = V - 500 = 0, \qquad V = 500 \text{ lb}$$
$$\Sigma M_D = 500 \times 4 - M = 0, \qquad M = 2000 \text{ lb-ft}$$

Problems

2. Solve Prob. 1 by drawing a free-body diagram of the portion of DG on the right-hand side of section mm and applying the equations of equilibrium to forces acting on this portion.

3. Calculate the internal forces in member BK in Fig. 2 at a section midway between C and D.   *Ans.* $V = 750$ lb; $H = 250$ lb; $M = 0$.

4. Calculate the internal forces at section *mm* of the body shown in Fig. 3. Let $P = 1000$ lb and $Q = 500$ lb. The bar has a square cross section 2 in. on each side.

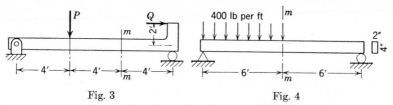

Fig. 3   Fig. 4

5. Calculate the internal forces at the section *mm* of the body shown in Fig. 4: (*a*) by considering the left-hand portion, (*b*) by considering the right-hand portion.

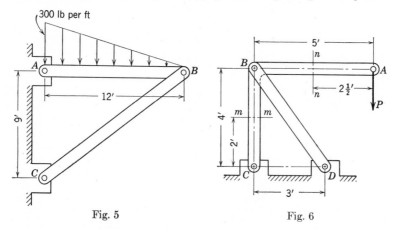

Fig. 5   Fig. 6

6. Calculate the internal forces in the member *AB* of Fig. 5 at a section midway between *A* and *B*.   *Ans.* $V = 150$ lb; $H = 800$ lb; $M = 2700$ lb-ft.

7. Calculate the values of the internal forces on section *mm* of the frame shown in Fig. 6. Let $P = 1800$ lb.

8. Calculate the values of the internal forces on section *nn* of the frame in Fig. 6. Let $P = 600$ lb.

9. In Fig. 7 let $P = 1500$ lb. (*a*) Determine the internal forces on section *mm*; (*b*) determine the internal forces on section *nn*.

10. The bar shown in Fig. 8 is subjected to an axial load *P*. Determine, in terms of *P* and *θ*, the internal forces on section *mm*.

11. The crank pressures P_1 and P_2 on the crankshaft shown in Fig. 9 are 6000 lb and 4800 lb, respectively. The bearing reactions are R_1 and R_2,

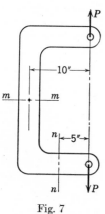

Fig. 7

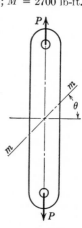

Fig. 8

and the moment Qq is applied to hold the crankshaft in equilibrium. Determine the internal forces (a) at a vertical section through B, and (b) at a vertical section just to the right of C.

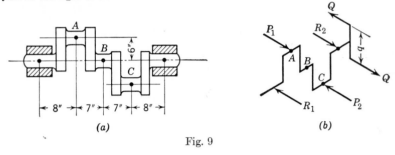

(a)   (b)

Fig. 9

5. Stress.   If an internal force Q is distributed on an area a at a section mm as in Fig. 10a and b, the stress at any point on the area is

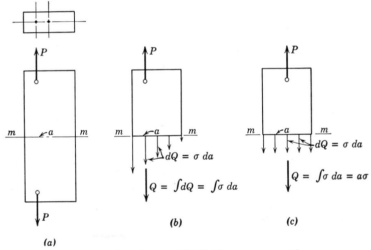

Fig. 10.   Normal stress distribution on cross section.

defined to be the force per unit area. Thus, if ΔQ is the force on a small area Δa including the point, the definition of stress may be written

$$\text{Stress} = \underset{\Delta a \to 0}{\text{limit}} \frac{\Delta Q}{\Delta a} = \frac{dQ}{da} \tag{1}$$

Normal Stress.   If the stress acts in a direction perpendicular to the area, it is called a normal stress and will be denoted by σ. The normal stress is called a tensile stress if it pulls on the area, and a compressive stress if it pushes on the area. In Fig. 10b, Q is distributed nonuniformly on the area, and hence $\sigma = dQ/da$ or

$$Q = \int \sigma \, da \tag{2}$$

It is evident from the foregoing expression that, in order to evaluate the integral, and hence to express Q in terms of the stress at any point of the area (which is a necessary step in the solution of the problem outlined in Art. 1), the manner in which σ is distributed on the area must be determined. The method of doing this is discussed in Arts. 8 and 9.

If the conditions are such that Q is distributed uniformly on the area, we may write

$$Q = \int \sigma \, da = \sigma \int da = \sigma a \quad \text{or} \quad \sigma = \frac{Q}{a} \tag{3}$$

and, since Q must hold P in equilibrium, $Q = P$, and hence also $\sigma = P/a$. However, at this point in the discussion we are primarily interested in expressing the *internal* force at the section in terms of the stress on the section [the relation of the stress to the *external* force (load) will be treated in more detail in Art. 9].

Shearing Stress. If the internal force Q lies in (acts tangent to) the area a at a given section, as in Fig. 11, it is called a shearing force. If

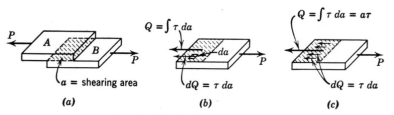

Fig. 11. Shearing stress on an area.

the force Q is distributed nonuniformly on the area, the stress at any point in the area, designated by τ, may be written

$$\tau = \frac{dQ}{da} \quad \text{or} \quad Q = \int \tau \, da \tag{4}$$

If, however, Q is distributed uniformly on the area, we may write

$$Q = \tau \int da = \tau a \quad \text{or} \quad \tau = \frac{Q}{a} \tag{5}$$

Units of Stress. A stress has the dimensions of force divided by length squared (F/L^2) and may be expressed in various units such as pounds per square inch (written lb per sq in. or lb/in.^{2}; the abbreviation psi is also used), kilograms per square centimeter (kg per sq cm), tons per square inch (tons per sq in. or tons/in.^{2}), kips per square inch (kips per sq in. or kips/in.^{2}) in which a kip is 1000 lb.

Problems

12. The straight bar shown in Fig. 12a has a rectangular cross section and is loaded so that the distribution of tensile stress on section mm is as shown in Fig.

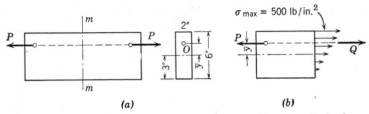

(a)   (b)

Fig. 12. Nonuniform distribution of stress caused by eccentric load.

12b. (a) Determine the magnitude of the internal force Q on section mm, and (b) find the distance $\bar{y}$ to the action line of Q.   *Ans.*   Q = 3000 lb; $\bar{y}$ = 1 in.

13. If the stress on section mm in Fig. 13a is distributed as shown in Fig. 13b, calculate the internal moment on section mm by using the centroidal axis of the section as the moment axis.

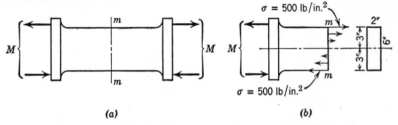

(a)   (b)

Fig. 13. Nonuniform distribution of stress caused by bending loads.

14. The stress distribution on section mm of Fig. 12 (Prob. 12) may be obtained by superimposing the two component distributions shown in Fig. 14b and c.

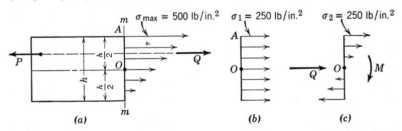

(a)   (b)   (c)

Fig. 14. A nonuniform stress distribution considered to be a superposition of two component distributions.

This is equivalent to resolving the force Q into a force acting through the centroid O of the section and a couple whose moment is M. From the values given in Fig. 14b and c, calculate the value of Q in Fig. 14b and of M in Fig. 14c.

6. Deformation and strain. *Tensile and Compressive Strain.* The *deformation* in any direction of a member subjected to loads is defined to be the total change in dimension (or change in some portion of the length) of the member in the given direction; it will be denoted by e. *Strain* in any direction is defined to be the deformation per unit of length in the given direction; it will be denoted by ϵ. If e is an increase in length, it is called an elongation or tensile deformation, and a decrease in length is called a shortening or compressive deformation. The strain ϵ is designated in the same way.

Thus, in Fig. 15a let mm and nn be two parallel planes before the loads P are applied to the member, the length of each fiber between the

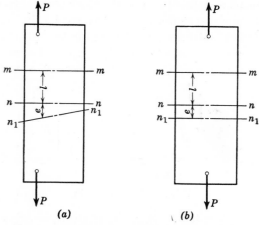

Fig. 15. Nonuniform and uniform tensile strain.

planes being l. If e denotes the tensile deformation or elongation (greatly exaggerated in Fig. 15) of any fiber of length l, the average tensile strain of the fiber is expressed by

$$\epsilon = \frac{e}{l} \qquad\qquad (6)$$

If the member is straight, is centrally loaded, and has a constant cross section over the length l as in Fig. 15b, the value of l will be the same for all fibers,* and e will be distributed uniformly along the length of

* Frequently it is convenient to consider that the member is composed of longitudinal rods or fibers, each fiber having a differential cross-sectional area da and acting as an axially loaded tensile (or compressive) bar.

the fiber; thus, the average strain then is also the value at any point along the fiber. The value of e, however, will not be the same for all fibers if the load is eccentric as shown in Fig. 15a. But, if P is a central (axial and concentric) load as in Fig. 15b, the plane n_1n_1 will be parallel to nn, and thus e and hence ϵ will have the same value for all fibers.

Frequently ϵ varies along the length of the fibers of a member, and its values for the fibers *at a given cross section* of the member are needed. We then consider the deformation to be Δe for a very small length Δl, and hence ϵ at the point on a fiber at the section considered may be defined by the expression

$$\epsilon = \lim_{\Delta l \to 0} \frac{\Delta e}{\Delta l} = \frac{de}{dl} \tag{7}$$

Shearing Strain. Let Fig. 16a represent an elemental cube of the material at a point at which shearing stresses exist in a member. The shearing stress on each face is τ, and the block of material is deformed from the original shape shown by Fig. 16a and by the dotted lines in Fig. 16c to that indicated by the solid lines in Fig. 16b or c.

The total shearing deformation in the length l is e_s as indicated in Fig. 16c, and hence the shearing strain, denoted by γ, is given by the

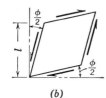
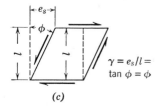

(a)   (b)   (c)

Fig. 16. Shearing strain.

expression $\gamma = e_s/l = \tan\phi$. Shearing strain is sometimes called detrusion. Since shearing strains are usually limited to small values, $\tan\phi$ may be considered to be equal to ϕ (expressed in radians). Therefore, for small shearing strains,

$$\gamma = \frac{e_s}{l} = \tan\phi = \phi \tag{8}$$

Thus, a small shearing strain at any point in a member is measured by the change in angle (expressed in radians) of two lines in the member that pass through the point and that were originally at right angles and in the directions of the shearing stresses.

7. Relation between stress and strain. Elasticity. *Normal Stresses.* Let a bar, as indicated in Fig. 17a, be subjected to an increasing load P in a testing machine under conditions such that P and e can be measured and the normal stress and strain can be calculated by use of Eqs. 3 and 6: namely, $\sigma = P/a$ and $\epsilon = e/l$. In such a test it will be found that, for many materials, σ is approximately proportional to ϵ up to a certain value of the stress that is called the proportional limit. Thus, a linear relationship exists between stress and strain, *provided that the values of the strain are small.*

This relationship is represented in Fig. 17b by the straight-line portion *OA* of the curve *OAB*; this curve is called the stress-strain curve or diagram for the material. For stresses above that corresponding to

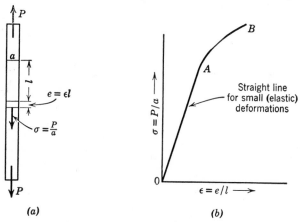

Fig. 17.   Stress-strain curve for elastic strains.

the proportional limit *A* on the curve, the form of the stress-strain diagram may vary greatly for different materials (as will be discussed in Art. 16), but the first portion of the diagram for nearly all materials is approximately a straight line.

Hooke's Law. The fact that, for small strains, stress is proportional to strain is called Hooke's law for unidirectional stress: that is, for normal stress in one direction only. Hooke's law for biaxial and tri-axial stresses will be discussed later.

Elasticity. If in the test suggested in the foregoing discussion the load (and stress) is decreased to zero from a value represented by the ordinate to any point on the straight-line portion of the stress-strain curve of Fig. 17b, the bar will return approximately to its original shape and dimensions. In other words, the bar may be assumed to act elastically. Thus a linear relation between stress and strain may usually be interpreted as evidence of elastic behavior of the material.

Modulus of Elasticity. Hooke's law may be stated mathematically by the expression $\sigma/\epsilon =$ a constant, in which the value of the constant is denoted by E and is called the modulus of elasticity. Thus, for stresses within the proportional limit, we may write

$$E = \frac{\sigma}{\epsilon} \quad \text{or} \quad \sigma = E\epsilon \tag{9}$$

This equation points out a very useful fact: namely, that the normal (unidirectional) stress at any point on a section of a load-resisting member made of a given material (for which E is known) can be determined, provided that the elastic tensile or compressive strain at the point is known or can be measured. Thus, for elastic strains, the distribution of stress on the section is the same as the distribution of strain.

Shearing Stress. A similar linear relationship holds for shearing stress and shearing strain: namely, $\tau/\gamma =$ a constant. The constant is called the *shearing modulus of elasticity* of the material and is denoted by the symbol G. Thus, for small (elastic) shearing strains,

$$\frac{\tau}{\gamma} = G \quad \text{or} \quad \tau = G\gamma \tag{10}$$

The constant G is also sometimes called the modulus of rigidity.

Lateral Strain—Poisson's Ratio. The bar in Fig. 17a will decrease in diameter as the load P increases; the ratio of the lateral strain to the longitudinal strain is a constant denoted by μ and is called Poisson's ratio.

Problems

15. The body or member B in each of the parts (a) and (b) of Fig. 18 is made of the same material and carries the same load P, but the arrangements of the supports are different. Assume that, before P is applied, each of the two supports in each arrangement is in contact with the member B, but that the pressure on the

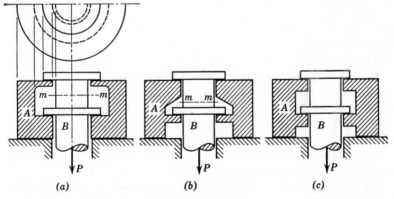

(a) (b) (c)

Fig. 18.   Influence of strains in a member on the stresses developed in the member.

supports is negligible since the weight of B is assumed to be negligible in comparison to P. Assume also that, when the load is applied, member B and the supports act elastically. (a) Will the elastic stresses on the section mm in each of the arrangements in (a) and (b) be equal? If not, in which arrangement is the stress on mm the greater? Why? (b) It is often assumed that, when the two supports are the same as in Fig. 18c, the reactions at the supports are equal. Is this assumption correct? If not, explain why.

16. Two wires, each 6 ft long, are stretched elastically the same amount: namely, 0.10 in. One wire is made of steel and the other of aluminum. Moduli of elasticity for steel and aluminum are $E_{st} = 30 \times 10^6$ and $E_{al} = 10 \times 10^6$, respectively, both values being expressed in pounds per square inch. The steel wire has a cross-sectional area of 0.02 sq in. and the aluminum wire 0.03 sq in. (a) What is the tensile stress in each wire, and (b) what is the tensile internal force in each wire?

17. Shearing strains are especially important in members subjected to twisting or torsional loads as in Fig. 19, where a twisting moment T is shown acting on a

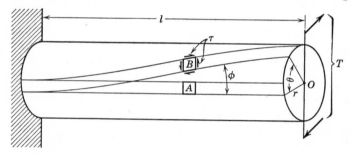

Fig. 19.   Shearing strains in a bar subjected to torsion (twisting).

cylindrical bar of radius r and length l. As T is applied, a rectangular element or block A at the surface of the cylinder is displaced and deformed elastically as shown at B (exaggerated), the shearing stress on each face of the block being τ. If the free end of the cylinder is turned through the angle θ, show that $\gamma = r\theta/l$ and $\tau = Gr\theta/l$.

8. General procedure for deriving load-stress relationship.

One part of the general problem as outlined in Art. 1 requires that a relationship be found between the loads acting on a member and the stress (usually the maximum normal or maximum shearing stress) at a point on a cross section of the member. Before attempting to carry out this requirement for any specific type of member and loading, it is very important that the general procedure used repeatedly throughout this book shall be understood thoroughly. The method or procedure for obtaining the relationship between loads and the resulting stresses may be stated as follows.

Step 1. By use of the method of sections (see Art. 4) and the equations of equilibrium, express the relation between the loads acting on the member and the internal forces at the section of the member considered.

Step 2. Express the internal forces at the section in terms of the stresses at the section; this requires that the distribution of the stresses on the section must be found. This distribution of the stresses is determined as follows:

(*a*) First, the distribution of the strains in the fibers of the member at the section is determined experimentally; it should be observed that strains can be observed (and often measured) whereas stresses cannot. The manner in which the strains vary (are distributed) at the section depends mainly on the shape (geometry) of the member and on the type of loading (axial, bending, etc.), but not on the properties of the material of which the member is made.

(*b*) The relation must then be found between strain and stress for the material of which the member is made. If the stresses on the section are primarily uniaxial, this relationship is found experimentally and expressed in the form of a stress-strain diagram; for many materials, a linear relationship exists between stress and strain for small (elastic) strains (see Art. 7). The information obtained under (*a*) and (*b*) makes it possible to express the *internal* forces in terms of the stresses and the dimensions of the cross section.

Step 3. By substituting the results found in step 2 into the equations obtained in step 1, we obtain the desired relationships between the loads acting on the member and the stress at any point of the section considered.

It should be noted that the limitations of the resulting relationship for a given type of member and loading are to be found in the assumptions made in carrying out the steps in the foregoing procedure. The procedure is applied in the next article to one of the simpler types of members and loading.

STATIC CENTRAL LOADS.   UNIAXIAL STRESS

§ 1   Elastic Behavior

9. Relation between central load and stress on section normal to load. In Fig. 20*a* the member is subjected to an axial load. Let it be required to express the stress σ at any point on the area a at section mm in terms of the load P and area a. In accordance with the procedure outlined in the preceding article, Fig. 20*b* is drawn; the force on the area da of each longitudinal fiber of the member is $\sigma\, da$. We do not know how these $\sigma\,da$ forces vary over the area, but, since they hold in equilibrium the force P, we may write

$$\Sigma F = 0 \quad \text{or} \quad P = \int \sigma\,da \tag{11}$$

It should be noted that, if P were an eccentric load and hence did not pass through the centroid of the area a, additional equilibrium (moment) equations could be written, giving further relationships between loads and stresses.

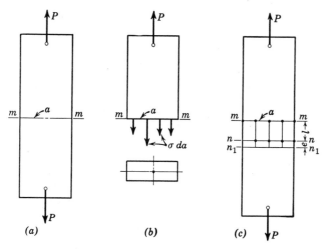

Fig. 20. Method for determining relation between axial load and stress.

In accordance with (a) of step 2, the deformation e of the fibers between the sections mm and nn of Fig. 20c are found (or assumed) to be equal, and, since ..ll the fibers have the same length l, the strain ϵ of each fiber may be expressed as $\epsilon = e/l$. Note that this statement requires that the member be straight and that the load be axial or central, but does not involve any property of the material except that it can deform. For example, it does not demand that the deformations be restricted to elastic deformations or that all the imaginary fibers be made of material having the same modulus of elasticity E, although they must of course act so that plane sections remain plane.

Next, in accordance with (b) of step 2, the stress σ on any fiber can be determined in terms of the load. *When the fiber is strained elastically, the stress is given by the expression $\sigma = E\epsilon$.* If, then, all fibers are made of the same material, the value of E will be the same for all the fibers, and hence σ is distributed uniformly over the area a ($\sigma = a$

constant, since E and ϵ are constants). Hence, by use of step 3, Eq. 11 may be written

$$P = \int \sigma \, da = \sigma \int da = a\sigma \quad \text{or} \quad \sigma = \frac{P}{a} \tag{12}$$

in which σ is the uniformly distributed normal (tensile) stress on a section normal to the load P.

It is important to remember that Eq. 12 is limited to the conditions imposed by the assumptions made in its derivation. The student should review the limitations and observe that they include the following:

1. The strains of the fibers are equal, and hence
   (a) The member must be straight for some distance on either side of the section on which σ occurs, and
   (b) The cross-sectional area must be constant over the straight portion.
2. The load P is a static central axial load.
3. The member is a one-material homogeneous body, for which E is a constant.

The significance of these (and other) conditions or limitations on the use of Eq. 12 is discussed later. It may be said here, however, that, if the member is made of *ductile* material, the harmful effects of moderate deviations from the required conditions are not, as a rule, serious.

Equation 12 gives the desired (maximum) *normal* stress in the member for the conditions stated. However, it was pointed out in Art. 1 (see also Art. 10) that for some materials the *shearing* stress is more significant in determining the load-carrying capacity of a member than is the normal stress. The shearing stress on an oblique section of the member in Fig. 20a is considered in the next article.

Central Shearing Load. At this point, however, attention should be directed to the fact that the load causing stress on a section of a member may be a central *shearing* load; that is, it may lie in the plane of the section and pass through the centroid of the area as already indicated in Fig. 11. If the shearing stress τ on the area is assumed to be distributed uniformly (τ = a constant), equilibrium for the forces in Fig. 11c may be expressed by the equation

$$P = \int \tau \, da = \tau \int da = a\tau \quad \text{or} \quad \tau = \frac{P}{a} \tag{13}$$

The shearing stress caused by a direct or central shearing load seldom is distributed uniformly, and hence τ in Eq. 13 usually is the average shearing stress on the shearing area, but in many problems the assumption that τ is constant over the area leads to satisfactory though approximate results.

Problems

18. Why is the equation $\sigma = P/a$ not strictly applicable to the section mm in each of the members shown in Fig. 21? Make clear at what point or stage in the

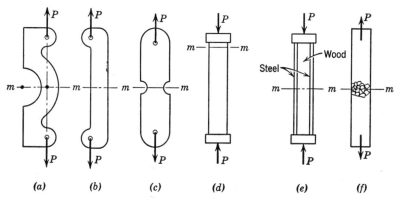

Fig. 21. Various members that do not satisfy the conditions required to make Eq. 12 applicable.

derivation of the equation each of the conditions represented in Fig. 21 was excluded; Fig. 21f is meant to indicate that the bar is made of metal which, of course, is not homogeneous but is made up of crystals.

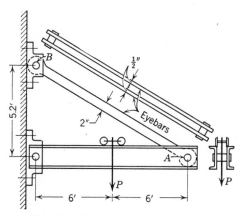

Fig. 22. Pin-connected wall bracket.

19. The wall bracket in Fig. 22 carries a load P of 6 tons. Compute the tensile stress at any section of the straight portions in each of the two eyebars.

20. The tie rod in Fig. 23 is 1.25 in. in diameter. It is used to help resist the lateral uniform pressure against the walls of a bin. If the tensile stress σ in the tie rod is 10,000 lb/in.^{2}, what diameter d should the washer have in order to keep the bearing pressure (assumed uniform) against the wall from exceeding 200 lb/in.^{2}?   *Ans.* $d = 8.95$.

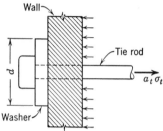

Fig. 23. Bearing pressure of washer on wall.

21. If a specimen of wood is tested as shown in Fig. 24 and the maximum tensile stress the specimen can resist is 8000 lb/in.^{2}, (a) what is the maximum axial load P that can be applied to the specimen; (b) what is the shearing stress in the heads of the specimen when resisting the tensile load P?

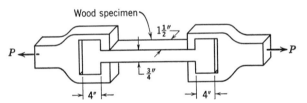

Fig. 24. Tensile and shearing stresses in wood specimen.

22. The pin-connected pin-loaded truss shown in Fig. 25a is subjected to loads that cause the internal forces shown in Fig. 25b in members AC and BC. If the

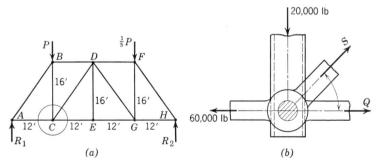

Fig. 25. Stresses in members of pin-connected pin-loaded truss.

cross-sectional areas of CD and CE are 2 in.^{2} and 3 in.^{2}, respectively, what is the normal stress in each of these members?   *Ans.* $\sigma_{CD} = 12,500$ lb/in.^{2}

10. Relation between central load and stresses on oblique plane. As stated in Art. 1, one of the main problems in resistance of materials is the determination of the relationship between the loads acting on a member and the resulting maximum normal and shearing stresses in the member.

In Art. 9 the maximum *normal* stress σ in a straight member having a constant cross-sectional area a was expressed in terms of the axial load acting on the member ($\sigma = P/a$). It is important that the maximum *shearing* stress in the same member also be expressed in terms of the load. This may be done by first determining the stresses on an oblique plane inclined any angle θ to the plane normal to the load.

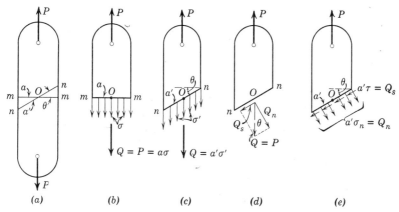

Fig. 26. Stresses on oblique plane in a tension member.

In accordance with the method previously discussed, Fig. 26c shows a free-body diagram of the upper part of the member in Fig. 26a; it will be observed that the force Q holds the force P in equilibrium, and hence $Q = P$. Furthermore, it is evident that $Q = a'\sigma'$, in which σ' is the uniformly distributed stress on the oblique plane nn having the area a'; thus $\sigma' = P/a'$. But σ' is less than $\sigma = P/a$, since a' is greater than a, and hence σ' has little significance by itself; its significance lies in its relation to the shearing stress on the area a'. This shearing stress may be found as follows: Let the force Q be resolved into normal and shearing components, Q_n and Q_s, respectively, as shown in Fig. 26d. Since these components pass through the centroid of a', the stresses σ_n and τ on a' may be assumed to be constant, as indicated in Fig. 26e. Hence, the following equations may be written:

$$Q_n = a'\sigma_n = \frac{a}{\cos\theta}\sigma_n \quad \text{and} \quad Q_s = a'\tau = \frac{a}{\cos\theta}\tau$$

But
$$Q_n = Q \cos \theta = P \cos \theta \quad \text{and} \quad Q_s = Q \sin \theta = P \sin \theta$$

Therefore,
$$P \cos \theta = \frac{a}{\cos \theta} \sigma_n \quad \text{and} \quad P \sin \theta = \frac{a}{\cos \theta} \tau$$

or
$$\sigma_n = \frac{P}{a} \cos^2 \theta \quad \text{and} \quad \tau = \frac{P}{a} \sin \theta \cos \theta = \frac{1}{2} \frac{P}{a} \sin 2\theta \qquad (14)$$

From Eq. 14 the normal and shearing stresses on any section inclined at an angle θ to the cross section that is perpendicular to load P may

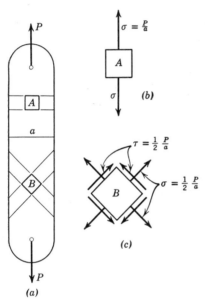

be found. The maximum value of σ_n occurs when $\theta = 0$, that is, on the plane perpendicular to P, and its value is $\sigma = P/a$, which agrees with Eq. 12. The maximum value of τ, as given by Eq. 14, occurs when $\theta = 45°$, and hence

$$\tau_{\max} = \frac{1}{2} \frac{P}{a} \qquad (15)$$

Thus, the maximum value of the shearing stress in an axially loaded straight bar having a constant cross section is equal to one half of the maximum normal stress in the bar, and it occurs on planes making angles of 45° with the plane on which the maximum normal stress occurs.

Fig. 27. Stresses on 45° planes in tension member.

But, even though the maximum shearing stress in the bar is only one half of the maximum normal stress, it may be the significant stress for the reason that the shearing *strength* of many materials is much less than the tensile or compressive strength of the material.

It will be observed from Eq. 14 that the normal stress σ_n on the 45° plane is also equal to $\frac{1}{2}P/a$. Thus, the stresses on the faces of a small block or cube B (Fig. 27a) oriented so that $\theta = 45°$ are shown in Fig. 27c; if each face of the block is considered to have an area equal to unity, the stresses shown could also be considered to be the forces acting on the faces.

11. Relation between axial load and deformation.   In Art. 1
it was pointed out that one important part of the general problem in
resistance of materials is to determine the relation between the loads
acting on a member and the resulting deformation of the member.
For a straight member subjected to a central load the desired relationship may be found as follows.

Tensile or Compressive Deformation.   If the central load is a longitudinal (axial) force acting on a straight bar of length l, the tensile or
compressive deformation de of an element of length dl is (see Eq. 7)

$$de = \epsilon \, dl \tag{16}$$

in which ϵ is the strain (deformation per unit length); ϵ may be assumed
to be constant in the length dl but may, of course, vary along the finite
length l.   The total deformation e of the length l then is

$$e = \int_0^l \epsilon \, dl \tag{17}$$

If the material is homogeneous and only elastic strains occur, we may
substitute $\epsilon = \sigma/E$ in Eq. 17, in which E is the modulus of elasticity of
the material.   Hence,

$$e = \int_0^l \frac{\sigma}{E} \, dl \tag{18}$$

Furthermore, if the stress σ on any given cross section is distributed
uniformly, its value is $\sigma = P/a$, but its value may vary from section
to section along the bar if the cross section of the bar varies gradually
(see Fig. 36 and Prob. 33), or if P varies along the bar even though a
remains constant (see Prob. 23).

Thus Eq. 18 may be written

$$e = \int_0^l \frac{P}{aE} \, dl \tag{19}$$

If, however, the cross section of the straight homogeneous member
is constant and if the member is subjected to loads at its ends only,
the term P/aE in Eq. 19 is constant, and hence

$$e = \frac{P}{aE} \int_0^l dl = \frac{Pl}{aE} \tag{20}$$

which expresses the elastic longitudinal deformation e of a straight bar
of constant cross-sectional area a and of length l, made of homogeneous
material having a modulus of elasticity E and loaded at its ends by an
axial load P.

It should be observed that the stress in such a bar, as expressed by $\sigma = P/a$, does not depend on any property of the material, whereas the deformation e depends on the value E for the material. Thus, if two bars with the same dimensions, one made of steel and the other of an aluminum alloy, were stretched elastically by equal axial loads P, the normal stresses in the two bars would be equal, but the elongation of the aluminum bar would be three times that of the steel bar since the modulus of elasticity of the aluminum-alloy material is only one-third that for steel.

Shearing Deformation. In Eq. 8, if we replace the total shearing deformation e_s in the length l by a differential part de_s in the length dl, the shearing strain γ (shearing deformation per unit length) at any point in the length l would be

$$\gamma = \frac{de_s}{dl} \tag{21}$$

and, hence,

$$de_s = \gamma \, dl \tag{22}$$

Thus, the total shearing deformation in the length l is

$$e_s = \int_0^l \gamma \, dl \tag{23}$$

If we assume that only elastic shearing strains occur, we may substitute $\gamma = \tau/G$ (Eq. 10) in Eq. 23, which gives

$$e_s = \int_0^l \frac{\tau}{G} \, dl \tag{24}$$

in which G is the shearing modulus of elasticity of the material.

If τ caused by the shearing load P_s is uniformly distributed on the shearing area a_s, we may write $\tau = P_s/a_s$; such a condition seldom is strictly true, but in many problems the approximation leads to useful results. Thus, for such conditions we may write

$$e_s = \int_0^l \frac{P_s}{a_s G} \, dl \tag{25}$$

Illustrative Problem

Problem 23. A bar shown in Fig. 28 is l in. long, has a constant cross-sectional area of a sq in., and weighs w lb per ft of length per sq in. of cross section. Find the total elongation of the bar when it is suspended from one end and is subjected to no downward load except its own weight. If the bar is made of steel and is 400 ft long, calculate the total stretch of the bar. (A steel bar having a cross-sectional area of 1 sq in. weighs 3.4 lb per ft of length.)

Solution. The tensile stress σ_t on a section at any distance y in. (Fig. 28) from the lower end expressed in pounds per square inch is

$$\sigma_t = \frac{awy}{12a} = \frac{wy}{12}$$

and the strain at this section is

$$\epsilon_t = \frac{\sigma_t}{E} = \frac{wy}{12E}$$

The elongation of the short length, dy in., along which the strain may be assumed to be constant is

$$de_t = \epsilon_t \, dy$$

and the total elongation (in inches) in the length of l in. is

$$e_t = \int_0^l \epsilon_t \, dy = \int_0^l \frac{wy}{12E} dy = \frac{w}{12E} \int_0^l y \, dy$$

$$= \frac{w}{12E} \frac{l^2}{2} = \frac{3.4 \times (400 \times 12)^2}{12 \times 30,000,000 \times 2}$$

$$= 0.108 \text{ in.} = \text{elongation of steel bar 400 ft long}$$

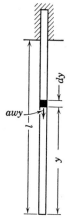

Fig. 28. Bar stretched by its own weight.

Problems for Articles 9, 10, and 11

24. In Fig. 29, AB is made of an aluminum alloy for which $E = 10 \times 10^6$ lb/in.^{2}, and it has a rectangular cross-sectional area of 2 in. by $\frac{1}{4}$ in. It is specified (a) that the maximum tensile stress in AB must not exceed 12,000 lb/in.^{2}, (b) that the maximum shearing stress shall not exceed 7200 lb/in.^{2}, and (c) that the elastic stretch of AB shall not exceed 0.20 in. Assume that the member deforms elastically. Determine whether or not each specification is satisfied.

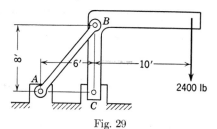

Fig. 29

25. In Fig. 30 two bolts, each $\frac{1}{2}$ in. in diameter, are used to connect the flanges of the members (one bolt on each side). The load P is 8000 lb. Calculate the tensile and shearing stresses in each bolt on a section inclined 30° to the horizontal as shown. Neglect friction between surfaces.

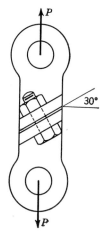

Fig. 30

26. A straight bar 50 in. long has a constant circular cross section 1.2 in. in diameter. It is made of steel, for which $E = 30 \times 10^6$ lb/in.^{2} The bar is subjected to a tensile axial load which causes a maximum elastic shearing stress in the bar of 12,500 lb/in.^{2} Calculate the tensile deformation of a 30-in. gage length of the bar.   *Ans.*   0.025 in.

27. It is specified that a straight brass rod when subjected to a tensile axial load of 30,000 lb. must not resist a tensile stress greater than 10,000 lb/in.^{2} and must not be stretched more than 0.02 in. The rod has a length of 100 in. Determine the least cross-sectional area for the rod. Which one of the two requirements determines the area? Assume that the rod deforms elastically and that for brass $E = 14 \times 10^6$ lb/in.^{2}

28. In Fig. 31, when the load Q is equal to 200 lb, the arm AB is horizontal, and BC is vertical. If an increment $\Delta Q = 800$ lb is added to Q, the deflection of

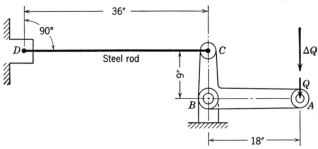

Fig. 31

the point A is $\delta = 0.125$ in. What is the diameter d of the steel rod CD? The rod is made of high-strength steel having a tensile proportional limit of 65,000 lb per sq in. Assume that CD is strained elastically and that ABC is a rigid body; the deflection of A, therefore, is caused solely by rotation of ABC about B due to the elongation of DC. Assume $E = 30 \times 10^6$ lb per sq in. for steel. After determining the value of d, calculate the tensile stress in CD to determine whether or not the assumption that CD acts elastically is justified.   *Ans.* $d = 0.20$ in.

29. A pulley (Fig. 32) transmits a turning moment Pd of 10,000 lb-ft to a 4-in. shaft, relative motion between the pulley and shaft being prevented by a flat key

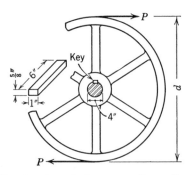

Fig. 32. Shearing stress in key connecting pulley and shaft.

1 in. wide, $\frac{5}{8}$ in. deep, and 6 in. long. Compute the average shearing stress in the key.   *Ans.*   10,000 lb/in.^{2}

30. Rubber frequently is used in shear as a vibration damper. In Fig. 33, rubber is bonded to two concentric cylindrical steel shells, and subjected to shearing stresses and strains in resisting the load P. The shearing stress varies from the inner surface to the outer surface of the rubber since the shearing area varies.

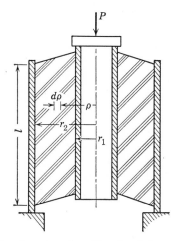

Fig. 33.   Shearing stress in rubber bonded to two cylinders.

Assume that τ on each cylindrical section of the rubber is constant and that the shearing modulus of elasticity G is constant. Show that the total shearing elastic deformation is

$$e_s = \int_{r_1}^{r_2} \gamma \, d\rho = \int_{r_1}^{r_2} \frac{P}{2\pi\rho l G} \, d\rho = \frac{P}{2\pi l G} \log \frac{r_2}{r_1}$$

31. In Fig. 34 the load P acting on the pin-connected frame is 6000 lb. The tie rod AC is made of structural steel and has a cross-section area of 0.25 sq in.

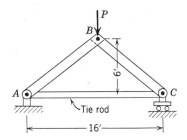

Fig. 34.   Pin-connected frame with steel tie rod.

Will the tie rod act elastically? If so, calculate the stretch of the tie rod. (See Table 1.)

32. In Fig. 35 is shown a rubber sandwich for supporting a machine on the concrete floor so that vibration and noise will not be objectionable. The dimension perpendicular to the paper is l. (a) Show that, when a load P is applied to the flat

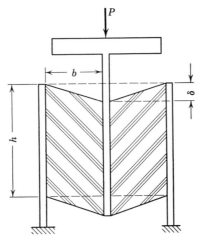

Fig. 35. Deflection of a rubber sandwich used for reduction of vibration.

steel plate to which the rubber is bonded, the plate and the load P will deflect elastically an amount

$$\delta = \frac{Pb}{2hlG}$$

(b) Write the dimensional equation for the foregoing expression for δ to show that δ is expressed correctly as a length. (c) If the permissible shearing stress in the rubber is limited to $\tau = 50$ lb per sq in., what is the maximum permissible value for the deflection δ; let $h = 4$ in., $l = 6$ in., $b = 2$ in., and $G = 100$ lb per sq in.?

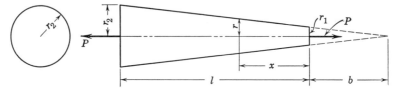

Fig. 36. Elastic deformation of axially loaded member having varying cross section.

33. In Fig. 36 let it be assumed that the known quantities are P, r_1, r_2, l, b, and the tensile modulus of elasticity E. Calculate in terms of these quantities the elastic elongation of the tapered bar.

$$Ans. \quad e = \frac{Pb}{\pi r_1^2 E}\left[\frac{l}{l+b}\right].$$

12. Two-material member. In Art. 9 the derivation of the expression $\sigma = P/a$ was based on the assumption that the load P

caused all the longitudinal fibers of the straight axially loaded member to strain elastically the same amount ϵ, and that, in addition, the material was homogeneous; it then followed that the elastic stress σ in all fibers at any normal cross section a would also be equal. This condition of homogeneity was required by the fact that the expression $\sigma = E\epsilon$ was used in the derivation. Thus, σ is a constant only if E and ϵ are constants; but ϵ is constant by virtue of the conditions imposed on the shape (geometry) of the body and on the loading, and E is constant only if the member is a homogeneous (one-material) body.

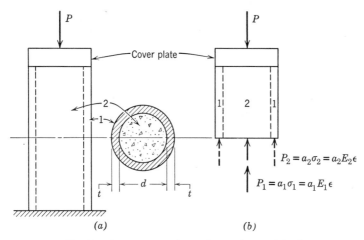

Fig. 37. A two-material member under axial load.

Let a member be composed of two parts (two bodies of different materials acting as one member) so that all the conditions required by the expression $\sigma = P/a$ are satisfied, except that the member as a whole is not made of homogeneous material although the material in each part is homogeneous. Such a member is shown in Fig. 37a, and may, for example, be thought of as a steel pipe filled with concrete and subjected to the total axial load P. Let it be required to determine the stress in each part. Let the subscript 1 refer to one part or body and the subscript 2 to the other body.

From the conditions of equilibrium of a portion of the member on one side of any cross section of the member as indicated in Fig. 37b, we obtain the fact that

$$P = P_1 + P_2 = a_1\sigma_1 + a_2\sigma_2 \qquad (26)$$

It is evident that the two desired values σ_1 and σ_2 cannot be determined from Eq. 26 alone, and hence another relation between σ_1 and

σ_2 must be found. When the conditions of equilibrium are not sufficient to determine the unknowns in a problem, the problem is said to be statically indeterminate, and equations in addition to the equilibrium equation are usually obtained by considering the relations between the strains imposed on the member by virtue of its shape and manner of loading and the stresses that accompany such strains; this relation between stress and strain depends on the material of which the body is made, and, as previously noted, for elastic strains the accompanying stresses are given by Hooke's law $\sigma = E\epsilon$ for uniaxial stress.

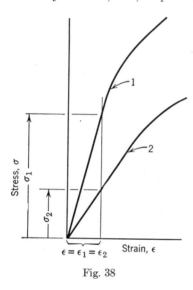

Fig. 38

For the problem here considered, the strains imposed on the member are expressed by stating that the longitudinal strain has the same value for the two parts, and hence $\epsilon =$ a constant, although the values for E are different. Thus, we may write

$$\sigma_1 = E_1\epsilon \quad \text{and} \quad \sigma_2 = E_2\epsilon \quad (27)$$

Therefore,

$$\frac{\sigma_1}{E_1} = \frac{\sigma_2}{E_2} \quad \text{or} \quad \frac{P_1}{a_1E_1} = \frac{P_2}{a_2E_2} \quad (28)$$

which gives an additional equation involving σ_1 and σ_2 or P_1 and P_2. Equation 27 may be interpreted in terms of the stress-strain diagrams of the materials as shown in Fig. 38, which should be self-explanatory. Combining Eqs. 26 and 28, we obtain

$$P_1 = \frac{P}{1 + a_2E_2/a_1E_1} \quad \text{and} \quad P_2 = \frac{P}{1 + a_1E_1/a_2E_2} \quad (29)$$

and, since $\sigma_1 = P_1/a_1$ and $\sigma_2 = P_2/a_2$, the stress in each of the two parts may be found from the foregoing equations if the property of E for each part is known in addition to the cross-sectional areas a_1 and a_2 and the total load P.

Illustrative Problem

Problem 34. A steel bolt extends through a cast-iron tube or sleeve as shown in Fig. 39a. The pitch of the threads on the steel bolt is $\frac{1}{8}$ in.; the diameter of the bolt (and inner diameter of the tube) is $\frac{3}{4}$ in., and the outer diameter of the tube is $1\frac{1}{2}$ in. Let subscript 1 refer to the steel and subscript 2 to the cast iron, and let it be assumed that $E_1 = 30 \times 10^6$ and $E_2 = 15 \times 10^6$ lb per sq in. Let it be as-

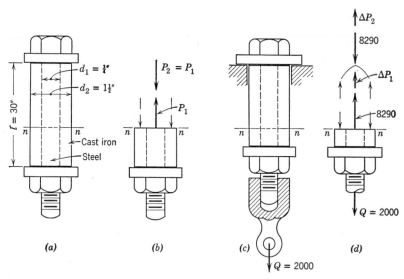

Fig. 39. Stresses in a two-material body under various conditions of loading.

sumed also that the two bodies act elastically. (a) If the nut is tightened by one fourth of a turn after it comes in contact with the cast-iron sleeve, what will be

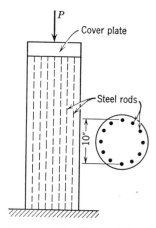

Fig. 40. Concrete compression block reinforced with steel rods.

the tensile stress in the steel bolt? (b) If then an additional force $Q = 2000$ lb is applied to the steel bolt as indicated in Fig. 39c, what will be the tensile stress in the bolt?

Solution. (a) From the conditions imposed on the deformations and type of loading, we have

$$e_1 + e_2 = \frac{1}{4} \times \frac{1}{8} = \frac{1}{32} \text{ in.} \quad \text{or} \quad \epsilon_1 + \epsilon_2 = \frac{1}{32 \times 30} \text{ in. per in.}$$

From the conditions of equilibrium as indicated in Fig. 39b, we obtain

$$P_1 = P_2 = P$$

But, from Eq. 20, we find

$$e_2 = \frac{P \times 30}{\frac{\pi}{4}\left[\left(\frac{3}{2}\right)^2 - \left(\frac{3}{4}\right)^2\right] \times 15 \times 10^6} \quad \text{and} \quad e_1 = \frac{P \times 30}{\frac{\pi}{4} \times \frac{9}{16} \times 30 \times 10^6}$$

Hence,

$$P = P_1 = P_2 = 8290 \text{ lb} \quad \text{and} \quad \sigma_1 = \frac{P_1}{a_1} = \frac{8290}{0.442} = 18{,}700 \text{ lb/in.}^2$$

and

$$\sigma_2 = \frac{P_2}{a_2} = \frac{8290}{1.33} = 6220 \text{ lb/in.}^2$$

(b) The condition imposed on the strains is that the changes or increments in the strains in the two materials caused by the change in the load Q from zero to $Q = 2000$ lb are equal. Thus,

$$\Delta\epsilon_1 = \Delta\epsilon_2 = \Delta\epsilon$$

each strain being an elongation (tensile strain). From the condition of equilibrium as indicated in Fig. 39d, we have

$$\Delta P_1 = Q - \Delta P_2 = 2000 - \Delta P_2$$

But

$$\Delta P_1 = \Delta\epsilon E_1 a_1 = \Delta\epsilon \times 30 \times 10^6 \times 0.442$$

$$\Delta P_2 = \Delta\epsilon E_2 a_2 = \Delta\epsilon \times 15 \times 10^6 \times 1.33$$

Hence

$$\Delta\epsilon = \frac{2000}{33.26 \times 10^6} = \frac{60.4}{10^6} \text{ in. per in.}$$

$$\Delta\sigma_1 = E_1\Delta\epsilon = 1820 \text{ lb/in.}^2, \qquad \sigma_1 = 18{,}700 + 1820 = 20{,}500 \text{ lb/in.}^2$$

$$\Delta\sigma_2 = E_2\Delta\epsilon = 908 \text{ lb/in.}^2, \qquad \sigma_2 = -6220 + 908 = -5310 \text{ lb/in.}^2$$

Note. It is of importance to note that, in the foregoing problem, when the additional load Q was applied to the steel bolt, the load already on the bolt (applied by the cast-iron sleeve) decreased. Thus the actual change in stress in the steel is 1820 lb/in.^{2} instead of $Q/a_1 = 2000/0.442 = 4520$ lb/in.^{2} that would normally occur if the axial load were applied without the nut first being tightened. This favorable action frequently occurs in engineering machines and structures and has an important influence on the resistance of the members involved, especially under conditions of repeated stress.

Problems

35. A relatively short concrete cylindrical compression member of 13 in. diameter is reinforced with 12 steel rods, $\frac{1}{2}$ in. in diameter, arranged in a circle with a radius of 5 in. as shown in Fig. 40. A uniform pressure or load P is applied to each end surface of the member. The concrete outside of the reinforcing rods furnishes fire protection to the rods in addition to helping resist the load. If the load P causes an elastic compressive stress of 750 lb per sq in. in the concrete, what is the elastic stress in the steel rods, and what is the total load P acting on the member? Assume that the cover plates bear initially against the ends of the rods as well as against the concrete. The compressive moduli of elasticity of the concrete and the steel are, respectively, $E_1 = 2,000,000$ lb per sq in. and $E_2 = 30,000,000$ lb per sq in.

36. Two blocks, each 4 in. by 8 in. by 20 in., are placed side by side and used as a compression member, as shown in Fig. 41. A pressure or load P is applied to the top and bottom surfaces so that the two blocks shorten elastically the same amount. If one of the blocks is made of cast iron and the other of oak, what is the magnitude of the load P when the elastic compressive stress in the cast iron is 15,000 lb per sq in.? Also determine how far from the vertical center line of the member P acts. The compressive moduli of elasticity of oak and cast iron may be assumed to be 2,000,000 and 15,000,000 lb per sq in., respectively.

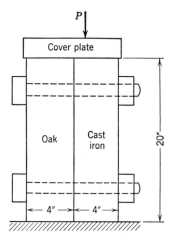

Fig. 41. Two-material compression block.

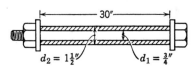

Fig. 42. Two-material member.

37. A brass bolt extends through a gray (cast) iron tube as shown in Fig. 42. Calculate the change in the internal force in the brass and in the gray iron by tightening the nut by one fourth of a turn. The pitch of the bolt threads is $\frac{1}{8}$ in. Assume that both members behave elastically. Use values in Table 1. *Ans.* 4370 lb.

38. A brass tube is attached firmly to the enlarged portions of a steel shaft to form the body shown in Fig. 43. An axial tensile load $P = 1450\pi$ lb is applied to the shaft as shown. The tube and shaft between the enlarged portions deform

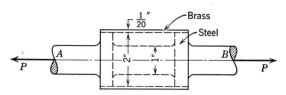

Fig. 43. Two-material member.

elastically the same amount. If the tensile modulus of elasticity for brass is two-fifths that for steel and E for steel is 30×10^6 lb per sq in., what is the tensile stress in the tube and in the shaft between the enlarged portions?

39. In Prob. 34 what value for Q would be required to reduce to zero the pressure of the cast-iron sleeve on the steel bolt, assuming that it could be done without the elastic properties of the material being exceeded?   *Ans.* 13,800 lb.

40. In the steel bolts in the flanged cast-iron pipe connection shown in Fig. 44, the nuts on the steel bolts are initially tightened (before the water enters the pipe) so that the tensile elastic stress in each of the eight bolts is σ_1. Let the subscript 1 refer to steel and the subscript 2 to the cast-iron flange. (*a*) Assume that the flanges are made of rigid material, and calculate the stretch e_1 of each bolt in

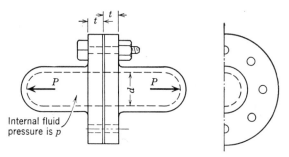

Fig. 44. Stresses in bolts of flange under various conditions of loading.

terms of σ_1, E_1, and t. (*b*) Assume next that the flange material is elastic and has a modulus of elasticity of E_2. Most of the deformation in the flanges occurs near the bolts. Let it be assumed that an area a_2 of the flanges is compressed uniformly and that the compressive deformation in this part of the flanges is one tenth of that of the bolts. Under this condition, will the stress in the bolts be greater or less than that caused by the condition under (*a*)? (*c*) After the bolts have been tightened under condition (*b*), let water be pumped in the pipe until the hydraulic pressure is p lb per sq in., causing a total tensile load on the eight bolts of $P = (\pi d^2/4)p$ lb. Calculate the stress in each bolt; the known quantities are E_1, E_2, t, d, the total area of the bolts a_1, and p. (*d*) What value of p would be required to reduce the value of the pressure between the flanges to zero and hence permit the joint to leak?

13. Stresses resulting from loads caused by temperature change.

When the temperature of a body is raised (or lowered), the material expands (or contracts) unless it is restrained from doing so by the forces exerted on it by other bodies; such restraining forces frequently do occur in machines and structures. The stresses caused by these forces may be found by first determining the expansion or contraction that would occur if the body were free to change its dimensions in response to the change in the temperature, and then assuming that the stress in the restrained body is the same as would be developed by forces causing elastic deformations that restore the body to its original dimensions. Thus the stress and restraining force in a bar whose thermal longitudinal expansion (or contraction) is prevented may be found as follows.

Let Δt denote the change in temperature of an unrestrained bar of material, and let n denote the coefficient of thermal expansion of the material (defined as the change in length of the bar per unit length per degree change in temperature). The total change in length e of the bar of length l for a somewhat limited range Δt of moderate temperatures in which the material does not change its structural properties may be expressed as follows:

$$e = nl\,\Delta t \quad \text{or} \quad \epsilon = \frac{e}{l} = n\,\Delta t \tag{30}$$

Certain nickel alloys, two of which are called Invar and Elvinar, have very low coefficients of thermal expansion and are therefore used for accurate measuring devices.

Average values of n for several structural materials, for use with temperature changes expressed by the Fahrenheit temperature scale, are as follows:

Brick	0.000 0050
Concrete	0.000 0062
Cast iron	0.000 0062
Steel	0.000 0065
Brass	0.000 0092
Aluminum	0.000 0130

If, however, the bar is attached to fixed supports at its ends and its temperature is changed, the thermal expansion or contraction will be prevented by the axial restraining forces P at its ends which cause an axial stress σ; the value of σ for any given temperature change Δt is the same as that developed by a force P which causes an elastic deformation equal (but opposite) to the expansion or contraction e accompanying the temperature change Δt. Thus

$$\sigma = E\epsilon = En\,\Delta t \tag{31}$$

It is very important to note that this value of σ is developed in the bar *only if the ends of the bar are completely restrained* so that no change in length of the bar occurs. The corresponding force P acting at the ends of the bar is

$$P = a\sigma = aEn\,\Delta t \tag{32}$$

In the foregoing discussion it was assumed that the change in temperature of the member occurred slowly so that an uneven distribution of temperature (temperature gradient) throughout the member would be avoided; in other words it was assumed that a temperature gradient Δt existed between the member and the restraining bodies to which it was attached but that no temperature gradient existed within the body.

Thermal Stresses. When a material is heated rapidly and hence is subjected to a temperature gradient or when a composite member consisting of two or more materials of different coefficients of expansion is heated (either slowly or rapidly), the various fibers of the member tend to expand different amounts. But, since the member is assumed to remain continuous (does not fracture), a system of stresses, called *thermal stresses*, is introduced, depending on the variation of temperature and of material throughout the member, and these thermal stresses may be superimposed on the stresses caused by the restraining forces of the outside contact bodies. These latter stresses are also frequently called thermal stresses but should be designated as steady-state thermal stresses to differentiate them from the former stresses.

Thermal Shock. When the member is subjected to a large and transient temperature gradient by very rapid heating or cooling, as, for example, when a hot body is submerged quickly in a cold solution (quenching), very large thermal stresses are developed which in turn sometimes cause fracture of the member before a steady-state temperature is reached. The term "thermal shock" is often used to indicate this transient condition. Repeated applications of thermal shock (sometimes called thermal stress fatigue) probably are involved in such fractures.

Illustrative Problem

Problem 41. Since 1932 several American railroads have been using continuous-welded rail in relatively short sections of the track. The temperature to which the rails in the track of one railroad are subjected varies from $-15°$ F in winter to $135°$ in summer. (*a*) If a continuous-welded steel rail (see Fig. 45) is 1 mile

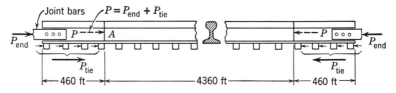

Fig. 45. Stress and deformation in continuous-welded railroad rail due to change of temperature.

long when its temperature is $60°$ F, how much will its length be increased by raising its temperature to $135°$ F, if it were free to expand? (*b*) Calculate the restraining forces required to be applied at its ends to prevent the expansion if the cross-sectional area of rail is 13 sq in. (*c*) Since the rail (see Fig. 45) expands very little in the track, the restraining forces calculated under (*b*) are actually applied to the rail. A part of the restraining force at each end is applied as a frictional force exerted by the joint bars on the rail; the magnitude of this frictional force depends mainly on the tensions in the bolts which cause the pressure of the joint bars against the rail. (In winter the play in the bolt holes is likely to be taken up, allowing the rails to come to a solid bearing against the bolts, and in summer to come to a solid bearing against abutting rail ends; when either of these conditions occurs, the end restraining forces may be expected to be greater than the frictional force mentioned.) The remaining portion of the required restraining force is applied by the ties through the fastenings which attach the rail to the ties. It has been found that the frictional force exerted by the joint bars on the rail can develop an axial compressive stress of as much as 5000 lb per sq in. on the rail cross section (that is, the end force due to friction can be as much as 5000 $\times$ 13 = 65,000 lb); it has been found also that a tie with the proper type of tie fastening can exert a restraining force on the rail as large as 700 lb per tie per rail. Assume that the end restraint of the joint bars on the rail 1 mile long is 65,000 lb and that a tie offers a restraint of 500 lb per rail, and calculate the number of ties adjacent to each end of the rail needed to prevent expansion of the main portion of the rail; also calculate the distance along the rail from each end in which the ties develop this restraining force, assuming that the distance between center lines of ties is 22 in. (For further details see "How Long Can a Rail Be?", *Railway Age*, Feb. 12, 1944, vol. 116, p. 340.)

Solution.

(a) $e = nl \, \Delta t = 0.0000065 \times 5280 \times 75$
        $= 2.57$ ft $= 30.8$ in. $=$ total expansion of free rail

(b) $\sigma = E\epsilon = En \, \Delta t$
        $= 30,000,000 \times 0.0000065 \times 75$
        $= 14,600$ lb/in.^{2} $=$ stress in rail if it is prevented from expanding by forces at its ends

        $P = 14,600 \times 13 = 190,000$ lb $=$ total force required to be applied at ends of rail to prevent expansion (see Fig. 45)

(c) $P_\text{tie} = P - P_\text{end} = 190,000 - 65,000 = 125,000$ lb $=$ resisting force required to be developed by ties near ends of rail (see Fig. 45)

        $N = \dfrac{125,000}{500} = 250 =$ number of ties at each end of rail needed to develop required resistance

        $L = 250 \times \frac{22}{12} = 460$ ft (approx.) $=$ length along rail from each of its ends in which ties resist expansion of rail

Thus, under the foregoing assumptions, the central 4360 ft of the rail would be completely restrained from expanding, as indicated in Fig. 45. The end lengths of 460 ft would expand somewhat, but experience shows that the expansion of the rail in the track does not cause serious trouble. It should be noted that this problem is really statically indeterminate; the simplifying assumption that all ties near the rail ends exert the same forces is known to be incorrect but may be used for approximate results.

Problems

42. A thin brass ring when at a temperature of 200° F just fits over a steel cylinder having a diameter of 4 in. and a temperature of 70° F. If the ring is left on the cylinder, what will be the stress in the ring when it and the steel cylinder have attained a temperature of 70° F, if we neglect the deformation of the cylinder caused by the pressure of the ring? For brass $E = 12 \times 10^6$ lb per sq in.

43. A slab of concrete is 25 ft long in winter when at a uniform temperature of 30° F. (a) How much longer will it be on a day in summer when its temperature is 120° F, if it is free to expand? (b) If the slab is partially restrained from expanding by abutments at its ends so that only one third of the free expansion is permitted, what will be the compressive elastic stress developed in the concrete? For concrete, $E = 2 \times 10^6$ lb per sq in.   *Ans.*   (a) 0.014 ft; (b) 745 lb/in.[2]

44. A steel tie rod containing a turnbuckle has its ends attached to rigid walls and is tightened by the turnbuckle in summer when the temperature is 90° F to give a stress of 1000 lb per sq in. What will be the stress in the rod in winter when the temperature of the rod is −20° F, assuming that the rod acts elastically? If for steel $E = 30 \times 10^6$ lb per sq in. and the elastic limit of the steel used is 35,000 lb per sq in., is the assumption of elastic action justified?

45. A steel cable of a small suspension foot bridge is 150 ft long on a warm day in summer when the temperature is 100° F. How much will it shorten when the temperature drops to −30° F in winter if it is assumed that the stress in it does not change as the length decreases?

46. The distance between two points is exactly 100 ft. This distance is indicated correctly on a surveyor's steel tape when used at a temperature of 70° F and subjected to a pull of 10 lb. If in measuring a certain distance the tape indicates the distance to be 100 ft when the tape is subjected to a temperature of 100° F and a pull of 20 lb, what is the correct distance being measured? The tape is $\frac{1}{32}$ in. thick and $\frac{3}{8}$ in. wide.   *Ans.*   100.022 ft.

47. A thin steel hoop on a wooden tank is tightened at a temperature of 70° F until the tensile stress in the hoop is 3000 lb per sq in. The outside diameter of the tank is 6 ft. (a) What will be the stress in the hoop when the temperature is −10° F, if it is assumed that no deformation in the circumferential direction occurs in the wooden tank, and hence no change occurs in the diameter of the tank? (b) If the wood does deform elastically as the stress in the hoop increases with decrease in temperature, what influence would this deformation have in changing the value of the stress calculated under (a)?

48. The Trans-Arabian pipe line for transporting oil from the Persian Gulf to the Mediterranean Sea is 1067 miles long. (See *Mechanical Engineering*, Oct. 1949.) A length of 350 miles of the pipe was laid above ground, and the operating

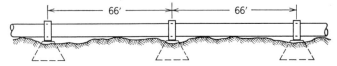

Fig. 46.   Stress and deformation of steel water pipe line due to change in temperature.

temperature of this portion in certain periods of the year increases 70° F above the temperature at which it was laid. The pipe is made of steel and has a diameter of 30 in. and a wall thickness of 0.25 in. Assume the pipe line to be straight. It is supported on concrete piers spaced 66 ft apart and rests on the ground between the piers (see Fig. 46). The pipe line was laid without expansion joints, but instead, at each concrete pier, the pipe was reinforced by a stiff steel ring which holds the pipe rigidly to the concrete pier, thereby preventing the longitudinal expansion of the pipe and thus developing an accompanying longitudinal (axial) stress in the pipe wall. (*a*) Calculate the increase in length per mile of the pipe that would be caused by the temperature change of 70° F, if the pipe were free to expand in length. (*b*) Calculate the axial compressive elastic stress caused by restraining the pipe from expanding in length. (*c*) Calculate the magnitude of the axial force required to cause the stress found in (*b*); this force is applied mainly by the concrete piers in much the same way that, in Prob. 41, the ties applied their forces to the rail.

14. Stresses in thin-walled circular cylinders. A *thin-walled* (hollow) circular cylinder subjected to uniform pressure on its inner surface is one in which the thickness of the wall or shell is small in

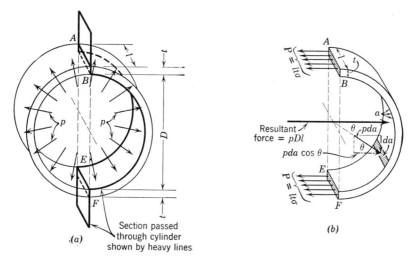

Fig. 47.   Stress in thin-walled cylinder caused by internal pressure.

comparison with the inner diameter of the cylinder. When this condition is satisfied, we may assume without serious error that the strains ϵ in the circumferential direction of all the circumferential fibers throughout the thickness of the shell are equal. Furthermore, if the (ideal) material is strained elastically and the hollow cylinder has open ends, the tensile stress σ, as well as the strain ϵ, in the shell will be uniaxial and distributed uniformly on each longitudinal cross section since $\sigma = E\epsilon$.

A hoop or tire shrunk on a wheel, an open-ended tank (standpipe), relatively large water, oil or gas pipe line, etc., satisfy rather closely these assumed conditions. In pressure vessels (boilers, tanks), the closed ends give rise to longitudinal stresses and strains on each transverse cross section of the shell in addition to circumferential stresses and strains. For approximate but useful results, however, it may be assumed that the circumferential stress in the shell is not influenced by the longitudinal stress and vice versa; the topic of biaxial stresses is discussed in Chapter VIII. Therefore, the following analysis of the stresses in a thin-walled cylinder will be assumed to be applicable to thin-walled pressure vessels, in addition to hollow cylinders in which the stress is uniaxial.

Circumferential Stress on Longitudinal Section of Shell. In accordance with the procedure given in Art. 8, a section represented by the heavy lines in Fig. 47a may be passed through the body. A free-body diagram of the portion of the body to the right of the section (consisting of one half of the shell) is shown in Fig. 47b. The equations of equilibrium applied to the forces shown in this figure give the relations between the circumferential tensile stress and the internal fluid pressure and dimensions of the hollow cylinder. The result is $\sigma_t = pD/2t$ which may be obtained as follows:

Let σ_t = circumferential tensile stress

p = uniform pressure (force per unit area) on inner surface of hollow cylinder

t = thickness of shell

D = inner diameter of cylinder (also approximately equal to outer diameter since t is small)

R = inner radius of cylinder

P = resisting circumferential force on one cross-sectional area of shell

The pressure of the fluid on the internal surface of the cylinder at any point is normal to the surface at that point, as indicated in Fig. 47; the resultant pressure (load) on one half of the shell (Fig. 47b) is resisted and held in equilibrium, by the internal forces P, P exerted by the other half of the shell at the areas AB and EF. One condition of equilibrium, therefore, may be expressed as follows:

Resultant horizontal force = total resisting force, or

$$p\,Dl = 2P = 2lt\sigma_t$$

The expression $p\,Dl$ for the resultant horizontal force follows from the fact that it is the sum of the horizontal components of the forces acting on the elementary areas. The force on an elementary area da is $p\,da$, and its horizontal component is $p\,da\cos\theta$. The resultant horizontal force, therefore, is $\int p\,da\cos\theta$, which may be written $p\int da\cos\theta$ since the pressure p is the same at all points on the semicylindrical area a.

But $da \cos \theta$ is the area formed by projecting the area da on a vertical plane, and, hence, $\int da \cos \theta$ is the area formed by projecting the semi-cylindrical area on a vertical plane, and is, therefore, equal to Dl. Thus, the resultant horizontal force is $p\,Dl$.

Furthermore, the fact that the internal resisting force P in Fig. 47b is the same at each of the two cross-sectional areas of the shell is obtained from the condition of symmetry or from the moment-equilibrium equation, and the expression $P = lt\sigma_t$ follows from the condition that σ_t is uniformly distributed on the area. Hence

$$\sigma_t = \frac{pD}{2t} = \frac{pR}{t} \tag{33}$$

in which R is the inner radius of the hollow cylinder.

Alternative Method. The section passed through the body may be the plane shown by the heavy line in Fig. 48a. The forces acting on

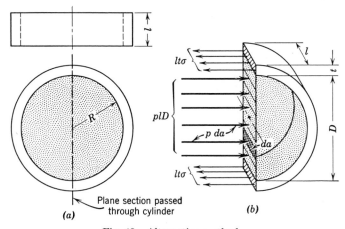

Fig. 48. Alternative method.

the portion of the body (half-shell and half of the fluid) that lie to one side of this section are shown in Fig. 48b. The equations of equilibrium applied to these forces give

$$p\,Dl = 2lt\sigma_t, \qquad \sigma_t = \frac{pD}{2t} = \frac{pR}{t} \tag{33a}$$

Stress in Transverse Section. The total force of the fluid against the end of the cylinder in Fig. 49 or against the spherical surface in Fig. 50 must be held in equilibrium by the total resisting force on a transverse section of the cylinder or sphere as indicated in Figs. 49 and 50. The total force (load) against the end of each body is $p(\pi D^2/4)$, and the

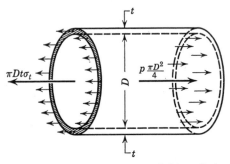

Fig. 49. Stress on transverse sections of thin-walled cylinder.

total resisting force in each case is $\pi D t \sigma_t$. Hence, the condition of equilibrium requires that

$$p\,\frac{\pi D^2}{4} = \pi\, Dt\sigma_t$$

Thus

$$\sigma_t = \frac{pD}{4t} = \frac{pR}{2t} \tag{34}$$

In Eqs. 33 and 34, p and σ_t must be expressed in the same units (usually pounds per square inch), and D and t must be expressed in the same units (usually inches).

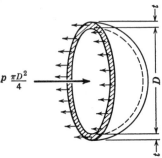

Fig. 50. Stress in thin-walled sphere.

A comparison of Eqs. 33 and 34 shows that the stress on a *longitudinal* section of a thin-walled cylinder due to an internal fluid pressure is twice as great as that on a *transverse* section of the same cylinder.

Problems

49. Large welded-steel pipe lines, 30 to 34 in. in diameter, are used for the long-distance transmission of oil and gas. Pumping stations are located along this pipe line, usually 75 to 100 miles apart. As the gas leaves a pumping station, its pressure may be as high as 700 to 1000 lb/in.[2] This pressure decreases as the gas flows at a speed of 15 to 20 miles per hour through the pipe to the next station. One such pipe line has a wall thickness of $\frac{3}{8}$ in. and an outer diameter of 30 in. The maximum gas pressure is 850 lb/in.[2] What is the maximum circumferential tensile stress in the wall of the pipe caused by the gas pressure? (For additional information see "Design Features of the Trans-Arabian Pipe Line" by S. P. Johnson in *Mechanical Engineering*, Oct. 1949, pp. 821–823.)

50. A steel standpipe, 8 ft in diameter, is 60 ft high. When it is full of water, what is the circumferential stress in the plate near the bottom of the standpipe if the thickness of the plate is $\frac{3}{8}$ in.? *Hint.* Since water weighs 62.5 lb per cu ft, the pressure (in all directions) at the bottom of the standpipe is 62.5×60 lb per sq ft.

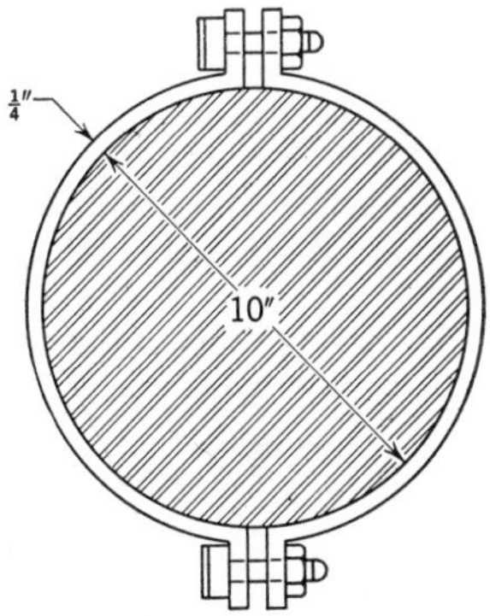

51. An aluminum band, $\frac{1}{4}$ in. thick and 3 in. wide, is tightened on a steel cylinder (Fig. 51) by turning the nuts on the bolts until the tensile force in each of the two bolts is 15,000 lb.

Fig. 51. Band tightened on smooth cylinder.

Assume that the aluminum acts elastically and that the cylinder is rigid but has a smooth surface. (*a*) What is the pressure per unit area of the cylinder on the band? (*b*) How much does each half band stretch? (*c*) What is the stress in the band?

Ans. (*a*) 1000 lb/in.[2]; (*b*) 0.0314 in.; (*c*) 20,000 lb/in.[2]

52. A standpipe having a diameter D of 72 in. resists an internal water pressure p of 120 lb per sq in. at a given section of the standpipe. The two ends of the cylindrical shell at this section are connected by a double-riveted lap joint (see Fig. 52). The thickness t of the shell or plate is $\frac{7}{16}$ in., and the two rivets occur every 3.5 in. ($l = 3.5$ in.). Calculate the force P transmitted in the circumferential direction through each pair of rivets along the joint. (*b*) After calculating the value of P, use this value in determining the circumferential stress in the shell of the plate, and check the result with the result obtained from Eq. 33.

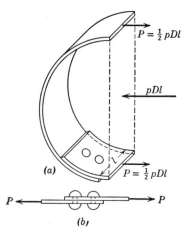

(a)

$P = \frac{1}{2} pDl$

pDl

$P = \frac{1}{2} pDl$

$P \longleftarrow \qquad \longrightarrow P$

(b)

Fig. 52. Stress in boiler joint.

53. The steel tire for a locomotive driving wheel has an internal diameter $\dfrac{d}{1500}$

less than that of the wheel on which the tire is to be shrunk, where d is the diameter of the wheel. The value of d is 60 in., and the value of t, the thickness of the tire, is $\frac{3}{4}$ in. If it is assumed that, after the tire is shrunk on the wheel, the diameter of the wheel is not changed by the pressure of the tire, find (a) the elongation of the tire, (b) the tensile stress (hoop tension) in the tire, and (c) the pressure of the tire on the wheel. *Ans.* (a) $e = 0.126$ in.; (b) $\sigma = 20,000$ lb per sq in.; (c) $p = 500$ lb per sq in.

54. A high-strength steel ring or hoop, having a proportional limit of 100,000 lb per sq in., an inside diameter of 39.9 in., and a thickness of $\frac{1}{4}$ in., is heated until it just fits over a smooth rigid cylinder which is at room temperature. The diameter of the cylinder is 40 in. After the ring has cooled to room temperature, (a) what is the stretch of the ring per unit of length, if it is assumed that the diameter of the cylinder does not change; (b) what is the tensile stress in the ring; and (c) what is the pressure of the cylinder on the ring? *Ans.* (a) 0.0025; (b) 75,000 lb per sq in.; (c) 937 lb per sq in.

55. The pressure in the cylinder of a steam engine (Fig. 53) is 120 lb per sq in., and the internal diameter D of the cylinder is 14 in. How many $\frac{3}{4}$-in. bolts are

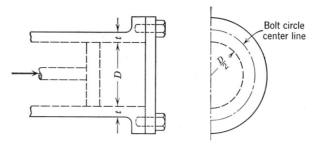

Fig. 53. Steam cylinder and piston.

required for strength if the tensile stress in the bolts is not to exceed 8000 lb per sq in.? What should be the thickness t of the walls of the gray-(cast-)iron cylinder to satisfy the requirement for strength if the tensile stress must not exceed 800 lb per sq in.? *Note.* The maximum stress specified is taken relatively low, owing to the fact that the load is applied with more or less impact. Moreover, the requirement for strength in many problems is not the governing requirement. In this problem, for example, the bolts should be large enough to prevent a workman, with ordinary tools, from twisting off the heads. Further, the requirement for tightness of the joint may determine the number of bolts. Similarly, the thickness of the wall may be influenced by the considerations of heat loss or of ease and reliability in casting, etc.

56. In the original design of a long pipe line for transmitting oil (see Prob. 49) it was proposed to install eight pumping stations distributed along the pipe line to maintain the desired rate of flow of the oil. It was later decided to decrease the number to six pumping stations by increasing the discharge (exit or down-stream) pressure at each station. In order to strengthen the pipe to resist this increased pressure, it was necessary to increase the pipe wall thickness from $\frac{1}{4}$ in. to the next size of $\frac{7}{16}$ in. on the down-stream side of each pumping station. If the pressure drop in the pipe is a linear function of the distance along the pipe and the total pressure drop between two stations 175 miles apart is 800 lb/in.[2], how many miles of pipe with a wall thickness of $\frac{7}{16}$ in. must be used between the two stations? Assume that circumferential stress in the pipe is 33,800 lb/in.² and that the pipe has an inside diameter of 30 in.

15. Stresses at abrupt change in cross section. Stress concentration. Let an axially loaded member have an abrupt change in section such as an axially loaded flat plate containing semicircular grooves, or fillets, or a circular hole as shown in Figs. 54 to 57. The

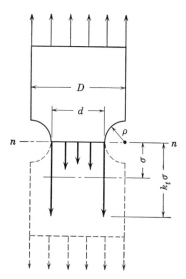

Fig. 54. Stress distribution at abrupt change in cross section.

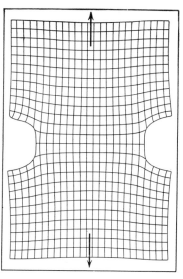

Fig. 55. Effect of abrupt change in cross section on elastic strain distribution at the change in section.

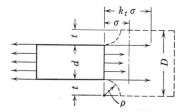

Fig. 56. Stress distribution at fillet.

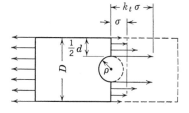

Fig. 57. Stress distribution at hole.

longitudinal elastic strains at any change in section are not uniformly distributed over the section, as is indicated in Fig. 55 for the plate containing the semicircular grooves. Figure 55 represents the strains in a rubber model of the actual plate. In rubber the strains are relatively large and hence may be observed with the naked eye, but they are distributed approximately the same as would be the very small elastic strains in a similarly shaped and similarly loaded metal member. The elastic-stress distribution at section nn, as shown in Fig. 54, may be determined approximately by multiplying the longitudinal strain at each point in the section nn, as shown in Fig. 55 by the modulus of elasticity ($\sigma = E\epsilon$) as explained in Art. 7. The elastic-stress distributions shown in Figs. 56 and 57 may be obtained in the same manner. However, it is difficult to measure the strains accurately over the short lengths of fibers involved, and, hence, the stress distribution is usually found by other means, one of which is the photoelastic method.

The maximum elastic stress that occurs at each abrupt change in cross section is greater than the average stress P/a where a is the area of the net or small portion of the section at the abrupt change of section. The maximum stress at such changes in section usually is called a stress concentration, and the factor by which P/a must be multiplied to obtain the value of the maximum stress for axially loaded members is called an ideal, theoretical, or elastic-stress-concentration factor and is denoted by k_t. Thus,

$$\sigma_{\max} = k_t P/a \tag{35}$$

The value of k_t depends on the geometry * of the member: that is, on the relative values of the dimensions of the member in the neighborhood of the stress concentration.

Values of k_t for the types of abrupt change of section indicated in Figs. 54 to 57 are given as ordinates to the curves in Fig. 58; the abscissas for the curves are values of the ratio ρ/d, which takes account of the geometry or shape of the change in section.

An important fact should be noted in Fig. 58: namely, that, if the radius ρ at the change in section is relatively large ($\rho/d = 0.5$ approx.), the value of k_t is relatively small. On the other hand, when the radius ρ is relatively small, the value of k_t is relatively large. This fact means that, whenever possible, a fillet in a load-resisting member should have as large a radius as practicable, so that the change in cross section is made as gradual as is feasible. Likewise, any other change in cross section should be made as gradually as possible so that k_t will be small.

Significance of Stress Concentration. Since nearly all machine and structural members have abrupt changes of cross section at which

---

* The value of the *effective* stress concentration, which is influenced by the properties of the material as well as by the geometry of the member, is discussed in Art. 17.

stress concentrations occur, it would appear that it would always be necessary to use the stress-concentration factor in determining the value of the significant stress in the member and computing the load to which the member is to be subjected. Indeed this is especially important if the material in the member is brittle or if the loads on a ductile member are repeated many times as will be discussed in Chapter IX. How-

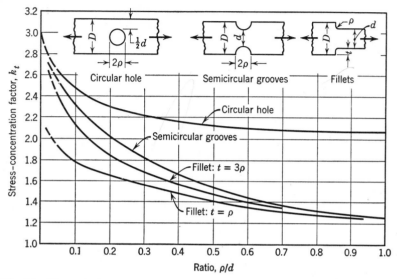

Fig. 58. Theoretical stress-concentration factors for three types of abrupt changes in cross section.

ever, for members made of ductile metal and subjected to static loads and to essentially unidirectional stress, stress concentrations fortunately are usually relatively unimportant, as will be shown in Art. 17.

Problems

57. A flat plate subjected to an axial load $P = 100,000$ lb has a thickness of $\frac{1}{2}$ in. and contains fillets as shown in Fig. 56. If the dimensions of the plate and fillet are $D = 10$ in., $d = 8$ in., $t = \rho = 1$ in., compute the maximum tensile stress in the plate. Assume that the maximum stress does not exceed the proportional limit of the material. *Ans.* 44,000 lb/in.²

58. Solve Prob. 57 if all quantities are as given except that $t = 3\rho = 1$ in., $\rho = \frac{1}{3}$ in.

59. Let it be assumed that a plate contains semicircular grooves and has the dimensions $D = 10$ in., $d = 8$ in., $\rho = 1$ in. If the plate is made of brittle material whose stress-strain diagram is approximately a straight line (elastic) up to the ultimate strength of the material, compute the ultimate load P that will cause fracture of the plate. The ultimate tensile strength of the material is 50,000 lb/in.^{2} The plate thickness is one inch. *Ans.* 180,000 lb.

60. Let a flat plate contain a hole as in Fig. 57, and let the values of P, D, d, and ρ have the same values as in Prob. 57. Compare the value of the maximum elastic tensile stresses in the two plates.

§ 2   Inelastic Behavior

16. Complete stress-strain diagram. Properties of Materials.
The terms stress and strain were defined in Arts. 5 and 6, respectively, and it was shown in Art. 7 that a definite relationship exists between stress and strain at any point in a load-resisting member; namely, stress is approximately proportional to the strain at the point, provided that the material acts elastically. This means that the stress must not exceed a value called the proportional limit of the material. This property of a material is of considerable importance as a measure of the useful strength of the material in a load-resisting member if the member will cease to perform its function satisfactorily when it is strained beyond its limit of elasticity; the member is then said to be given an inelastic strain or a plastic strain.

Since, under some service conditions, load-resisting members may be subjected to small amounts of inelastic strains without damaging their load-carrying function, it is important to consider the stress-strain diagram and the properties of a material beyond the elastic range of behavior of the material. Furthermore, a knowledge of the inelastic properties of material is of importance also in the process of forming and fabricating a member of the given material into a load-resisting member in a structure or machine.

In testing the material to obtain the experimental data for plotting the complete stress-strain diagram for the material, the test * sample or specimen usually consists of a straight bar of the material having a constant cross section for a distance on both sides of the midlength of somewhat more than $l/2$, where l is a gage length whose increase (or decrease) e in length is to be measured by an extensometer at regular intervals of increasing values of the axial load P. The strain is computed from $\epsilon = e/l$, and the stress caused by the load P is found from $\sigma = P/a$. Several corresponding pairs of values of ϵ and σ are obtained in the test and are plotted to give the stress-strain curve. The relation between stress σ and strain ϵ, found experimentally as indicated in the foregoing precedure, is represented, within approximate limits, by the stress-strain graph in Fig. 59a; the first part of the curve

---

* See p. 1389 to p. 1409 of the ASTM Standards, 1952, for description of methods of conducting tension and compression tests.

COMPLETE STRESS-STRAIN DIAGRAM

in Fig. 59a is drawn to a larger scale in Fig. 59b. The part of the curve from F to G will exist only if the material is ductile (which means that it will deform inelastically a considerable amount before fracture), such as structural steel and aluminum alloys used in airplane construction. Thus, if the material is relatively brittle,* such as heat-treated (hardened) high-carbon steel, and certain cast metals, the stress-strain curve will be represented by a graph like that shown in Fig. 60a.

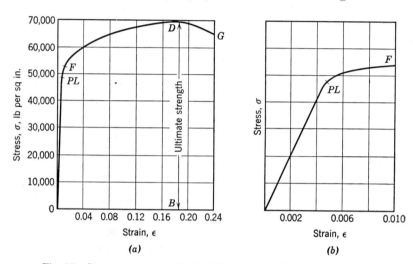

Fig. 59. Stress-strain curve for ductile material without a yield point.

Proportional Limit. As noted in Art. 7 and indicated in Fig. 59b it is found that, for most materials used for load-resisting members, the stress increases as the strain increases in practically the same ratio; thus, if the stress is doubled, the strain likewise is doubled, etc.; that is, the stress-strain curve is a close approximation to a straight line until the stress reaches a value called the proportional limit. This stress is represented by the ordinate to the point PL in Figs. 59 and 60. Therefore the *proportional limit* of a material is defined to be the greatest stress that can be developed in the material without causing a deviation from the law of proportionality of stress to strain.

---

* The stress-strain curves for concrete, gray-iron casting, alloyed aluminum, alloyed magnesium, bronze, stainless steel, etc., are curved slightly practically all the way from zero stress to the fracture stress, but it may be assumed, without serious error, that the first part of the curves, corresponding to relatively small stresses usually used in design, are straight lines. The proportional limit of materials such as these is difficult to obtain because it is difficult to determine just where the stress-strain relationship begins to be curved.

Stiffness. Modulus of Elasticity. The constant ratio between stress and strain below the proportional limit, called the modulus of elasticity, as noted in Art. 7, represents the rate at which the material deforms elastically with respect to stress, and, hence, is a measure of the general property of stiffness of the material, which is an important property of material in load-resisting members.

Elastic Limit. If the load on the bar or specimen is released after the bar has been stressed beyond the proportional limit, the bar usually will not return to its original length but will retain a part of its

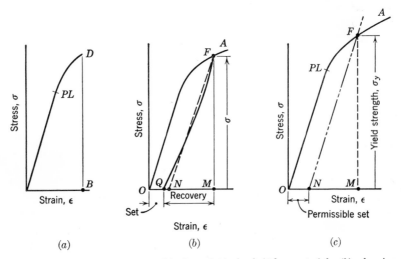

Fig. 60. Stress-strain curves (*a*) for relatively brittle material, (*b*) showing permanent set, (*c*) showing yield strength.

deformation. The deformation per unit of length (strain) retained by the bar after the load (and stress) has been reduced to zero is called the *permanent set* or merely the *set.* For example, let the bar be subjected to the stress σ, represented by the ordinate MF to the point F on the stress-strain curve in Fig. 60*b*, the strain corresponding to this stress being OM. If the load is released gradually, the stress-strain curve will be represented by a curve such as FQ, which can be represented approximately by the straight line FN drawn parallel to the straight-line * portion of the stress-strain curve below the proportional limit. That is, part of OM, represented by QM, is recovered, but a

---

* This deviation of the stress-strain curve (FQ), corresponding to unloading of the inelastically strained bar from a straight line (FN), was first noted by Johann Bauschinger and is known as the Bauschinger effect.

part, represented by OQ, is retained by the bar. OQ, therefore, represents the *set* corresponding to the stress σ.

The magnitude of the set depends on the stress σ to which the bar has been subjected. There is a stress σ called the elastic limit, such that the application of a stress larger than σ leaves a permanent set, but the application of a stress equal to σ or less than σ does not leave any set. Hence, the *elastic limit* of a material is defined to be the maximum stress that can be developed in the material without causing permanent set. It is found that for most elastic materials the elastic limit has approximately the same value as the proportional limit of the material, and in technical literature the proportional limit frequently is called (though incorrectly) the proportional elastic limit.

The elastic limit and proportional limit are important properties, especially if a member made of the material cannot be allowed to have any permanent set, such as, for example, a tooth of a spur gear or a bolt used to resist tension in a clamp which must remain tightly clamped. However, as already noted, there are many load-resisting members in which a small amount of permanent set does not damage seriously the load-carrying usefulness of the member, and hence another property called yield strength, as described in the next paragraph, based on a certain small permissible set, is often specified for determining the useful strength of the material in such a member.

Yield Strength. The yield strength of a material is defined to be the maximum stress that can be developed in a test specimen of the material without causing more than a specified permissible set; a permissible set of 0.10 or 0.20 per cent (which means a set of 0.001 or 0.002 in. per in.) frequently is specified as the permissible set for metals. The value of the yield strength may be found by first plotting a stress-strain curve (Fig. 60c) from test data and then laying off on the axis of strain the permissible set ON and drawing a line from N parallel to the straight-line portion of the stress-strain diagram. This line from N intersects the stress-strain curve at the point F; the ordinate FM is the yield strength.

This method of obtaining the yield strength is usually called the *offset method*, since the assumption is made that the distance ON, by which the line FN is offset from the straight-line portion of the curve, represents the permanent set in the material when the stress has the value represented by FM. This assumption, though usually somewhat erroneous as indicated in Fig. 60b where the actual set OQ is less than ON, gives a value of yield strength FM which corresponds to a permanent set that is equal to or less than ON.

It should be noted that a yield-strength value corresponding to a very small offset gives a reproducible and significant value approximately equal to the proportional limit and avoids the difficulties of determining the proportional limit as the point of tangency of the straight-line portion of the stress-strain diagram and a curved portion of very gradual curvature. Moreover, for most load-resisting members a yield strength corresponding to an offset of an appreciable amount (such as 0.2 per cent) is more meaningful than a value of the proportional limit, particularly for ductile metals subjected to static loads.

Yield Point. There are certain materials, such as mild steel, that have a stress-strain diagram as shown in Fig. 61a; this diagram is

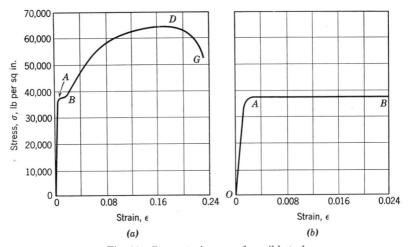

Fig. 61. Stress-strain curve for mild steel.

characterized by a flat, horizontal portion *AB* that follows immediately after the elastic limit and proportional limit, as shown by the part *OAB* from Fig. 61a which is replotted in Fig. 61b. Thus, when this stress is reached, the strains continue to increase without any increase in stress. The stress at which this action occurs is called the yield point, and is represented by the ordinate to the part *AB* of the stress-strain curve in Fig. 61. Thus, the yield point of a material is defined to be the minimum stress in the test specimen of the material at which the material deforms appreciably without an increase in stress.

Significance of Yield Point. The stretch that occurs in a bar subjected to direct axial tension while the stress is at the yield point is represented by the portion *AB* of the curve in Fig. 61. This stretch is large in comparison to the stretch that occurs in stressing the bar to the proportional limit. The stretch in a structural-grade steel bar 10 ft long at the proportional limit is about 0.0012 in./in., giving a total stretch of $e = \epsilon l = 0.0012 \times 120 = 0.144$ in. On the other hand, the stretch that occurs in the bar at the yield-point stress may be as much as 0.025 in./in., giving a total additional stretch of $e = 0.025 \times 120 = 3.0$ in. Thus, it can be seen that a substantial change in the length of the member occurs at the yield-point stress.

Usually, when such a bar is a part of a machine or structure, the change in length (or shape) that occurs while the stress is at the yield-point value is often sufficient to damage the load-resisting function of the machine or structure, although perhaps a greater load than the

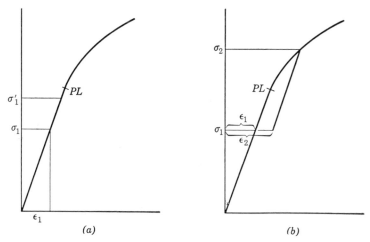

Fig. 62. Stress-strain diagrams indicating meaning of single-valued relationship between stress and strain.

yield-point load would be required to cause collapse or fracture of the machine or structure.

Single-valued Relationship between Elastic Stress and Strain. It is important to observe that, when the behavior of a material is elastic, a given stress is always accompanied by a definite value of strain, and vice versa. Thus, in Fig. 62a, when the stress at a point in the material has the value σ_1, the strain at the same point will always be ϵ_1 without regard to the manner in which the *elastic* stress was produced. For example, the stress could be caused by gradually increasing the stress from zero to the value σ_1, or it could be the result of causing an elastic stress σ'_1 considerably larger than σ_1 and then decreasing the load until the value to stress is σ_1. If, on the other hand, the stress σ_1 is attained by first causing an inelastic stress indicated by σ_2 in Fig. 62b, and then the load is decreased until the stress is σ_1, the strain will not be ϵ_1 but will be ϵ_2. Thus, for a given stress σ_1, the strain may have either of two values, depending on the previous stress history, and, hence, there is not a single-valued relationship between stress and strain except within the wholly elastic behavior of the material. It should be noted also that, even though inelastic strains are produced by a given load, when the load is decreased (the material is unloaded), the material acts approximately elastically since the stress-strain curve for unloading is nearly straight and parallel to the elastic curve for loading.

Increase in Elastic Strength after Inelastic Deformation. Strain Hardening. It is important to note also that, after the material is given an

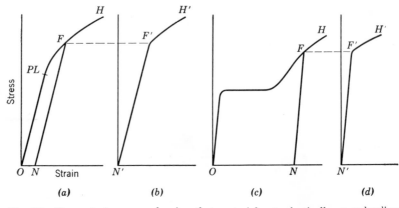

Fig. 63. Stress-strain curves showing that material acts elastically on unloading from a load that caused inelastic strain and also on loading a second time.

inelastic strain corresponding to the point F in Fig. 63a and c, and the load is reduced to zero (corresponding to the point N), the material will act approximately elastic on the second application until the stress reaches the value represented by the point F' as indicated in Fig. 63b and d. Further increase in the load (and stress) will then cause further increase in inelastic strains, approximately the same increase that would be caused if the load had not been reduced and applied a second time.

The increase in elastic strength caused by inelastic deformation is called strain hardening, and the process of producing the inelastic deformation is frequently called cold working. It is an important phenomenon in the use of load-resisting members at ordinary temperatures as well as in the fabrication of material.

Nature of Deformation That Occurs at Yield Point. An approximate, oversimplified description of the yield-point deformation may be given as follows: The deformation that occurs when the yield-point stress is first reached starts as localized slip bands visible as strain markings called Luder's lines; the slip planes or bands are often approximately in the direction of the maximum shearing stress. But the slip usually starts at a point of stress concentration or at a defect or weak point in the material.

The material that has been inelastically strained becomes stronger, as noted in the foregoing paragraph, but the inelastic strains cause stress concentrations in the adjoining elastic material which causes this material to deform inelastically with little or no increase in load. The slipping occurs along the planes of weakness determined by the crystalline orientation and the maximum shearing stress at the areas adjacent to the first inelastic strains. This process continues until all the material in the tension specimen has become deformed inelastically, after which further inelastic strains will occur only when a load greater than the yield-point load is applied. Sometimes the load required to start the inelastic deformation is greater than that required to continue the inelastic deformation. The names upper and lower yield points are sometimes used to indicate the two values of the yield points. The lower yield point, however, is the more significant as an indication of the useful strength of load-resisting members subjected to static loads.

As noted in a previous side heading, a material that requires an increasing load to cause additional inelastic strain is called a strain-hardening material. It should be noted that *fracture* occurs after the ability of the material to develop further inelastic deformation has been exhausted and the material has reached the limit to which it can be strain-hardened (strain-strengthened). Thus, fracture in a ductile metal is the end result of the inelastic-deformation process.

Ultimate Strength. If the load on the tensile test specimen is increased still further beyond the yield strength or yield-point load, the stress and strain will increase as indicated by the portion of the curve *FD* (Fig. 59a) if the material is ductile. The ordinate *BD* represents the maximum load divided by the original cross-sectional area and is called the tensile ultimate strength of the material. The ultimate strength for a brittle material is represented by the ordinate *BD* in Fig. 60a; a brittle material breaks when stressed to the ultimate strength, whereas a ductile material continues to stretch. The ultimate strength of a material, then, is defined to be the maximum stress that can be developed in the material, as determined from the original cross section of the bar or specimen; the cross section of the bar of a ductile material decreases somewhat as the bar is stressed above the yield strength and particularly as it is stressed beyond the ultimate strength.

After the ultimate strength of a ductile material is developed, the bar begins to "neck down," thereby rapidly reducing the area of cross section at the neck-down section, and the load required to cause the bar to continue to stretch decreases, as indicated by the curve DG (Figs. 59a and 61a). The load on the bar at the instant of rupture is called the *breaking* or *rupture load*. The breaking load divided by the area of the neck-down section is the value of the stress in the bar when rupture occurs, and this value is considerably greater than the ultimate strength, since the rate at which the cross-sectional area decreases is greater than the rate at which the load decreases as necking down occurs. This value of the stress at rupture is often called the *true stress* at rupture.

Ductility. Brittleness. Definitions. The capacity of a load-resisting material to undergo large permanent deformation while resisting a load is called ductility. Two quantities that are measures of ductility are usually found in the tension test. These are the percentage ultimate elongation and the percentage reduction of area at the fractured area. The per cent ultimate elongation is obtained by dividing the increase in gage length l of the tensile test specimen (Fig. 17a) after rupture has occurred by the original length l and multiplying by 100. The percentage of reduction in area is found by dividing the difference between the areas of the ruptured and the original sections by the area of the original section and multiplying by 100.

Significance of Ductility. A material that deforms inelastically only a small amount before fracture is designated as a *brittle* material. Ductility and brittleness are general properties and have significance depending on the conditions of use of the material. It is evident that a material that possesses a yield point is a ductile material, but many materials that do not exhibit a yield point have high degrees of ductility, such as aluminum alloys. The importance of ductility in decreasing the damaging influence of stress concentration is discussed in the next article.

Poisson's Ratio. As previously noted, if a bar is subjected to axial tensile forces at its ends, the bar elongates in the direction of the load: that is, in the longitudinal direction. It is found, however, that at the same time the lateral dimension of the bar decreases, and, hence, there is a lateral deformation accompanying the longitudinal deformation.

The ratio of the lateral *strain* (deformation per unit length in the lateral direction) to the corresponding longitudinal strain is called Poisson's ratio; it will be denoted by the symbol μ. The value of this ratio for steel for elastic strains is approximately $\frac{1}{4}$. Values of $\frac{1}{4}$ to $\frac{1}{3}$ frequently are used; the values for copper and aluminum for elastic strains

TABLE 1

VALUES OF STRENGTH, STIFFNESS, AND DUCTILITY OF VARIOUS STRUCTURAL MATERIALS

These are *average* values; test results for a specimen of a given material may deviate considerably from the values in the table.

Material	Tensile Strength, lb per sq in.		Compressive Strength, lb per sq in.		Shearing Strength, lb per sq in.		Modulus of Elasticity, lb per sq in.		Elongation in 2 in., per cent
	Yield Strength (See Art. 16)	Ultimate Strength	Yield Strength (See Art. 16)	Ultimate Strength	Yield Strength (See Art. 16)	Ultimate Strength	Tensile and Compressive	Shearing	
Structural steel (about 0.30% carbon), hot rolled	35,000	65,000	35,000	(a)	21,000	45,000	30,000,000	12,000,000	30
Steel (about 0.60% carbon), hot rolled	60,000	110,000	60,000	(a)	36,000	85,000	30,000,000	12,000,000	15
Structural nickel steel (3.5% nickel), hot rolled	55,000	110,000	55,000	(a)	30,000	65,000	30,000,000	12,000,000	25
Chrome–nickel (SAE 3245) steel, heat-treated (carbon 0.40–0.50%, Ni 1.50–2.00%, Cr 0.90–1.25%)	110,000	130,000	110,000	(a)	65,000	95,000	30,000,000	12,000,000	25
Gray (cast) iron *	......	20,000	......	75,000	......	30,000	15,000,000	6,000,000	1
Alloy (cast) iron *	......	45,000	......	90,000	......	55,000	20,000,000	8,000,000	1
Bronze,* rolled (copper 95%, tin 5%)	40,000	65,000	35,000	(a)	24,000	......	14,000,000	6,000,000	30
Brass,* rolled (copper 60%, zinc 40%)	40,000	60,000	35,000	(a)	24,000	......	12,000,000	5,000,000	30
Aluminum alloy,* rolled, tempered (aluminum 96%, copper 4%)	35,000	58,000	35,000	(a)	22,000	36,000	10,000,000	3,800,000	{20 15
Magnesium alloy,* high strength, extruded (magnesium 93%, aluminum 6.0%, zinc 0.7%)	30,000	42,000	28,000	(a)	16,000	20,000	6,500,000	2,600,000	16
Monel metal,* hot rolled (nickel 67%, copper 28%)	45,000	85,000	40,000	(a)	25,000	50,000	25,000,000	9,500,000	40
Plastic laminate,* glass fabric base, cross laminated	45,000	58,000	......	......	......	......	3,000,000	......	1
Concrete (1 cement:2 sand:3.5 crushed stone)	......	......	......	3,500	......	......	2,500,000	......	..
Timber { Yellow pine, small clear dry specimen	......	......	5,000	7,000	......	1,300	1,800,000	......	..
Timber { White oak, small clear dry specimens	......	......	4,300	7,000	......	1,800	1,600,000	......	..

(Compressive column for Timber: Parallel to grain)

* There are many materials in this classification with different compositions and made under different conditions which have a wide range of values (see, for example, Metals Handbook of the American Society for Metals. (Buckling is considered in Chap. VI.)

(a) The yield strength is considered to be the maximum static compressive strength of ductile metals.

are slightly larger than for steel. For inelastic strains the value is approximately $\frac{1}{2}$.

Caution. The equation $\sigma = E\epsilon$ has sometimes been interpreted (erroneously) to mean that, if an elastic strain ϵ occurs in a given direction, a stress equal to $E\epsilon$ is developed in that direction. But, in obtaining Poisson's ratio, we see that an elastic strain in the lateral direction occurs but no stress is developed in this direction; there are no external forces acting in the lateral direction to prevent the lateral deformation.

Properties of Structural Materials. Average values of various properties of a few of the more common engineering materials subjected to static loads are given in Table 1 for use in problems, particularly in the early chapters of this book. Various technical societies, governmental agencies, and industrial and research laboratories give, in their publications, values for an extensive list of materials for various uses. See, for example, *Metals Handbook*, of the American Society for Metals, *Strength of Metal Aircraft Elements* (Air Force, Navy, Commerce, ANC-5), Mar. 1955, etc.

It is important to note that values of properties of a material as given in tables are *average* values. The results of a test of a specimen of the material may deviate appreciably from the value given in a table. This arises from the fact that there are always uncontrollable factors in the method of manufacture, treatment, etc., of the material, and also in the method of testing. This fact usually is recognized in specifications of materials. For example, it is specified in the ASTM Standards that the ultimate tensile strength of structural steel for buildings shall be 60,000 to 72,000 lb per sq in.

Other Properties of Materials. There are other properties of materials that may be found from the stress-strain curve as obtained from the tension test, such as resilience and toughness; these are discussed in Chapter X. Furthermore, there are many properties that are obtained from tests other than the static-load tension test. One of these is the fatigue strength or endurance limit (see Chap. IX) which is a property that gives an indication of the resistance of a material to repeated loads. Likewise creep strength is a property of a material that indicates the resistance of the material to slow continuing deformation over long periods of time at elevated temperatures.

Problem

61. In a tension test of a steel bar 0.499 in. in diameter the elongation was measured over a gage length of 2 in. Successive readings of the load and of the extensometer were as given herewith. Determine the elastic limit, the proportional limit, the yield point and the yield strength for an offset of 0.2 per cent.

Load, lb	Reading of Extensometer, in.
500	0.0
1500	0.0004
500	0.0
3000	0.0008
500	0.0
4490	0.0014
500	0.0
5980	0.0018
500	0.0
7510	0.0024
500	0.0
8630	0.0029
500	0.0002
9500	0.0075
500	0.004
9600	0.0130

17. Influence of localized inelastic deformation on stress concentration in member made of material having yield point. If a load-resisting member made of ductile metal having a yield point (Fig. 61) contains an abrupt change in cross section and is subjected to a static load and uniaxial stress, the elastic-stress distribution at the abrupt change in section will be changed when the load is increased to a value that causes inelastic (plastic) strains to start in the most stressed portion of the material at and near to the abrupt change in section. The change in stress distribution caused by the inelastic strains reduces the stress concentration. This condition follows from the fact that the stress accompanying inelastic strains does not increase as the strains increase, but remains constant and equal to σ_y, as shown in the stress-strain diagram of Fig. 61 for a material having a yield point.

After the inelastic strains start in the elastically most stressed portion of the member, the load may be increased until it finally causes the inelastic strains to spread to all the other (elastic-strained) fibers at the cross section where the abrupt change is located. The deformation or deflection of the member as a whole is essentially elastic until the inelastic strains occur in all the fibers at the section where there is an abrupt change, as will be discussed in the next paragraph. Thus the load corresponding to this latter condition, often called the *fully plastic load,* for the member, may be considerably greater than the elastic-limit load, which is the load that causes inelastic strain to start in the most strained (and most stressed) fiber in the member.

These facts will be illustrated more specifically with respect to one type of abrupt change in change of section, as follows.

As shown in Fig. 64a, let a load-resisting member made of ductile metal having a yield point (Fig. 64b) consist of a plate that is subjected to a static central axial load P_y, called the <u>maximum elastic load</u>, and let the plate contain a centrally located transverse hole. The

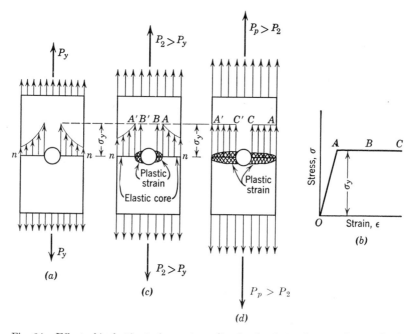

Fig. 64. Effect of inelastic strain on stress distribution in tension member made of material having a yield point.

load P_y causes the maximum elastic (concentrated) stress in the plate at a section nn through the hole to be equal to σ_y, which is the proportional limit of the metal (also the yield point for this material), as shown by the stress-strain curve in Fig. 64b. The stress distribution as shown by the ordinates to the curve in Fig. 64a indicates that there is a stress concentration at the hole (see Art. 15 and Fig. 57).

If the static load P on the plate is increased to a value P_2, greater than P_y, the strain in some of the fibers of section nn of the plate near the hole exceeds the proportional limit strain, as indicated by points along AB in Fig. 64b, and the stress distribution on section nn is as illustrated by the curves AB and $A'B'$ in Fig. 64c. The inelastic behavior in the member due to P_2, as indicated by experiments, is shown by the cross-hatched areas on either side of the hole in Fig. 64c. The remainder of the material near the cross section nn is still elastic, and the so-called elastic core insures that the deflection of the member as a

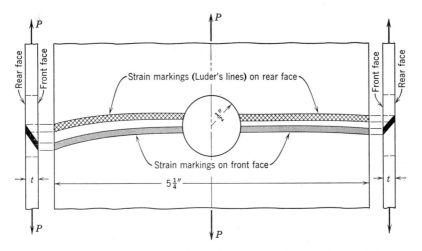

Fig. 65. Fully plastic condition in tension steel member containing a hole.

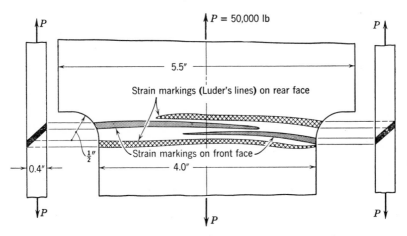

Fig. 66. Fully plastic condition in tension steel member containing a fillet.

whole will be essentially elastic until all the fibers in section nn are inelastically strained.

This latter condition will not occur until the axial load P is increased still more and reaches a value $P = P_p$, called the fully plastic load.

This load occurs when the strains and stresses of *all* the fibers at section nn have finally become stressed to their yield point stress. Under the action of the load P_p the stress distribution is as illustrated by the curve AC (and $A'C'$) in Fig. 64d, which means that under these conditions the stress distribution is uniform over the section through the hole; the stress concentration is almost completely removed, and the resulting value of the stress concentration factor is very nearly unity.

Experimental evidence of the behavior described in the foregoing paragraph is shown in Fig. 65, and similar behavior at an abrupt change in section caused by fillets is shown in Fig. 66. The sketches were made from photographs of the Luder's lines (strain markings) on surfaces of the two sides of the flat steel specimen soon after the tensile load P reached the fully plastic value. The solid black portions are the Luder's lines on the front face and the double cross-hatched portions are those on the rear face. The end or edge views of the material that has yielded are also shown. It will be observed that yielding occurs along planes that approximately coincide with the planes of maximum shearing stress.

Thus, although the fully plastic load causes only slight deformation of the member as a whole, a small increase in this load may cause large deformation of the member as a whole (constituting failure of the member by general yielding), provided that there is considerable elastically stressed material adjacent to the fully plastic section into which the plastic strains can penetrate rapidly; this adjacent material behaves elastically at the fully plastic load, but the stress in it may be only slightly less than the yield point, provided that the cross-sectional area of the elastically stressed adjacent portion is not markedly larger than the fully plastic section. This condition is satisfied in Fig. 66, but in Fig. 65 the size of the hole may be sufficiently large to cause fracture on the area through the hole before yielding of the adjacent material is developed (see Prob. 74).

Fully Plastic Load. When the load has reached the value shown in Fig. 64d, the dimensions of the plate in the sections near the hole usually will have become considerably distorted by the inelastic deformation, but this localized condition may or may not be sufficient to cause the member to cease to fulfill its function satisfactorily as a load-resisting member in a given structure or machine. Thus P_p is usually the failure load for the member although a larger load may be required to cause fracture of the plate. If the localized deformation that usually accompanies the load P_p does not cause failure of the member, the ultimate or fracture load as discussed in the next article may be the cause of failure.

Since the stress σ_y on the inelastically deformed section is nearly uniformly distributed and is caused by the load P_p, we may write

$$P_p = a\sigma_y \qquad (36)$$

This expression gives a value for P_p that usually is considerably larger than P_y, which is the load that first causes inelastic strain, given by the expression.

$$\sigma_y = k_t \frac{P_y}{a} \quad \text{or} \quad P_y = \frac{a\sigma_y}{k_t} \qquad (37)$$

After the fully plastic load is determined, the working load P_w is found by dividing the value of P_p in Eq. 36 by a factor of safety N_p. Thus,

$$P_w = \frac{P_p}{N_p} = \frac{a\sigma_y}{N_p} = a\sigma_w \qquad (38)$$

in which $\sigma_w = \dfrac{\sigma_y}{N_p}$ is a so-called working stress (see Art. 21).

Caution. Some confusion is likely to exist in the student's mind at this point in the analysis because the working load P_w in Eq. 38 will usually cause only elastic stresses in the member, although it is found from P_p which produces inelastic stresses. It may appear, therefore, that we are in reality using elastic stress analysis. Any such confusion or apparent inconsistency that may be suggested by this situation should be clarified by the observation that the main function of a member (as considered in this book) is to resist loads. Stresses are not of importance in themselves; their significance lies mainly in determining loads. Thus, after a reliable value of the safe or working load is found by any method, the stresses caused by it are of secondary importance.

The important value to be determined is a safe or working *load* based on a reliable value of the load that will cause failure of the member. For members subjected only to elastic behavior, this value may be determined satisfactorily by using a working stress since the stress is proportional to the load, but, if the member is strained inelastically, the fully plastic load or the ultimate load must be found (depending on which load is considered to be the cause of the failure of the member) in order to determine a working load.

The foregoing reasoning will be illustrated by applying it in the next paragraphs to a familiar member, namely, a simple riveted joint, and showing that, when the maximum load-carrying capacity of the joint is reached, the significant stresses on the areas involved are distributed approximately uniformly.

Fully Plastic Load for a Simple Riveted Joint. It is not the purpose of the following discussion to deal with riveted joints as such, but merely to make use of the riveted joint as an excellent example of a member in which several types of stresses occur and in which the fully plastic load (and ultimate load) for each type of stress is of importance in determining the maximum load-carrying capacity of the joint.

Figure 67 represents a single-riveted lap joint consisting of two ductile-steel plates of thickness t and width p joined by one steel rivet of diameter d. The joint is subjected to a direct axial load P. Let it be required to determine the fully plastic load on the joint. If it is assumed that the steel plates have a yield point σ_{ty} in tension and σ_{by} in bearing and that the steel rivet has a shearing yield point τ_y, the fully plastic load will be the smallest of three different values: namely, the fully plastic load P_{tp} that occurs when the stresses are uniformly distributed and equal to σ_{ty} in the section of the plate containing the hole (Fig. 67d), the fully plastic load P_{sp} that occurs when the shearing stress on the cross-sectional area of the rivet (Fig. 67g and f) is uniformly distributed and equal to τ_y, and the fully plastic load P_{bp} in bearing of the plate as described later in this article (Fig. 67i). Each of these three loads will now be determined.

Tensile Load P_{tp}. Let the joint be cut by a plane section through one plate, severing the plate through the center of the rivet hole (Fig. 67c), as was done in Fig. 64, and let the elastic-limit load be P_{ty} which will cause the maximum stress on the section to be equal to the yield point σ_{ty}. The tensile-stress distribution on the cut section under these conditions is approximately as shown in Fig. 67c. Although inelastic deformation of the plate starts at the load P_{ty}, the deformation will not usually be sufficient to damage the joint until the yield-point stress σ_{ty} is reached in all fibers (all fibers are plastically strained) across the cut section of the plate, as shown by the stress distribution in Fig. 67d. From Fig. 67d and the condition of equilibrium, the fully plastic load in tension may be written:

$$P_{tp} = t(p - d)\sigma_{ty} \quad \text{or} \quad \sigma_{ty} = \frac{P_{tp}}{t(p - d)} \tag{39}$$

Shear Load P_{sp}. Let the joint be cut by a plane section passing between the two plates and cutting the rivet in half. Figure 67e shows one part of the joint with the elastic-limit load P_{sy} that causes shearing stresses on the rivet cross section (Fig. 67f) probably as indicated by the ordinates to the curve over the rivet section, the maximum shearing stress being τ_y, the shearing yield point. The relationship between the elastic-limit load P_{sy} and the maximum shearing stress on the rivet

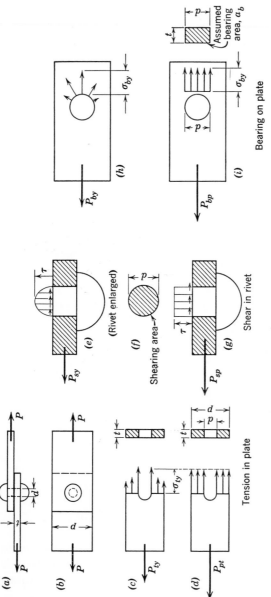

Fig. 67. Fully plastic condition in rivet joint.

section for elastic conditions is not known, and the curve shown in Fig. 67e is used here for illustrative purposes only.

Although inelastic deformation may begin in the rivet at the unknown elastic-limit load P_{sy}, it may not cause damage to the joint until the whole cross section of the rivet becomes inelastically stressed (fully plastic), as shown by the ordinates to the horizontal stress-distribution line in Fig. 67g, where the shearing stress is equal to τ_y at all points in the rivet cross section. Hence, we may say that the fully plastic load in shear is

$$P_{sp} = a_s\tau_y \quad \text{or} \quad \tau_y = \frac{P_{sp}}{a_s} \tag{40}$$

in which a_s is the area of the rivet cross section.

Bearing Load P_{bp}. Let the joint be cut so that we obtain Fig. 67h and let the bearing (compressive) stresses exerted on the inside of the rivet hole in the plate (or on the rivet) be as indicated by the radial arrows to the curve around the right side of the hole. The exact shape of this curve is not known, and the relationship between the elastic-limit load P_{by} and the maximum bearing stress σ_{by} is not known. However, as was true in tension of the plate and in shear of the rivet, the inelastic deformation due to the maximum bearing stress as shown in Fig. 67h usually does not damage the plate. Moreover, it may be assumed that inelastic deformation in bearing of the plate will not be excessive until the compressive stress σ_{by} is uniformly distributed over an assumed bearing area of dimensions t by d, where t is the plate thickness and d is the hole diameter. Thus the fully plastic load P_{bp} in bearing may be written

$$P_{bp} = a_b\sigma_{by} = td\sigma_{by} \quad \text{or} \quad \sigma_{by} = \frac{P_{bp}}{td} \tag{41}$$

The least of the three fully plastic loads as given by Eqs. 39, 40, and 41 is the fully plastic load for the joint, and, in some uses of rivets, this load may be considered to be the load that causes failure of the joint as will be discussed further in Art. 21. However, the load that causes failure of many riveted joints is the ultimate or fracture load, as will be discussed in Art. 20.

18. Influence of localized inelastic deformation on stress concentration in member of ductile material without yield point. If the member with an abrupt change in cross section such as that shown in Fig. 64 is made of a ductile metal that does not have a yield point, such as an aluminum alloy (Fig. 59), the stress continues to increase with the strain after inelastic strains start until the ultimate strength is approached, where there is usually a rather long part of the curve along which the stress remains nearly constant as the strains increase (Fig. 68).

Let the load on the member be increased to a value P_u that will cause the member to fail at section nn by a fracture (Fig. 68a) that begins at the edges of the hole. At this load the stress distribution on

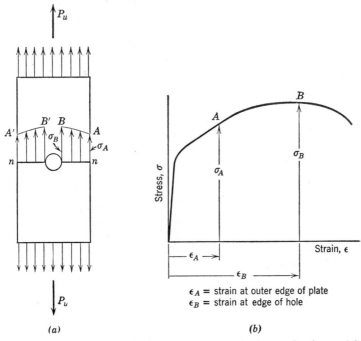

ϵ_A = strain at outer edge of plate
ϵ_B = strain at edge of hole

(a)   (b)

Fig. 68.   Influence of inelastic strains on stress in member made of material not having a yield point.

section nn may not be uniformly distributed but may be as shown by the curve AB (and $A'B'$), since the strain at the edge of the hole and at the outer edge of the plate correspond to different stress levels, say σ_B and σ_A, respectively, as shown in Fig. 68b. Consequently, the stress-concentration factor, though greatly reduced from the theoretical elastic value k_t, is not reduced to unity as was the case for the fully plastic load (see Eq. 39). The stress-concentration factor corresponding to the conditions described in Fig. 68 is called an effective or significant stress-concentration factor,* k_e. Its value depends on the geometrical

* This factor is usually greater than unity, although it is sometimes less than unity. For example, if a plate of structural-grade steel that contains a line of closely spaced holes perpendicular to the line of action of a tensile load that is applied to the plate to fracture it, the ultimate tensile strength of the plate based

shape at the abrupt change of section and also on the type of material. In riveted, bolted, and welded joints of aircraft structures a factor * of 1.15 to 1.20, equivalent to k_c, is usually assumed (see Art. 21). In the design of most pressure vessels and heavy structures the value of k_e is usually absorbed into what is called a factor of safety (see Art. 21).

Ultimate Load. The maximum stress at an abrupt section, such as at nn in Fig. 68a, in a centrally loaded member subjected to the ultimate load P_u is equal to the ultimate strength σ_u of the material. The equation relating P_u and σ_u is written as

$$\sigma_u = k_e \frac{P_u}{a} \quad \text{or} \quad P_u = \frac{a\sigma_u}{k_e} \tag{42}$$

in which k_e is the significant or effective value of the stress-concentration factor and a is the original (net) cross-section area.

The foregoing methods will be illustrated in a treatment of riveted joints in Art. 20 and of welded joints in Art. 19.

19. Ultimate load for a welded joint. A member, such as a welded or a riveted joint may fulfill its load-resisting function satisfactorily until the ultimate load for the member is reached, even though it is part of a structure that must act elastically or with only small inelastic deformations. This fact arises from the condition that such joints usually can yield relatively little compared to the primary members which they connect in the structure, because only a small amount of material in the joint can yield (deform inelastically) as the yielding spreads over the most stressed areas when the load is increased from the elastic-limit load at which yielding starts to the ultimate load of the joint. In other words, inelastic deformation starts as local yielding and remains mainly localized until rupture or fracture occurs, and hence it influences very little the deformation of the primary members connected by the joint. Thus the load-resisting capacity of such a joint usually is considered to be the ultimate load for the joint.

To illustrate the foregoing ideas let it be required to find the ultimate load for the fillet weld shown in Figs. 70 and 71. However, before doing so, it will be helpful to give a few brief comments concerning welding.

on the original net area of the plate through the section containing the holes will be greater than the ultimate tensile strength of a similar plate without the holes; that is, k_e is approximately 0.9 in this test. The reason for this apparently increased tensile ultimate strength of such a plate with the holes is that the holes tend to prevent lateral contraction (necking down) of the member at the section where the fracture occurs.

* Usually called a fixture factor in aircraft structural stress analysis.

Types of Welds. Welding consists primarily of the joining of two or more pieces of metal (called base metal) by the application of heat, causing localized consolidation of the metal of the pieces. The most common method of welding load-resisting members involves fusion (melting) of the metal, the heat being supplied in several different ways; in fusion welding, pressure between the pieces is not applied. Arc welding, gas welding, and Thermit welding are classified as fusion welding. The most widely used method is metal arc welding, which

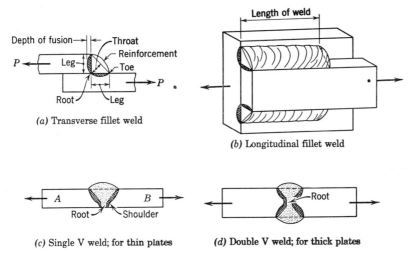

(a) Transverse fillet weld

(b) Longitudinal fillet weld

(c) Single V weld; for thin plates   (d) Double V weld; for thick plates

Fig. 69. Common types of welded joints.

is a localized progressive melting and flowing together of adjacent edges of the base-metal parts caused by high temperatures produced by an electric arc between a metal electrode or rod and the base metal. The welding material in the form of a welding rod or electrode, together with the adjacent base metals, melts and, on cooling, solidifies, thus joining the two or more pieces by continuous material.

The two main classes of welds are fillet welds and butt welds. These two types of welds with the names of the various parts of the welds are shown in Fig. 69. Attention should be called to the fact, however, that the sketches in Fig. 69 are rather misleading in indicating lines of demarcation between the base metal and the deposited weld metal, for, as already noted, in a satisfactory welded joint the weld consists of nearly uniform metal from the base metal of one member to the base metal of another member. The cross-hatched areas indicate the depth of fusion of the weld material with the base metal.

Fully Plastic Load on Welded Joints. Let the two ductile-metal plates in Fig. 70a that are joined by the longitudinal fillet welds be loaded as shown by the direct central static load P. It is required that the fully plastic load P_p for this joint be determined.

Let the planes nn cut the fillet welds through the section at the throat of each weld, and let the upper bar and the upper half of each weld be removed as shown in Fig. 70b. The significant shearing stress is considered to occur on the throat section. The load P is transmitted

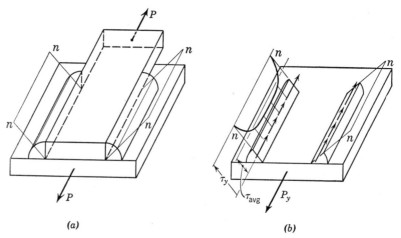

(a)   (b)

Fig. 70. Elastic loads for a fillet weld.

through the throat sections by the resisting shearing forces, as shown in Fig. 70b. The elastic shearing stresses which accompany this load are not uniformly distributed over the length of the throat of the weld. This fact is shown by the ordinates to the curve in Fig. 70b in plane nn where the ordinate represents the magnitude of the shearing stress on the throat area. At the ends of the weld the elastic shearing stress has its maximum value and is much larger than that at midlength of the weld. When the maximum elastic shearing stress first reaches a value equal to the shearing yield point τ_y, the corresponding load P_y on the joint is called the elastic-limit load. But, as already noted, this load does not represent the load-carrying capacity of the joint.

Value of Fully Plastic Load. If the load on the joint is increased to values above P_y, the shearing stress at the ends of the weld increase only slightly, because, at the yield point of metals used in such welds, the stresses do not increase very much when additional inelastic strains occur, as previously explained. But, in the middle portion of the length of the weld, the elastic shearing stresses, which are very much below the yield-point stress τ_y, will continue to increase (in welds of moderate length) until the distribution will be nearly uniform and will be approximately equal to the value τ_y as shown in Fig. 71a. When this distribution is attained, the load is called the fully plastic load and is designated by P_p. Under these conditions * the shearing stresses over the entire length of the weld approach the value of τ_y, and hence we may assume that the average stress τ_{avg} is nearly equal to τ_y. The

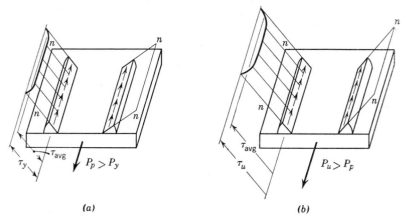

(a) (b)

Fig. 71. Fully plastic loads for a fillet weld.

total resisting shearing force is, therefore, $2a_t\tau_y$ where a_t is the area of the throat section of one of the fillet welds. From the conditions of equilibrium, we have

$$P_p = 2a_t\tau_y \quad \text{or} \quad \tau_y = \frac{P_p}{2a_t} \tag{43}$$

But, as already noted, P_p does not represent the load-carrying capacity of the joint.

Ultimate Load on Fillet Weld. The ultimate or fracture load for the welded joint of Fig. 70a will usually be greater than the fully plastic

---

* If the load is applied very rapidly, as under impact conditions, there may not be sufficient time for the inelastic strains to occur as they do under static loads, and hence the elastic-limit load may be important under impact conditions. Furthermore, in some metals, relatively low temperatures have the effect of reducing the ductility of the metal so that, for conditions of low temperatures, the inelastic strains may not occur. Under either of these conditions, the nonuniformity of the shearing stress over the weld-throat area must be taken into account in computing the ultimate load for the joint. Also, repeatedly applied loads tend to cause progressive fracture, called fatigue. This condition is especially important because the loads that cause such failures are usually much smaller than the fully plastic load, and hence the complete redistribution of stresses cannot occur.

load, because of the increases in resisting shearing stress due to strain hardening of the metal at the larger inelastic strains which occur before fracture. It may be shown, in the same way as in the foregoing paragraph, that the shearing-stress distribution on the weld-throat section that occurs just before fracture of the joint is approximately as shown by the ordinates to the curve in Fig. 71b. The average stress τ_{avg} represented by this distribution curve is nearly equal to the ultimate shearing strength. Hence the ultimate shearing resisting force is very nearly equal to $2a_t\tau_u$ in which a_t is the weld-throat area. Therefore

$$P_u = 2a_t\tau_u \quad \text{or} \quad \tau_u = \frac{P_u}{2a_t} \tag{44}$$

The use of the relationship in Eqs. 43 and 44 for design of welded joints is illustrated in Art. 21.

Illustrative Problem

Problem 62. A steel flat bar, 3.5 in. wide, 0.5 in. thick, and 20 ft long, is connected by a fillet-welded joint at one end to a wider bar or plate as shown in Figs. 69b, 70, and 71. The length of the weld on each side is 3 in., and the leg is $\frac{1}{2}$ in. The joint and bar together will be referred to as a simple structure consisting of the two parts. Determine the maximum load P that can be applied to the structure if the following requirements are met: (a) The behavior of the structure as a whole must be essentially elastic; the joint alone may be subjected to its ultimate load without contributing appreciable inelastic deformation to the structure, and the length of the joint may be considered to be negligible compared to the length of the structure; furthermore, the bar can resist loads up to its fully plastic load without causing appreciable inelastic deformation of the bar as a whole. The following values (in pounds per square inch) are given:

For the weld: $\tau_y = 20,000$, and $\tau_u = 45,000$; for the plate: $\sigma_{ty} = 35,000$, $\sigma_{tu} = 70,000$, and $E = 30 \times 10^6$.

Solution. The maximum load for the joint is the least of the following two values. Ultimate load for the welded joint:

$$P_{su} = 2a_t\tau_u = 2 \times 3 \times \frac{1}{2} \times \frac{\sqrt{2}}{2} \times 45,000 = 96,000 \text{ lb}$$

Fully plastic load for the bar:

$$P_{tp} = 3.5 \times 0.5 \times 35,000 = 61,500 \text{ lb}$$

This is the load that will cause a stress on each cross section of the bar just equal to the yield point, and any larger load will cause a large inelastic deformation.

Since the behavior of the structure must be essentially elastic, the maximum load is 61,500 lb.

The fully plastic load for the welded joint alone is only 42,500 lb:

$$P_{su} = 2a_t\tau_u = 2 \times 3 \times \frac{1}{2} \times \frac{\sqrt{2}}{2} \times 20,000 = 42,500 \text{ lb}$$

but this inelastic deformation of the joint alone in the fully plastic condition is not considered to be sufficient to destroy the elastic behavior of the structure.

Problems

63. In Fig. 72, $t_1 = t_2 = \frac{1}{2}$ in., and $b = 6$ in. Calculate the ultimate load P for the joint. It may be assumed that each weld transmits one-half the load and that $\tau_u = 35,000$ lb per sq in. for the weld material.

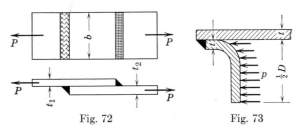

Fig. 72   Fig. 73

64. In Fig. 73, $t = \frac{3}{8}$ in., and the diameter D of the pressure vessel or boiler is 5 ft. If the steam pressure p in the boiler is 100 lb per sq in., calculate the shearing stress on the section through the throat of the weld. Also calculate the fully plastic load and the ultimate load for this joint if the shearing yield point and the shearing ultimate strength of the weld materials are 20,000 lb/in.^{2} and 42,000 lb/in.^{2}, respectively.   *Ans.* Fully plastic load = 500 lb/in.^{2}

65. Figure 74 shows a fixture in an aircraft structure in which a gusset plate of thickness $t = 0.050$ in. is welded into the corner of two intersecting tubes, each

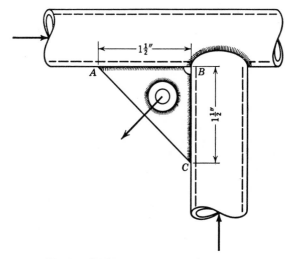

Fig. 74. Welded joint in aircraft structure.

of which has a wall thickness of 0.058 in. The gusset plate transmits a diagonal (45°) load P to the tubes. The gusset plate and tubes are made of an alloy steel, and the ultimate shearing strength on the throat area of the fillet weld connecting the gusset plate and tubes is τ_u = 43,000 lb per sq in. (see Table 2.61212 ANC-5, Mar. 1955). A factor of safety of 1.5 based on the ultimate strength of the material is usually required for primary members of an aircraft structure, and an additional factor equivalent to a stress-concentration factor at the ultimate load (see Art. 17) of k_e = 1.2 sometimes is employed for connections or fixtures that are used to join the primary members. Let it be required to find the working load for this fixture, using a factor of safety of 1.5.

66. In Fig. 75 is shown a part of an aircraft structure consisting of a streamlined tubular strut with a flat plate welded into the end of the tube for a distance of

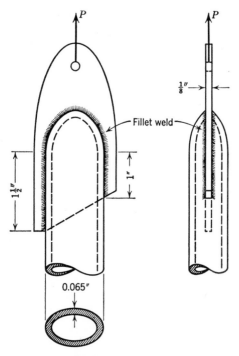

Fig. 75. Welded joint in aircraft structure.

$1''$ on one side and $1\frac{1}{2}''$ on the other (the weld along the rounded end is neglected). The ultimate strength of the weld material on the throat area in shear is τ_u = 43,000 lb per sq in. Determine the ultimate load P_u for the member. *Hint.* The weld throat is $2\frac{1}{2}$ in. long and 0.065 in. wide and occurs on two sides of the plate, making a total throat area of 5 in. by 0.065 in. *Ans.* P_u = 14,000 lb.

20. Ultimate load for a riveted joint. A riveted joint, as well as a welded joint, is usually considered to fulfill its function satisfactorily in a load-resisting structure until the ultimate or breaking load of the joint is reached, especially when the strength (rather than tightness) of the joint is the main factor considered. Three values of the ultimate load, however, must be obtained since the ultimate load for the joint may be limited by the stresses on any one of three areas: namely, the ultimate shearing stress on the cross section of the rivet as in Fig. 76a, the tensile stress on the cross section of the plate through the holes as in Fig. 76b, and the bearing (compressive) stress of the rivet on the plate indicated in Fig. 76b. It is assumed that other modes of failure will not occur if the usual joint dimensions are specified.

Before determining the three ultimate loads for a riveted joint it will be helpful to present brief comments concerning riveted joints,

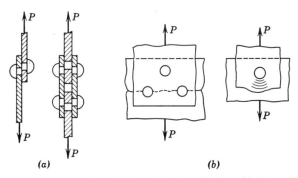

Fig. 76. Modes of failure of structural riveted joint.

even though the riveted joint is used here merely as an illustration of a member or structure that is made of ductile metal and that does not cease to function satisfactorily (does not fail) as a load-resisting member until the ultimate (fracture) load for the joint is reached.

Types of Rivets and Riveted Joints. It is convenient to divide riveted joints into three general groups: (1) structural joints used in connecting members in bridges, buildings, cranes, and other so-called heavy structures, usually made of steel, (2) boiler, tank, or pipe joints used in connecting plates in various types of pressure vessels, and (3) structural joints used in connecting relatively thin sheets and plates of aluminum alloys, magnesium alloys, or stainless steel such as used in aircraft structures and in railway-car construction. In structural joints, strength is the main requirement, whereas, in boiler and pipe joints, tightness in addition to strength must be considered. In the first two types of joints, rivets of the type shown in Fig. 77a are commonly used. However, if one end of the rivet must be flush with the surface, as in the outer surface of aircraft structure, one of the rivets of Fig. 77b, c, or d may be used. Rivets of the dimpled type, as in Fig. 77c or d, when properly assembled will produce a joint that resists permanent set (often called slip in connection with riveted joints) between the fastened plates and thus improve the tightness of the joint.

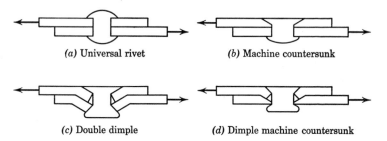

(a) Universal rivet   (b) Machine countersunk

(c) Double dimple   (d) Dimple machine countersunk

Fig. 77. Single-riveted lap joint with different types of riveting for aircraft structures.

Riveted joints may also be classified as to arrangement of the plates and rivet patterns. Two widely used types are lap joints and butt joints (see Fig. 78), and both lap and butt joints may be single, double,

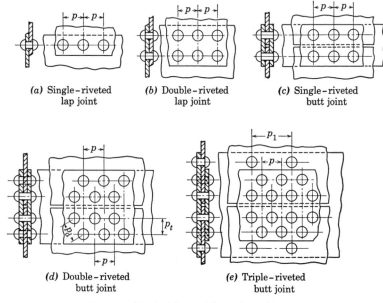

(a) Single-riveted   (b) Double-riveted   (c) Single-riveted
lap joint   lap joint   butt joint

(d) Double-riveted   (e) Triple-riveted
butt joint   butt joint

Fig. 78. Typical lap and butt riveted joints.

or triple riveted, etc., according to whether one, two, or three rows of rivets pierce each of the two plates that are connected. Furthermore, a butt joint may have two cover plates (or straps) or only one cover plate, and both lap and butt joints may have the rivets arranged in the form of chain riveting (Fig. 78b) or in the form of staggered riveting (Fig. 78d and e).

Definitions. The terms defined in the following are used in the subsequent paragraphs.

An ideal riveted joint is one in which the ultimate loads in shear, tension, and bearing are equal.

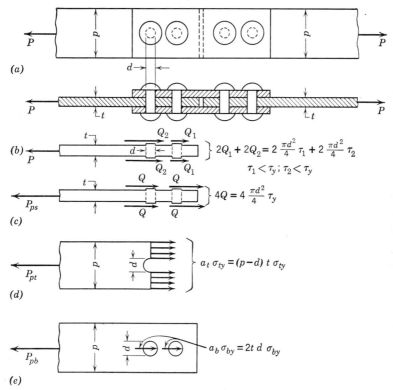

Fig. 79. Elastic and fully plastic stresses in double-riveted butt joint.

The *pitch* of a row of rivets is the distance between the centers of any two adjacent rivets in the row. The pitch is not necessarily the same for all rows. Thus, in Fig. 78e the pitch for the inner rows is denoted by p and for the other row by p_1 in which p_1 equals $2p$.

A *gusset plate* or *splice plate* is a plate used in structural joints to form part of the joint in connecting two or more members of a structure (see Fig. 83b). It corresponds to a cover plate or strap in a boiler or pipe butt joint.

The term *efficiency* of a riveted joint is the ratio of the ultimate (fracture) strength of the joint to the ultimate tensile strength of the solid (unpunched or undrilled) plate.

Method Explained. To illustrate the method of determining the ultimate strength of a joint, one particular type of joint (a double-riveted butt joint) as indicated in Fig. 79a will be used, but the method is the same for all riveted joints. In Fig. 79 the load P is held in equilibrium as shown in Fig. 79b by the elastic shearing forces Q_1 and Q_2 on the rivets, which are, at the lower values of the load P, relatively large on the outer rivet (nearer to P) and relatively small on the inner rivet. As the load P is increased, the shearing stress in the outer rivet reaches the shearing yield point τ_y of the material and yields at the constant stress until the stress on the inner rivet also reaches the yield point. The load P will then be the fully plastic load P_{sp} for shear in the rivets. Thus, from the condition of equilibrium, we obtained the following equation from the forces in Fig. 79c in which all shearing areas are assumed to be equally stressed:

$$P_{sp} = a_s \tau_y = \frac{4\pi d^2}{4} \tau_y \quad \text{or} \quad \tau_y = \frac{P_{sp}}{\pi d^2} \tag{45}$$

It should be noted that, if the joint were a double-riveted *lap* joint, each rivet would have only one shearing area, and hence the total shearing area would be $2\pi d^2/4$ instead of $4\pi d^2/4$.

Similarly, the fully plastic loads for tension in the plate and bearing of rivet on plate, P_{tp} and P_{bp}, are found from Fig. 79d and e to be

$$P_{tp} = a_t \sigma_{ty} = (p - d)t\sigma_{ty} \quad \text{or} \quad \sigma_{ty} = \frac{P_{tp}}{(p - d)t} \tag{46}$$

and

$$P_{tb} = a_b \sigma_{by} = 2td\sigma_{by} \quad \text{or} \quad \sigma_{by} = \frac{P_{bp}}{2td} \tag{47}$$

in which the simplifying assumption is made that the bearing area on which σ_{by} is constant is td for each rivet rather than the semicylindrical area of contact of the rivet and the plate. The smallest of the three fully plastic loads is the fully plastic load for the joint.

These equations may be important in determining the maximum or limiting load that the joint can be permitted to resist, especially if loosening of the rivets causes failure.

Equations for Ultimate Loads. If the load P is increased further, the stress on each of the three areas may reach the ultimate strength of the material in shear, tension, and bearing designated by τ_u, σ_{tu}, and

σ_{bu}, and hence, if these values are used in Eqs. 45, 46 and 47, respectively, the ultimate loads in shear, tension, and bearing may be written

$$P_{su} = a_s\tau_u = \frac{4\pi d^2}{4}\,\tau_u \tag{48}$$

$$P_{tu} = a_t\sigma_{tu} = (p - d)t\sigma_{tu} \tag{49}$$

$$P_{bu} = a_b\sigma_{bu} = 2td\sigma_{bu} \tag{50}$$

The smaller of these three loads is the ultimate strength of the (double-riveted) joint if made of ductile metal having the ultimate strengths τ_u, σ_{tu}, and σ_{bu} in shear, tension, and bearing (compression) and subjected to a central static load at ordinary temperatures. One of these equations will give the maximum load that the joint may be allowed to resist before failure occurs, provided that the strength of the joint is the governing factor.

Illustrative Problem

Problem 67. Two steel flat bars are connected by a double-riveted butt joint as shown in Fig. 79a. The over-all length of the two plates and the joint (forming a simple structure) is 20 ft. Determine the maximum load P that can be applied to the structure if the following requirements are met: (a) The behavior of the structure as a whole must be essentially elastic; the joint itself may be loaded to its ultimate load without contributing appreciable inelastic deformation to the structure, if the length of the joint is negligible compared to the length of the structure. (b) The total stretch (deformation) of the structure must not exceed 0.25 in. Other values (see Fig. 79) are: $t = \frac{1}{2}$ in., $d = \frac{5}{8}$ in., $p = 3$ in., $\tau_y = 25,000$, $\sigma_{ty} = 45,000$, $\sigma_{by} = 60,000$ lb/in.^{2}, $E = 30 \times 10^6$ lb/in.^{2}, $\tau_u = 40,000$, $\sigma_{tu} = 60,000$, $\sigma_{bu} = 90,000$ lb/in.^{2}

Solution. A stretch of $e = 0.25$ in. means that the tensile stress σ in the plate could have a maximum value of

$$\sigma = E\epsilon = 30,000,000 \times \frac{0.25}{20 \times 12} = 31,300 \text{ lb/in.}^2$$

Hence the maximum load that could be applied to the structure would be

$$P = 31,300 \times 3.0 \times 0.5 = 46,900 \text{ lb}$$

unless the ultimate load for the joint in the structure is less than this load.

The ultimate load for the joint in shear is the ultimate load for the joint, and its value is $P_{tu} = \frac{1}{2}\left(3 - \frac{5}{8}\right)60,000 = 71,400 \qquad P_{bu} = 2\left(\frac{5}{8}\right)\frac{1}{2} \times 90,000 = 56,200$

$$P_{sp} = a_s\tau_u = \pi d^2 \times \tau_u = \pi\left(\tfrac{5}{8}\right)^2 \times 40,000 = 49,000 \text{ lb}$$

Hence the maximum load that can be applied to the structure is limited by condition b and is 46,900 lb.

Problems

68. In an ideal joint the ultimate loads in shear, bearing, and tension are equal. (*a*) By equating the ultimate shearing load to the ultimate bearing load, show that the diameter of the rivets in a *lap* joint is 2.55 times the thickness of the plate ($d = 2.55t$), if the value of $\tau_u = 60,000$ lb per sq in. and $\sigma_{bu} = 120,000$ lb per sq in. are used. (*b*) Similarly, show that, in an ideal butt joint having two cover plates, $d = 1.27t$. Which of these two types of joints is better suited for boilers, pipes, etc., having thick plates? *Hint.* If n represents the number of rivets we have for (*a*),

$$n \cdot \frac{\pi d^2}{4} \tau_u = ntd\sigma_{bu} \quad \text{or} \quad d = \frac{4}{\pi} \frac{\sigma_{bu}}{\tau_u} \cdot t$$

69. By equating the ultimate tensile load to the ultimate bearing load, show that the pitch in an ideal double-riveted lap joint is four times the diameter of the rivets ($p = 4d$), if $\sigma_{tu} = 80,000$ lb per sq in. and $\sigma_{bu} = 120,000$ lb per sq in. Also, show that the efficiency of an ideal double-riveted lap joint of this material is 75 per cent.

70. A boiler 60 in. in diameter is designed to withstand an internal fluid pressure of 80 lb per sq in. The longitudinal joint is a single-riveted lap joint; the rivets have a pitch of $2\frac{1}{2}$ in.; the plates are $\frac{3}{8}$ in. thick, and the rivets are $\frac{7}{8}$ in. in diameter. Find the shearing, tensile, and bearing ultimate loads for the joint using the following values (in pounds per square inch). $\tau_u = 60,000$, $\sigma_{tu} = 75,000$, and $\sigma_{bu} = 120,000$. Also find the efficiency of the joint.

71. In Fig. 80 is shown a riveted lap joint connecting two aluminum-alloy sheets of Alclad 24S-T3 fastened by rivets of aluminum-alloy 24S-T31. Compute the

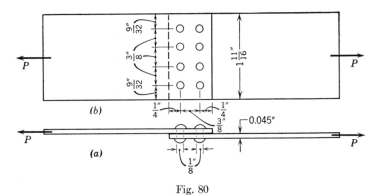

Fig. 80

ultimate load for the joint. The ultimate shearing strengths of the sheet and rivets, as given in *Strength of Metal Aircraft Elements* (ANC-5 Bulletin) are as follows: In shearing of the rivets $\tau_u = 41,000$ lb per sq in., in tension of the sheet $\sigma_{tu} = 60,000$ lb per sq in., in bearing of the sheet $\sigma_{bu} = 114,000$ lb per sq in. *Note.* The value of σ_{bu} specified is less than the value given here when the ratio d/t of the rivet diameter to the sheet thickness is greater than 3 for rivets in single shear and is greater than 1.5 for rivets in double shear. The factors for use in reducing

σ_{bu} are given in Table 3.6111(a) of ANC-5 Bulletin. The reason for the reduction in compressive strength is that thin sheet tends to buckle around the rivet hole, owing to the high compressive stresses where the plate is in contact with the rivet.

§ 3 Design of a Member

21. Procedure for design of a member. *Factor of Safety.* The foregoing articles have been concerned mainly with analyses leading to relationships among loads, stresses, and deformations, based on certain simplifying assumptions. The main value or importance of the analyses lies in their use in the design of a load-resisting member.

The rational design of such a member usually involves certain general considerations as follows: First we must know or decide (from a knowledge of experimental results or from experience) what action or behavior of the member will limit, under the service conditions, the maximum loads that can be applied to the member without destroying its required load-resisting function. In short, the first consideration is to determine the *mode of failure* of the member.

For most members that are subjected to static loads and uniaxial stress at ordinary temperatures, the mode of failure will usually consist of one of the four following behaviors.

(*a*) The failure of the member may be by fracture, if the material is truly brittle; the material will act elastically until rupture or fracture occurs.

(*b*) The failure may also be by fracture, even though the member is made of ductile metal; fracture in a ductile metal occurs, as previously pointed out, only after large inelastic strains exhaust the ductility of the material, but, if the shape of the member is such that the large inelastic strains are localized as in a welded joint (Fig. 71), the deformation of the member as a whole may be small at fracture (see Prob. 67).

(*c*) The maximum load that may be applied to a member may be limited (failure may occur) by a small (specified or permissible) inelastic strain in the most stressed fibers; in this condition of failure, it is assumed that the material is ductile and that the shape of the member is such that the inelastic strain in the most stressed fibers is not localized as under (*b*), but would spread to other portions of the member if the load exceeded that corresponding to the permissible value of strain, and thus would lead to failure by excessive plastic deformation of the member (see Prob. 62).

(*d*) The maximum load may be limited by a specified or permissible elastic deformation of the member, and hence only elastic behavior is involved, but the member would fail to perform its load-resisting function if its elastic deflection exceeded the specified value. As previously stated, failure of slender compression members by buckling is excluded from this discussion.

It is usually possible and convenient to indicate when each of these failure conditions is reached by specifying a critical value of the normal stress or of the shearing stress. This critical value of the stress (here called the critical stress) must then be reduced for use in design by dividing it by a factor, called the factor of safety and denoted by N, in order to obtain a *working stress* or *allowable stress;* this latter step takes account of the uncertainties involved in the service conditions. Thus, a working stress may be defined as the maximum stress that is considered (in the design of the member by use of the equations obtained in the stress analysis adopted) to be safe for the member to resist in service, and it may be obtained from the expression

$$\text{Working stress} = \frac{\text{critical stress}}{N} \quad \text{or} \quad N = \frac{\text{critical stress}}{\text{working stress}}$$

After the working stress has been found, it will be used in the equations in the foregoing articles, in order to determine the dimensions of the member required to resist a given load.

Values of Critical Stresses. The stresses for each of the four failure behaviors previously mentioned are usually considered to be as follows:

(a) For fracture of brittle material, the critical stress is the ultimate strength of the material; (b) for fracture of ductile metal, the critical stress is considered to be the ultimate strength; (c) for a small amount of inelastic deformation of ductile material, the critical stress is the yield point or the yield strength for a specified offset; and (d) for elastic deflection, the critical stress is the stress accompanying the maximum specified elastic deflection.

If, in the design of a member, the critical stress is considered to be as stated under (a), (b), or (c), the member is said to be designed for strength, and, if the critical stress is considered to be as stated under (d), the member is said to be designed for stiffness. Frequently, when stiffness governs, the stress corresponding to the specified deflection or strain is so small that the member has excess strength.

Need of a Margin of Strength. The need for creating a margin of strength by selecting a working stress considerably less than the critical stress arises mainly from (1) the uncertainties concerning the properties of the materials used, (2) the uncertainties concerning the loads to be resisted by the structure or machine as a whole and also by the various members of the structure, and (3) the uncertainties in the influence of the simplifying assumptions introduced in developing the methods of calculating the stresses in the members.

In deciding on the importance of these uncertainties and in selecting a value for the working stress, many factors must be considered, such as the care used in inspecting the materials and the methods of construction, the extent of the damage to property and life likely to be caused by a failure of the structure or machine, the degree of permanence or the length of useful life of the structure, the extent to which deterioration is likely to occur, and the employment of periodic inspection. The more the uncertainties are reduced, the higher the working stresses may be.

In the design of heavy construction such as buildings, bridges, and machines in general, working stresses, especially in the design of buildings, have become standardized to a large degree. Thus, the building codes of many of the larger cities specify the properties of materials and the maximum allowable working stresses to be used for the common structural materials. Codes are also formulated by other groups, such as the Boiler Code Committee of the American Society of Mechanical Engineers for use in the design of pressure vessels, the Air Force, Navy, and Commerce Depts. which give specifications in *Strength of Metal Aircraft Elements* (usually referred to by the short title ANC-5), American Institute of Steel Construction, American Concrete Institute, etc.

Caution. It should be emphasized that the primary function of members as considered in resistance of materials is to resist *loads*. Therefore, if loads are to be limited to specified safe values by limiting stresses to safe or working values, the stresses must be directly proportional to the loads. Thus, when inelastic behavior is permitted in the member, it is preferable to use the critical stress for the working stress, and multiply the actual or working loads by a factor of safety to obtain the design loads. For elastic behavior the two methods, of course, lead to the same results.

The method or procedure of design discussed in this article will be illustrated in the following problems.

Illustrative Problems

Problem 72. A straight flat bar having semicircular grooves as indicated in Fig. 58 is made of hardened steel having a stress-strain curve shown in Fig. 60a and is subjected to an axial static load P. Determine the cross-sectional area of the bar if $P = 10,000$ lb and a factor of safety $N = 5$ is specified. Let the value of the ultimate strength σ_u be 100,000 lb/in.[2]

Solution. The material is brittle, and failure is by fracture; the material acts elastically (approximately) until it fractures. The member will fracture when the tensile stress in the most stressed fiber reaches the ultimate strength of the material. The critical or limiting stress therefore is the ultimate strength, and the working stress is

$$\sigma_w = \frac{\sigma_u}{N} = \frac{100,000}{5} = 20,000 \text{ lb/in.}^2$$

The stress on the most stressed fiber is

$$\sigma_{\max} = k_t \frac{P}{a}$$

Let it be assumed that the grooves (see Fig. 58) are such that $\rho/d = 0.20$ and $k_t = 2.0$. Therefore,

$$\sigma_{\max} = \sigma_w = 20,000 = 2.0 \frac{10,000}{a}$$

$$a = 1.0 \text{ sq in.}$$

Problem 73. The diameter of the rivets in the butt joint shown in Fig. 81 is $\frac{7}{8}$ in., and the thickness of the main plates is $\frac{3}{4}$ in. The plates and rivets are of

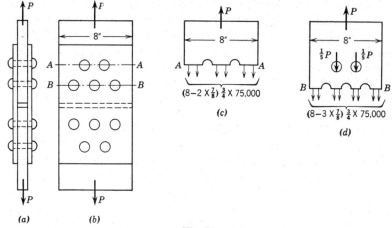

Fig. 81

alloy steel, for which the ultimate strengths in shear, tension, and bearing are $\tau_u = 60,000$ lb per sq in., $\sigma_{tu} = 75,000$ lb per sq in. and $\sigma_{bu} = 120,000$ lb per sq in., respectively. Calculate the allowable load P_w for a factor of safety of 5.

Solution. In accordance with the discussion in Art. 20, failure will be by fracture, and the rivets will carry equal parts of load; hence the factor of safety will be based on the ultimate load for the joint. Since each rivet is in double shear, the ultimate load in shear is

$$P = 2 \times 5 \times \frac{\pi(\frac{7}{8})^2}{4} \times 60,000 = 10 \times 0.601 \times 60,000 = 360,600 \text{ lb}$$

The ultimate load in bearing is

$$P_{bu} = 5 \times \tfrac{7}{8} \times \tfrac{3}{4} \times 120,000 = 393,600 \text{ lb}$$

The load P is transmitted across the section AA (Fig. 81c). The ultimate load in tension for section AA is, therefore,

$$P_{tu} = (8 - 2 \times \tfrac{7}{8})\tfrac{3}{4} \times 75,000 = 351,500 \text{ lb}$$

The load resisted by, or transmitted across, section BB (Fig. 81d) is $\tfrac{3}{5}P$ since $\tfrac{2}{5}P$ is resisted by the two upper rivets. Therefore, the ultimate load based on the ultimate tensile stress on section BB is

$$P_{tu} = \tfrac{5}{3}(8 - 3 \times \tfrac{7}{8})\tfrac{3}{4} \times 75,000 = 504,000 \text{ lb}$$

The ultimate load for the joint is, therefore, 351,500 lb. This load is divided by the factor of safety of 5, which gives an allowable or working load P_w.

Thus,

$$P_w = \frac{P_u}{5} = \frac{351,500}{5} = 70,300 \text{ lb}$$

Problem 74. Let an axially loaded bar with semicircular grooves (shown in Fig. 82, in which $D = 4$ in., $d = 2$ in.) be made of steel for which the stress-strain

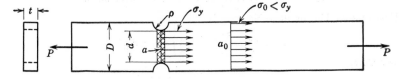

Fig. 82. A tension member with fully plastic condition at abrupt change of section, and with elastic condition in main body of member.

diagram is similar to that shown in Fig. 61. Let the yield point be $\sigma_y = 36,000$ lb/in.^{2} and the ultimate strength be $\sigma_u = 65,000$ lb/in.^{2} The bar must act essentially elastically when subjected to the load $P = 30,000$ lb, in order to fulfill its load-resisting function. The bar has a rectangular cross section of thickness t. Calculate the value of the thickness necessary for a factor of safety of $N = 2$.

Solution. The maximum load that can be applied to the bar is limited to the value that causes inelastic strains to start at sections away from the grooves or to the load that will cause fracture across the bar at the reduced section. The fully plastic load P_p occurs when the stress distribution is constant over the area a at the reduced section and equal to the yield point σ_y. Thus, the first inelastic strain to occur will be at the reduced section, but the elastic deformation of the whole bar will not be influenced appreciably by the inelastic strains in the small volume of material at the reduced section. If the load P is increased above P_p, the bar may fracture at the reduced section, or inelastic strains may spread along the bar on either side of the reduced section and result in inelastic behavior of the whole bar, which would also constitute failure of the bar. Therefore, the critical or failure load will be the smaller of the following loads:

$$P_{\text{fracture}} = \sigma_u a = \sigma_u t d = 65,000 \times 2t = 130,000t$$

$$P_{\text{yielding}} = \sigma_y a_0 = \sigma_y t D = 36,000 \times 4t = 144,000t$$

Therefore, the bar will remain essentially elastic until it fails by fracture at the reduced section. Therefore,

$$P_{\text{fracture}} = 130,000t = NP = 2 \times 30,000$$

Hence,

$$t = \frac{60,000}{130,000} = 0.46 \text{ in.}$$

It should be noted that in most cases the area a at the reduced section of a member will be made large enough so that yielding will occur in the unreduced sections a_0 before fracture occurs at the reduced section.

Problem 75. A steel bar of constant cross section a is subjected to a static central load $P = 30,000$ lb. Determine the value for a in order to meet the specifications that the bar must not be given an elastic deformation (elongation) of more than 0.05 in. in a length of 60 in., and that a factor of safety of 2 be used. The modulus of elasticity of steel is $E = 30 \times 10^6$ lb/in.^{2} and the elastic limit (or yield point, see Fig. 61) is 36,000 lb/in.^{2}

Solution. Stiffness governs the design; the failure of the member occurs when the elastic strain reaches the value

$$\epsilon_{cr} = \frac{0.050}{60} = 0.000833 \text{ in./in.}$$

The stress corresponding to this elastic strain is

$$\sigma_{cr} = E\epsilon_{cr} = 30 \times 10^6 \times 0.000833 = 25,000 \text{ lb/in.}^2$$

Hence the working or allowable stress is

$$\sigma_w = \frac{\sigma_{cr}}{N} = \frac{25,000}{2} = 12,500 \text{ lb/in.}$$

Therefore,

$$a = \frac{P}{\sigma_w} = \frac{30,000}{12,500} = 2.4 \text{ in.}^2$$

Problems

76. The members of the Fink truss shown in Fig. 83a are connected by riveted joints. The arrangement of the joint at C is shown in Fig. 83b. Show that the

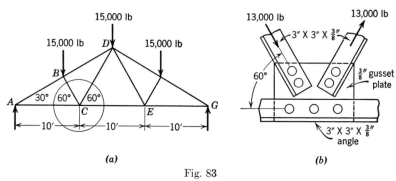

(a)   (b)

Fig. 83

forces in members BC and DC are 13,000 lb compression and 13,000 lb tension, respectively. The rivets are $\frac{3}{4}$ in. in diameter. The working or allowable stresses as given by the AISC are

$$\sigma_{tw} = 20,000 \text{ lb per sq in.,} \qquad \tau_w = 15,000 \text{ lb per sq in.}$$

and

$$\sigma_{bw} = 32,000 \text{ lb per sq in.} \quad \text{(when rivets are in single shear)}$$

Determine the shearing stress in the rivets connecting the members BC and DC to the gusset plate, and in the rivets connecting the gusset plate to the lower chord $ACEG$. Also find the bearing stress of the members BC and DC on the rivets, and the tensile stress in CD. Are the computed values less than the corresponding working values?

Note. It will be found that all these stresses, except the shear in the rivets in BC and DC, are considerably less than the allowable values. This result is not unusual in a truss such as this, because the force in a compression member such as BC is limited to lower values by its buckling strength as discussed in Chapter VIII. All values in the answer are given in pounds per square inch.

Ans. $\tau = 14,700$ in rivets connecting BC and DC

$\tau = 9800$ in rivets connecting gusset plate to lower chord

$\sigma_b = 23,000$ for BC and DC

$\sigma_b = 15,400$ for rivets on lower chord

$\sigma_t = 7100$

77. A boiler having a diameter D of 68 in. is designed to resist a working internal steam pressure R of 120 lb per sq in. The longitudinal joint is a double-riveted butt joint shown in Fig. 84. The thickness t of the plates is $\frac{7}{16}$ in., the diameter

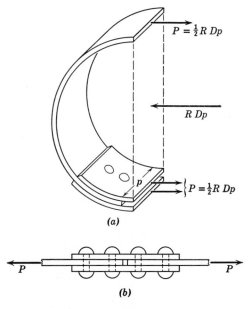

(a)

(b)

Fig. 84

d of the rivets is $\frac{3}{4}$ in., and the pitch p is $3\frac{1}{2}$ in. Let it be assumed that for the material in the rivets and plate $\tau_u = 40,000$ lb/in.^{2}, $\sigma_{tu} = 60,000$ lb/in.^{2}, and $\sigma_{bu} = 90,000$ lb/in.^{2} Determine whether this boiler is safe for use at the given pressure by a factor of safety of 5 based on the ultimate strength of the joint. Also determine the efficiency of the joint.

78. In Fig. 85 is shown a joint in an aircraft structure which consists of two aluminum-alloy sheets of Alclad 24S-T3 fastened by seven $\frac{5}{32}''$ diameter A17S-T3 aluminum-alloy rivets.   In ANC-5, June 1951, the following data are given for these metals: For the sheets, $\sigma_{tu} = 60,000$ lb per sq in. and $\sigma_{bu} = 114,000$ lb per sq in., and for the rivets $\tau_u = 30,000$ lb per sq in.   By making use of a factor of

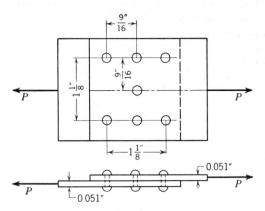

Fig. 85

safety of 1.5 based on the ultimate load and a stress-concentration factor of k_e = 1.2, determine the working load for this joint.   All marginal distances are $\frac{9}{25}$ in. $\supset 6 / 0$ *Ans.*   2250 lb.

79. In Fig. 86, the joints are steel pins 1 in. in diameter, and C is a yellow-pine timber member having a square cross section 6 in. on side.   The ultimate shearing strength of the timber parallel to the grain is 800 lb/in.^{2} In Fig. 86, assume that

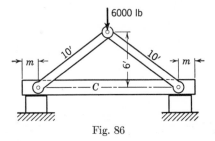

Fig. 86

the grain is horizontal and that the member does not fail until the ultimate shearing strength of the material on the shearing area $a_s = 12m$ is reached.   Use a factor of safety of 6, and calculate the minimum value for the dimension m.

80. A force P of 196 lb applied to the bell crank shown in Fig. 87 causes a bearing pressure of 15 lb/in.^{2} normal to the rubbing surfaces of the friction clutch. The coefficient of friction for the rubbing surfaces is 1/4.   It may be assumed that the clutch functions satisfactorily until a key shears off; that is, failure occurs when the shearing stress in the key reaches the ultimate shearing stress.   Each key is $\frac{1}{2}$ in. wide, $\frac{5}{16}$ in. deep, and $2\frac{1}{2}$ in. long. If a factor of safety of 5 was used in the design, what value was used for the ultimate shearing strength of the material? *Ans.* 10,150 lb/in.²

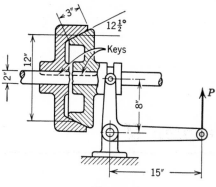

Fig. 87

81. In Fig. 22, let the load P be applied at A, and let it be assumed that the failure value for P occurs when the yield point of the eyebars is reached. The eyebars are made of steel for which $E = 30 \times 10^6$ lb per sq in. and the tensile yield point $\sigma_y = 35,000$ lb per sq in. If a factor of safety of 2 was used in the design of the eyebars, what value of P was considered to be the working or allowable load?

Chapter II

TORSION OF CYLINDRICAL BARS

22. Introduction. *Torsional Loads.* Forces that cause a bar to twist about its central axis are called torsional loads. The resultant of torsional loads acting on a shaft is a twisting couple (two equal opposite noncollinear forces); simple turning or twisting can be produced only by a couple. The resultant moment (or moment of the resultant couple) which causes the twisting is the algebraic sum of the moments of the torsional loads about the axis of the bar or shaft.

Twisting Moment. The twisting moment for a section of a shaft is the algebraic sum of the moments, about the axis of the shaft, of the torsional loads that lie to one side of the section. The symbol T will be used to denote the twisting moment (see Fig. 90).

It is here assumed that the torsional loads lie in planes perpendicular to the axis of the shaft. If the forces do not lie in such planes, the forces may be resolved into components perpendicular and parallel, respectively, to the axis, the components parallel to the axis being neglected in this chapter (see Chap. VIII).

Resisting Moment. At each transverse cross section of the shaft, an internal moment must exist in order to hold in equilibrium the (external) twisting moment of the loads that lie to either side of the cross section. The moment of the internal forces acting on the cross section is called the resisting moment at the section. The symbol T_r will denote this moment (see Fig. 90).

Problem Defined. The main problem here considered is similar to that considered in Chapter I for central loads. It consists of two parts: namely (1) to develop a rational analysis giving the relationships between (a) torsional static loads acting on a cylindrical bar or shaft and each of the resulting significant stresses in the bar (these stresses usually will be the maximum tensile stress and the maximum shearing stress) and also (b) the relationship between the loads and the deflection (angle of twist) of the bar, and (2) to present a rational method of design of a bar or shaft of a given material subjected to torsional loads.

As pointed out in Chapter I, these two considerations—analysis and design—are involved, in general, in all problems of resistance of materials, although the design features of the problem are intended to give primarily the procedure or method of approach rather than detailed information on design. The design procedure under (2) will make use of the relationships in the analysis under (1), provided that the stresses and deflections involved in the analysis are the *significant* stresses and deflections, by which is meant the stresses and deflections that reach values, as the loads are increased, which destroy the function of the member for resisting further loads, as discussed under the next side heading.

Modes of Failure. In order to determine what quantity (stress or deflection) may be significant as defined in the preceding paragraph, we must observe from experimental results and experience with service conditions the action or behavior of bars or shafts of different materials as they are subjected to gradually increasing (static) twisting moments.

Experiments and experience have shown that the maximum torsional loads that cylindrical bars of constant cross section may resist in a structure or machine are limited usually by one of the following actions or conditions: (1) The deflection (angle of twist, see Fig. 88), even though the deformation of the member is entirely elastic, may be sufficiently large to cause the member to fail to perform satisfactorily its function in the structure. (2) The shearing stress τ_V on a transverse plane (see Figs. 88 and 91) or the equal shearing stress τ_H on the longitudinal plane (see Figs. 88 and 102) may exceed the shearing elastic limit of the material which will cause the bar, if made of ductile material, to become permanently distorted and hence to fail if no permanent set can be allowed in the member. (3) The shearing stress τ_V may cause fracture of a ductile-metal bar on a transverse cross section, since, after considerable inelastic shearing strain has occurred, the stress τ_V

reaches the value of the ultimate shearing strength τ_u (see Art. 19, Chap. I); this type of failure is discussed further in Art. 30. (4) The

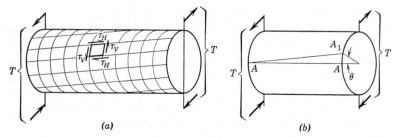

Fig. 88. Shearing stresses and strains in cylindrical bar subjected to torsional loads.

diagonal tensile stress σ_t (see Figs. 89 and 103) may reach a value that will cause the bar to fracture, if the bar is made of brittle material; brittle material usually is relatively weak in tension.

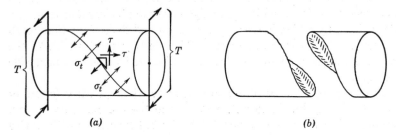

Fig. 89. Tensile stress accompanying shearing stress resulting in fracture of bar if made of brittle material.

§ 1   Elastic Behavior

23. The torsion formula. As indicated in Fig. 90, let a straight bar with a constant circular cross section be acted on by twisting moments (couples) T at its ends, and let it be assumed that the bar acts elastically. We wish to find the relation among the twisting moment, the shearing stress τ_V at any point in the shaft on a section perpendicular to the axis of the shaft, and the dimensions of the area of the section. Let a plane BC be passed through the shaft, and let the portion of the shaft to the right of the plane be removed. If the remaining (left) portion of the shaft (Fig. 90) is held in equilibrium (as it was when a part of the whole shaft), a moment equal and opposite to T must be applied to it. This moment (denoted by T_r, Fig. 90b) is exerted on the left portion by the right portion on the section DE cut by the plane

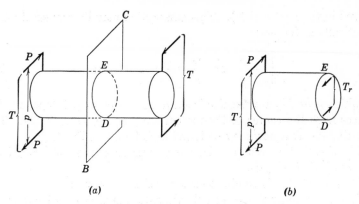

Fig. 90.   Internal resisting moment on any cross section of bar.

and is due to the shearing ($\tau\,da$) forces developed on the section; it is called the resisting moment.   Thus, the condition of equilibrium gives

Moment of external forces = moment of internal forces

that is,

Twisting moment = resisting moment   or $T = T_r$

Before the resisting moment T_r can be expressed in terms of the shearing stress at any point in the area and the dimensions of the area, the manner in which the stress varies over the area must be known.

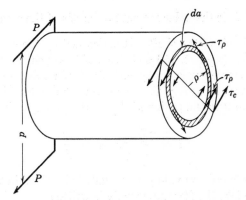

Fig. 91.   Distribution of shearing stress on cross section.

It is assumed that, if the material is not stressed beyond its shearing proportional limit, the shearing stress is zero at the center and increases at points along any radius c directly as the distance ρ from the center, as shown in Fig. 91 (the justification for this assumption is discussed in the next article). This assumption may be expressed mathematically as follows:

$$\frac{\tau_\rho}{\tau_c} = \frac{\rho}{c} \quad \text{or} \quad \frac{\tau_\rho}{\rho} = \frac{\tau_c}{c} = \text{a constant} \tag{51}$$

in which τ_ρ and τ_c are the elastic shearing stresses at points whose distances from the center of the section are ρ and c, respectively. The resisting moment now may be found as follows (see Fig. 91):

The shearing force on an element of area da at the distance ρ from center of shaft $= \tau_\rho \, da$.

Moment of this force about center of shaft $= \tau_\rho \, da \, \rho$.

Sum of moments of forces on all elements of area $=$ resisting moment $= T_r = \int \tau_\rho \rho \, da$. This may be written

$$T_r = \int \frac{\tau_\rho}{\rho} \rho^2 \, da \tag{52}$$

but

$$T = T_r \quad \text{and} \quad \frac{\tau_\rho}{\rho} = \frac{\tau_c}{c} = \text{a constant}$$

Therefore,

$$T = \frac{\tau_\rho}{\rho} \int \rho^2 \, da \tag{53}$$

in which $\int \rho^2 \, da$ is the polar moment of inertia of the area with respect to the central axis of the shaft. It is denoted by the symbol J and is equal to $\pi d^4/32$ (see Art. 156 and Prob. 431, Appendix I).

If now for convenience we let τ, instead of τ_ρ, denote the shearing stress on the area da at any distance ρ from the center where ρ may be any value from 0 to the radius of the shaft, we may write

$$T = \frac{\tau J}{\rho} \quad \text{or} \quad \tau = \frac{T\rho}{J} \tag{54}$$

But, since the maximum value of τ usually is involved in the use of the formula in design, the formula usually is written

$$\tau_{\max} = \frac{Tc}{J} \quad \text{or} \quad \tau_{\max} = \frac{T}{J/c} \tag{54a}$$

which is called the *torsion formula*, in which J/c is called the *section modulus*. Equation 54 or 54a is applicable only to a bar or shaft having a circular cross section, but the cylindrical bar may be either a solid or a hollow cylinder. However, many torsional members are of this form so that Eq. 54 is of considerable practical importance.

Units. In Eq. 54a, if τ is expressed in pounds per square inch, T must be expressed in pound-inches, J in inches to the fourth power (in.⁴), and c in inches.

24. Justification for assumption of stress distribution. In order to supply the evidence and reasoning leading to the assumption that the shearing stress at any point in the section of the cylindrical shaft varies directly as the distance of the point from the center of the section, it is necessary, in accordance with the method of Art. 8, to consider (*a*) the manner in which the shearing strains of the fibers of the shaft vary when the shaft is twisted, and (*b*) the relation between the shearing strain at a point in a material and the shearing stress at the point.

Thus, let Fig. 92 represent a cylindrical shaft twisted by the twisting moment T or Pp. It is assumed that, when a cylindrical * shaft is

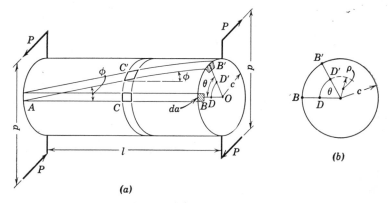

(*a*)

Fig. 92.   Distribution of shearing strain on cross section.

twisted, a normal plane section of the shaft before twisting is approximately a plane section after twisting, and it is assumed also that a diameter in the section before twisting is a diameter (straight line) after twisting.† An outer element or fiber AB, having a cross-sectional

---

* A plane section of a shaft whose cross section is not circular does not remain plane when the shaft is twisted. For torsion of shafts having noncircular sections see our *Advanced Mechanics of Materials.*

† Although these assumptions seem reasonable, it is very difficult to obtain direct experimental verification. The justification for the assumptions is to be found in the agreement of results calculated from the formula based on these assumptions with experimental results.

area da, takes the form of a helix AB' when the shaft is twisted.* Thus a small portion of the fiber, which is at C before the shaft is twisted, is at C' after the shaft has been twisted and is deformed as shown in the figure by the shearing stresses on its faces.

Furthermore, as discussed in Art. 6, the shearing strain γ at any point of a body is equal to the tangent of the angle of deviation from a right angle of two planes passing through the point. Therefore, the shearing strain γ_c at the surface of a cylindrical shaft when twisted is

$$\gamma_c = \tan \phi$$

But $\tan \phi$ (Fig. 92) is equal to the arc BB' divided by the length l of the shaft, and $\overline{BB'}$ is equal to the radius c times the angle of twist θ expressed in radians. Therefore,

$$\gamma_c = \tan \phi = \frac{BB'}{l} = \frac{c\theta}{l} \tag{55}$$

Similarly, since a diameter remains a straight line, the shearing strain γ_ρ at a point at the distance ρ from the center of the shaft (Fig. 92) is

$$\gamma_\rho = \frac{DD'}{l} = \frac{\rho\theta}{l} \tag{56}$$

If Eq. 55 is divided by Eq. 56, the result obtained is

$$\frac{\gamma_c}{\gamma_\rho} = \frac{c}{\rho} \tag{57}$$

That is, when a cylindrical shaft is twisted, the shearing strains of the fibers vary directly as the distances of the fibers from the central axis of the shaft.

But, as stated in Art. 7, the shearing stress at any point in the material is proportional to the corresponding shearing strain at that point, provided that the stress does not exceed the shearing proportional limit of the material. Therefore, since the shearing strains of the fibers are proportional to the distances of the fibers from the center of the shaft, and since the shearing strains of the fibers are also proportional to the shearing stresses on the fibers, it follows that:

The shearing stress on a fiber at any section of the shaft varies directly as the distance of the fiber from the axis of the shaft.

* It should be noted that, since the outer longitudinal fibers become longer as the bar is twisted, there must be longitudinal tensile stress in these outer fibers, but, for the small angles of twist to which cylindrical shafts usually are subjected, these longitudinal stresses are very small and may be neglected.

It is important to note that the torsion formula is applicable only to a right circular cylinder, solid or hollow, in which the shearing stress does not exceed the shearing proportional limit, for otherwise the shearing stresses on the fibers at any section of the shaft will not vary as the distances of the fibers from the center of the shaft.

Illustrative Problem

Problem 82. In Fig. 93 the maximum elastic shearing stresses developed on sections AA and BB by the twisting moments T_1 and T_2 are $\tau_A = 6370$ lb/in.[2]

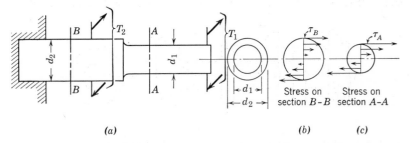

Fig. 93.   Distribution of shearing stress on two cross sections.

and $\tau_B = 4720$ lb/in.[2] The values of the diameters are $d_1 = 2$ in. and $d_2 = 3$ in. Calculate the values of T_1 and T_2.

Solution.

$$\tau_A = \frac{T_1 c}{J} \quad \text{or} \quad T_1 = \tau_A \cdot \frac{J}{c}$$

$$\frac{J}{c} = \frac{\frac{1}{32}\pi d_1^4}{d_1/2} = \frac{\pi d_1^3}{16} = \frac{\pi (2)^3}{16} = 1.57 \text{ in.}^3 \text{ for section } AA$$

Hence,

$$T_1 = \tau_A \cdot 1.57 = 6370 \times 1.57 = 10{,}000 \text{ lb-in.}$$
$$T_1 + T_2 = \tau_B \cdot 5.3 = 4720 \times 5.3 = 25{,}000 \text{ lb-in.}$$
$$T_2 = 25{,}000 - 10{,}000 = 15{,}000 \text{ lb-in.}$$

It should be noted that an increase in the diameter of the bar from d_1 to d_2 increases the section modulus J/c considerably; since J increases as the fourth power of the diameter and c increases as the first power of the diameter, J/c increases as the cube of the diameter. Thus, even though section BB is subjected to a twisting moment of $T_1 + T_2$ whereas section AA resists only the moment T_1, nevertheless the stresses on section AA are the larger because the J/c for section AA is relatively small.

Problems

83. A twisting moment of 12,000 lb-ft is applied to a solid cylindrical steel shaft having a 4-in. diameter. (a) Calculate the shearing stress on a transverse section at a point on the outer surface of the shaft; assume that the shearing elastic limit of the steel is 24,000 lb/in.² (b) Would the stress have the same value if the shaft were made of bronze or aluminum or any other elastic material provided that it was not stressed above its elastic limit?   *Ans.* (a) 11,400 lb/in.²; (b) Yes.

84. Compare the twisting moments acting on the following two shafts when stressed to their shearing proportional limits. The first is a solid shaft 21 in. in diameter, made of material having a shearing proportional limit of 26,000 lb/in.²; the second is a hollow shaft having an outside diameter of 20 in., an inside diameter of 15 in., and a shearing proportional limit of 32,000 lb/in.²

85. How much will the elastic strength of a solid cylindrical shaft be decreased by boring a concentric longitudinal hole through the shaft, the cross-sectional area of the hole being one half of the cross section of the solid shaft?

86. In Fig. 94, let the tube and shaft both be made of steel, and let the tube and shaft act as one body when subjected to a twisting couple of moment T ap-

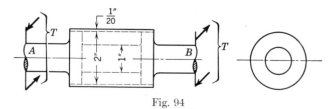

Fig. 94

plied at A and B. If the torsional shearing stress in the tube between the enlarged ends of the shaft is 10,000 lb per sq in., what is the value of T? Assume the radius of tube to be 1 in. in calculating J and c.

87. In Fig. 95 a force P of 196 lb will cause a normal pressure of 15 lb per sq in. on the rubbing surfaces of the friction clutch shown. If the coefficient of friction for the rubbing surfaces is 0.30 and the diameter of the shaft is 1.25 in., find the maximum shearing stress in the shaft at section AA. The shaft is made of steel which has a shearing proportional limit of 20,000 lb/in.²   *Ans.* $\tau = 7960$ lb/in.²

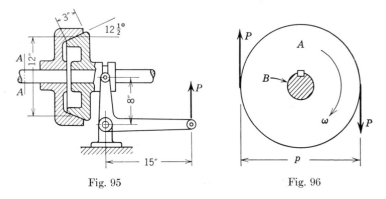

Fig. 95   Fig. 96

88. In Fig. 96 a disk A is keyed to a shaft B and a twisting moment $T = Pp$ is applied to the disk; the moment T is just sufficient to overcome the resisting moment offered by the machine that is driven by the shaft. Thus the disk and shaft rotate at a constant angular speed of ω radians per second. Show that the relation among the horsepower transmitted by the shaft, the twisting moment T, and the speed n in revolutions per minute (rpm) is given by the expression

$$\text{Hp} = \frac{T2\pi n}{12 \times 33,000} = \frac{T\pi n}{198,000}$$

in which T is expressed in pound-inches. (1 hp = 33,000 ft-lb per min = 550 ft-lb per sec.)

89. A cylindrical steel shaft having a diameter d in. is welded to a circular plate by means of a fillet weld, as shown in Fig. 97, in which h is small compared to d.

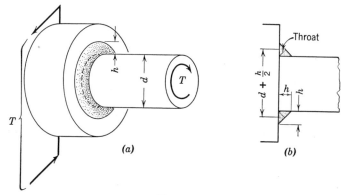

(a) (b)

Fig. 97

Equal and opposite twisting moments T lb-in. are applied to the ends of the member. If the shearing force on the throat section per inch of length of weld is q lb/in., show that

$$T = \frac{1}{2}\pi q \left(d + \frac{h}{2} \right)^2$$

Is this equation dimensionally correct? Also note that the shearing stress on the throat area of the weld is

$$\tau = \frac{q}{h \cos 45°}$$

90. In Fig. 98 let it be assumed that the diameter of the bolts of the coupling are small relative to r, so that the shearing stress on the cross section of each bolt

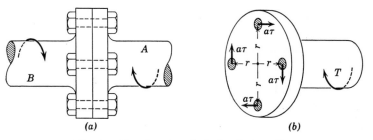

(a) (b)

Fig. 98. Shearing stress in bolts of a coupling.

may be considered to be distributed uniformly. Observe from Fig. 98b that equilibrium requires that the twisting moment T transmitted from one shaft to the other may be expressed as follows:

$$T = m \frac{\pi d^2}{4} \tau \cdot r$$

where m is the number of bolts and d is the diameter of each bolt. If, in Fig. 98, $d = \frac{3}{4}$ in., $r = 3$ in., $\tau = 8000$ lb/in.^{2}, and the speed of the shaft is 90 rpm, what horsepower is transmitted by the shaft? (See Prob. 88.)

91. A coupling is to be used to connect two shafts having diameters of 4 in. The maximum elastic shearing stress in the shafts is 10,000 lb per sq in., the diameter of the bolt circle is 8 in., and the elastic shearing stress in the bolts is 9000 lb per sq in. (a) Find the number of $\frac{3}{4}$-in. bolts used. (b) Calculate the horsepower transmitted by the shaft if its speed is 100 rpm. (See Prob. 88.)

92. A solid shaft 4 in. in diameter is to be connected to another shaft of the same size by means of a coupling, as shown in Fig. 98. If six $\frac{3}{4}$-in. bolts are used on a circle having a diameter of 10 in., what horsepower can the shaft transmit when rotating at 150 rpm, and when the shearing stress in the bolts is 10,000 lb per sq in.? (See Prob. 88.) What will be the maximum shearing stress in the shaft?   *Ans.*   hp = 315; τ = 10,540 lb per sq in.

93. In order to reduce the weight of a large solid shaft, a hollow shaft with a somewhat larger outside diameter may be used; this fact follows from the condition that the material near to the center of the shaft is very ineffective in contributing to the strength of the shaft since the stresses near to the center are small. The solid-steel propeller shaft of a large passenger ship delivers 40,000 hp at a constant speed of 200 rpm to the propeller. (a) If the outer diameter of the solid shaft is 24 in., what is the maximum torsional shearing stress in the shaft? (See Prob. 88.) Assume that the shaft acts elastically. (b) If a hollow shaft of the same material having an outer diameter of 26 in. is to replace the solid shaft without increasing the maximum shearing stress in the shaft, what should be the inner diameter of the hollow shaft? (c) How much weight per foot of length will be saved by use of the hollow shaft? Assume that steel weighs 0.28 lb per cu in.

94. The hydraulic turbines in the Keokuk waterpower plant are rated at 10,000 hp, with an overload capacity of 13,500 hp. The vertical shaft connecting the turbine and the generator is 25 in. in diameter and rotates at 57.7 rpm. What is

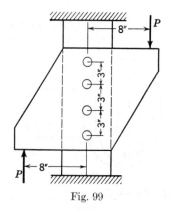

Fig. 99

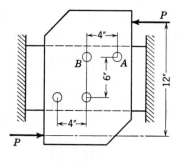

Fig. 100

the maximum shearing stress in the shaft when full load is being developed, and when maximum overload is being developed? (See Prob. 88.)

95. A plate (Fig. 99) is riveted to a fixed member by means of four $\frac{3}{4}$-in. rivets as shown. Calculate the elastic shearing stress at the center of each rivet area caused by the loads $P = 3000$ lb. Is the torsion formula applicable to this problem? Note that the shearing area of the rivets may be assumed to be two concentric annular areas equivalent to the cross sections of two concentric hollow cylinders.   *Ans.* 10,850 lb/in.²

96. Solve Prob. 95 if the rivets are arranged as shown in Fig. 100.

25. Longitudinal shearing stress. In Art. 23 the elastic shearing stress τ_V at any point in a *transverse* cross section of the shaft or bar was found in terms of the twisting moment (external forces) and dimensions of the section ($\tau_V = Tc/J$, see Fig. 101). But there are other

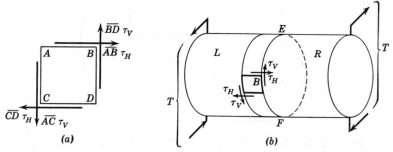

Fig. 101. Longitudinal shearing stress accompanying transverse shearing stress.

stresses at the point on different planes passing through the point, and these stresses, under some service conditions, may be the significant ones; the shearing stress τ_H on a *longitudinal* plane (Fig. 101) and the (maximum) tensile stress σ_t on a diagonal plane making an angle of 45° with the planes on which τ_V and τ_H occur are of special importance (see Fig. 103b and c). These stresses, however, will not be found here directly in terms of the external twisting moment, as τ_V was found, but will be expressed in terms of τ_V; then τ_V can be replaced by the expression Tc/J.

It will now be shown that $\tau_H = \tau_V$ (Fig. 101) by proving the following proposition:

Proposition. If a shearing stress occurs on a plane at a point in any stressed body, there must exist a shearing stress of equal magnitude at that point on a plane at right angles to the first plane.

Proof. Let an elementary rectangular block (Fig. 101a) be removed from a body in which the block is subjected to shearing stresses on a pair of parallel faces, such as faces BD and AC. As previously suggested, the block may be in the torsional bar, as illustrated in Fig. 101b where the part R causes shearing stresses τ_V on the transverse (vertical) plane BD and part L exerts equal resisting or opposite shearing stresses at the various points on face AC.

The shearing *forces* (average stress times area) acting on a pair of parallel faces of the block in Fig. 101a form a couple, and, since the block was in equilibrium when it was in the body, there must be shearing forces on the other pair of faces in order to satisfy the condition of

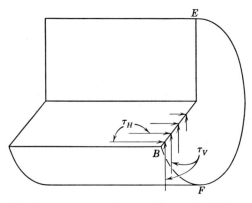

Fig. 102.   Distribution of transverse and longitudinal shearing stress.

equilibrium such that the moments of the two couples are equal and opposite. If the depth of the block perpendicular to the paper is assumed for convenience to be unity, then we may write

$$\overline{AB}\tau_H \cdot \overline{BD} = \overline{BD}\tau_V \cdot \overline{AB}$$

Hence

$$\tau_H = \tau_V \tag{58}$$

If now the dimensions of the block are considered to be indefinitely small, τ_H and τ_V may be considered to be the stresses at a point. Thus the magnitudes of the shearing stresses at any point in a stressed body on planes at right angles to each other are equal; this statement is true also when normal stresses act on the planes in addition to shearing stresses, as is illustrated in Fig. 27c. If *only* shearing stresses occur in the two planes at any point in a body, the state of stress at that point is said to be simple or *pure shear*.

Thus the shearing stresses in the torsional bar at various points on the radius of any transverse cross section of the bar may be shown as in Fig. 102, if all stresses are within the elastic limit of the material.

26. Diagonal normal stresses. *Proposition.* If a state of pure shear exists at a point in a body (as in Fig. 103a), there also exist normal (tensile and compressive) stresses at the point on planes that bisect the angles between the planes on which the shearing stresses act, and the magnitudes of the normal stresses are equal to those of the shearing stresses.

Proof. Let a diagonal plane AD be passed through the block of Fig. 103a, and let the forces acting on one part of the block be shown as

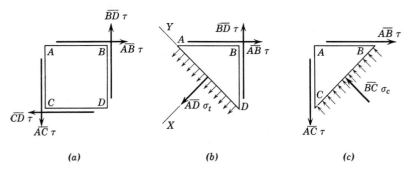

Fig. 103. Tensile and compressive stresses accompanying simple shear.

in Fig. 103b. The face of the block in Fig. 103 is assumed, for convenience, to have a thickness (perpendicular to the plane of the paper) of unity. The force on each face is equal to the area of the face times the stress on that face, and, since the block ABD (Fig. 103b) is in equilibrium, we have, by resolving the forces in the x direction,

$$\overline{AD}\sigma_t = \overline{AB}\tau \cos 45° + \overline{BD}\tau \cos 45° = \tau(\overline{AB} \cos 45° + \overline{BD} \cos 45°)$$

but

$$\overline{AB} \cos 45° + \overline{BD} \cos 45° = \overline{AD}$$

Therefore,

$$\sigma_t = \tau. \quad \text{Similarly, from Fig. 103c,} \quad \sigma_c = \tau \tag{59}$$

Furthermore, these values of σ_t and σ_c which occur on the two bisecting (45°) planes are the maximum values of the normal stresses that occur at the point; this may be proved by using θ (instead of 45°) in the equilibrium equation and showing that σ_t (or σ_c) has its greatest value on the plane for which $\theta = 45°$.

Thus, when a brittle material which usually is weak in tension is twisted as in Fig. 89, the material fails in tension on a plane inclined (approximately 45°) to the planes on which the shearing stresses occur. The student may demonstrate this fact by twisting a chalk crayon with his hands.   Furthermore, the diagonal *compressive* stress in a thin-walled cylindrical shell made of ductile metal may cause the shell wall to buckle (see Chap. VI) before the shearing stresses cause the thin-walled cylinder to fail by inelastic deformation (yielding).

Conclusion. It should be evident from the discussion in Arts. 25 to 27, that, in a cylindrical member (solid or hollow) subjected to torsion, any one of four stresses may be the significant stress; that is, any one of four stresses may limit the maximum torsional moment that can be applied to the member without causing structural damage to the member.   For example, the longitudinal shearing stress τ_H usually would be the significant stress in a torsional timber cylindrical member if the grain of the wood is parallel to the axis of the member; the transverse shearing stress τ_V usually is the significant stress in a ductile-metal bar that fails by inelastic yielding; the diagonal tensile stress causes failure by fracture if the member is made of brittle material, and the diagonal compressive stress is likely to cause failure by buckling in a thin-walled hollow member.   Buckling, however, will not be considered in this chapter.

Problems

97. Two cylindrical bars are connected by a coupling to form the member shown in Fig. 104.   The metal in body A is ductile; its shearing yield point is 30,000 lb/in.[2]   The material in body B is very brittle and acts elastically until rupture occurs; its ultimate tensile strength is 60,000 lb/in.[2]   If the member is twisted by gradually applied moments at its ends, will the member be damaged by excessive yielding of A or by fracture of B?   Assume $d_2 = 2d_1$.   Also assume that the member will not fail at the fillets or at the bolts of the coupling.

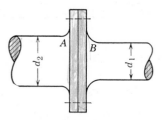

Fig. 104

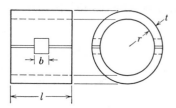

Fig. 105

98. A hollow cylindrical member is composed of two semicylindrical shells as shown in Fig. 105.   The shear key on each side of the cylinder is made of metal having a shearing yield point of 40,000 lb/in.[2], and the shearing yield point of the two cylindrical half-shells is 24,000 lb/in.[2]   The member is twisted by gradually applied moments at its ends.   If an allowable shearing stress for the keys is specified to be one half of the yield point, what is the allowable value of the twisting moment for the member?   Assume: $b = 2$ in., $t = \frac{1}{2}$ in., $r = 4$ in., $l = 6\frac{2}{3}''$.
Ans. $T = 343,000$ lb-in.

27. Torsion of thin-walled tubes. Shear flow. In thin plates or webs and thin-walled tubes, such as are used in airplane construction, the term *shear flow* frequently is used to denote the shearing force per unit length along a cross section of the web or tube.

In Fig. 106 is shown a thin-walled tube of constant wall thickness t. This tube is subjected to a twisting moment T, which develops a shearing stress τ at any point in the cross section in a direction tangent to the contour of the tube wall at that point. The shearing force on a differential area $t\,dL$ is $\tau t\,dL$ as shown in Fig. 106. The moment of this force with respect to any point O is $p\tau t\,dL$, and the moment of the shearing forces on all differential areas is $\int p\tau t\,dL$. Since

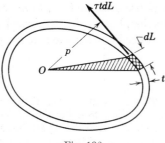

Fig. 106

this resisting moment must be in equilibrium with the applied twisting moment T, the following equation may be written:

$$T = \int p\tau t\,dL$$

But τt is the shear flow; for convenience let it be denoted by q. It is assumed to be constant for the reason that torsional tests of thin-walled tubes (including noncircular tubes) show that, within the elastic limit of the material, the measured value of the shearing strain γ times the wall thickness t is constant along the wall of the tube. Since γt is constant and $G\gamma = \tau$, we have $\tau t = q =$ constant. Furthermore, $p\,dL$ is equal to twice the cross-hatched area of the small triangle. Thus, the preceding equation may be written

$$T = q \int p\,dL = 2Aq$$

Thus,

$$q = \frac{T}{2A} \quad \text{and} \quad \tau = \frac{q}{t} = \frac{T}{2At} \tag{60}$$

in which A denotes the area enclosed by the median line of the shell.

Since q is assumed to be constant, the shearing stress at any point in a cross section with a variable thickness may be found by using the value of the thickness at that point. Thus,

$$q = \tau t_1 = \tau_2 t_2 = \text{constant} \tag{61}$$

The idea and name of shear flow comes from the fact that Eq. 61 is
similar to the equation of continuity for the flow of a liquid in a pipe:
namely,

$$Q = a_1 v_1 = a_2 v_2 = \text{constant}$$

in which Q is the volume of liquid flowing per unit time, v is the velocity
of the liquid, and a is the cross-sectional area of the pipe. The idea
and use of shear flow, however, is not restricted to shear developed in
torsion, but applies to shear in any thin plate or web, regardless of the
manner in which the shear is produced (see Art. 51).

Problems

99. Show that Eq. 60, when applied to a *cylindrical* thin-walled tube may be
transformed into the torsion formula $\tau = Tc/J$.

100. The shear flow in a thin-walled cylindrical tube is 100 lb per in. when the
tube is subjected to a twisting moment of 60,000 lb-ft. Calculate the mean radius
of the tube. If the thickness of the tube wall is $\frac{1}{8}$ in., what is the torsional shearing stress in the tube?   *Ans.*   800 lb/in.^{2}

101. If, in Fig. 107, t and b have the same values, respectively, in the two shapes,
compare the shear flows in the two shapes when the tubes are subjected to equal
twisting moments.

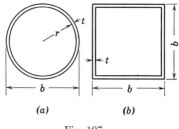

(a)   (b)

Fig. 107

28. Relationship of twisting moment and angle of twist. In
some problems the size of shaft required to transmit a given twisting
moment (or given horsepower at a given speed) is controlled by the
allowable elastic angle of twist rather than by the allowable elastic
shearing stress or allowable diagonal tensile stress. In other words,
stiffness rather than strength is the controlling factor in the design.
The angle of twist θ (Fig. 92) caused by a given twisting moment T
may be found as follows:

As explained in Art. 7,

$$\tau/\gamma = \text{a constant} = G$$

provided that τ does not exceed the shearing proportional limit of the material. But, as shown in Arts. 23 and 24,

$$\tau_c = Tc/J \quad \text{and} \quad \gamma_c = c\theta/l$$

Therefore,

$$G = \frac{Tc/J}{c\theta/l} = \frac{Tl}{J\theta}$$

Hence, the angle of twist θ, if the proportional limit of the material is not exceeded, is

$$\theta = \frac{Tl}{GJ} \tag{62}$$

Units. In Eq. 62, θ is expressed in radians, and any consistent units of force and length may be used to express the other quantities. Thus, T usually is expressed in pound-inches, l in inches, G in pounds per square inch, and J in inches to the fourth power.

If T or J (or both) vary with the distance z along the shaft, we have

$$\theta = \int d\theta = \int \frac{T\,dz}{JG} \tag{63}$$

where $d\theta$ is the angle of twist for a differential length dz and T, J, and G have the values for the given length dz.

Caution. An error is sometimes made by attempting to increase the stiffness of a steel cylindrical shaft (decrease θ for a given T) by using a steel that has a larger proportional limit (a stronger steel). But Eq. 62 shows that such a change would have no influence on the stiffness of the shaft since G is approximately the same for all grades of steel. It should be observed from an inspection of Eq. 62 that θ may be decreased for a given value of T in any one of three ways: namely (1) by use of a stiffer (not stronger) material which means that G would be increased (this would be difficult to accomplish with steel since steel is the stiffest material available for load-resisting members, (2) by decreasing the length l of the shaft, and (3) by increasing the diameter d which would increase the value of J, and since J varies as the fourth power of d, a small increase in d causes a relatively large increase in J.

Illustrative Problem

Problem 102. Cylindrical rubber springs frequently are used as spring mountings of automobiles, trucks, and buses. For example, one such spring is shown in Fig. 108 in which rubber is securely bonded to two concentric cylindrical steel shells denoted by S and H. The outer shell is attached to the frame or body of the automobile, and the inner shell is attached to the axle in such a way that the two shells twist relatively to each other when vertical relative motion between the axle and car body occurs as the car travels over rough road. The twisting moment or torque T transmitted from one shell to the other causes torsional shearing stresses and strains in the rubber. Find the total angle of twist of the outer shell relative to the inner shell, if it is assumed that the shearing modulus of elasticity G of the rubber is constant and that the torque is applied uniformly over the length L (Fig. 108).

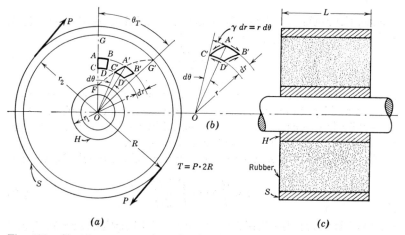

Fig. 108. Shearing stress and strains in a torsional rubber spring for reducing vibrations, sometimes called a torsilastic spring.

Solution. For convenience let it be assumed that the torque T is applied to the outer shell and that the inner shell is held rigidly. Before the torque T is applied, the line FG is any radial line, and the element $ABCD$ is any differential element in the cross section of the rubber. After the torque T is applied, the line FG and the differential element $ABCD$ take the positions FG' and $A'B'C'D'$, respectively (Fig. 108), as a result of the shearing strains in the rubber. The movement of the face $A'B'$ relative to the face $C'D'$ gives the outer shell an angular displacement $d\theta$ about the center of the shaft. Therefore, the total angle θ_T through which the outer shell turns relative to the inner shell (and to the center of the shaft) in response to the twisting moment T is equal to the sum of the angular displacements $d\theta$ of all of the differential elements along the line FG' or

$$\theta_T = \int d\theta$$

If the radial distance between the faces $A'B'$ and $C'D'$ is dr, $d\theta$ may be expressed in terms of dr, and then θ_T may be evaluated by integrating between the limits r_1 and r_2. This may be done as follows:

The distance through which the face $A'B'$ moves relative to the face $C'D'$ is the distance $r\, d\theta = \gamma\, dr$, in which γ is the shearing strain at a point r distance from the center (Fig. 108b), but $\tau/\gamma = G$. Hence,

$$d\theta = \frac{\tau}{G}\frac{dr}{r}$$

Therefore,

$$\theta_T = \int_{r_1}^{r_2} \frac{\tau}{G} \frac{dr}{r}$$

But τ varies with r, and hence the integration requires that τ be expressed as a function of r. This may be done by use of an equation of equilibrium; namely, the moment of the total shearing force on any concentric surface is equal to T. Thus

$$T = 2\pi r^2 L\tau \quad \text{or} \quad \tau = \frac{T}{2\pi r^2 L}$$

Hence

$$\theta_T = \frac{T}{2\pi LG} \int_{r_1}^{r_2} \frac{dr}{r^3} = \frac{T}{4\pi LG} \left(\frac{1}{r_1^2} - \frac{1}{r_2^2} \right)$$

It should be observed that the value of G for rubber is extremely small compared to that for metals, as is indicated in Probs. 103 and 104. Furthermore, the foregoing value for θ_T should be regarded as approximate (but useful) for the reason that for such large strains as are involved with rubber Hooke's law are not strictly applicable, as is assumed in the analysis of the problem.

Problems

103. A torsilastic spring (see Prob. 102 and Fig. 108) in service has rubber dimensions of 3.25 in. OD, 1.50 in. ID, and 9.40 in. in length. The shearing modulus of elasticity of the rubber is 175 lb per sq in. If a torque of 2500 lb-in. is applied to it, find the maximum shearing stress developed and the total angle of twist of the outer shell relative to the inner shell.   *Ans.* $\tau = 75$ psi; $\theta = 9.66°$.

104. A rubber with a shearing modulus of elasticity of 150 lb per sq in. is to be used in making a torsilastic spring (Fig. 108). The length of the spring is to be 3 in., and the maximum allowable shearing stress is 100 psi. It is estimated that the maximum torque to which the spring is to be subjected is 400 lb-in. Find the required diameters of the rubber material, if the angle of twist of the outer shell relative to the inner shell is not to exceed 15°.

Ans. $D_1 = 0.92$ in.; $D_2 = 2$ in.

105. A steel shaft 4 in. in diameter transmits 250 hp at a speed of 240 rpm. The distance between the driving and driven pulleys is 10 ft. Determine whether the following two requirements are satisfied: (*a*) Maximum shearing stress not to exceed 10,000 lb per sq in.; (*b*) twist of shaft not to exceed 1° per 20 diameters of length.

106. The steel shaft connecting a hydraulic turbine with an electric generator was so long that, under fluctuating load, the changing angle of twist of the shaft caused electrical trouble in the generator. Does Eq. 62 indicate that the angle of twist would be decreased by replacing the shaft by a higher-strength steel? (See Table 1.) For a given twisting moment T, which of the following two changes would decrease the angle of twist the more: decreasing the length of the shaft by one half or doubling the diameter? How much more?

107. Let the body shown in Fig. 36 (Chap. I) be subjected to equal and opposite twisting moments T at its ends instead of axial loads P. Let it be required to find the angle of twist θ of one end of the body relative to the other end in terms of T, G, and the dimensions of the body given in Fig. 36.

108. A hollow bronze shaft having an outside diameter of 4 in. and an inside diameter of 2 in. is 12 ft long. If the shaft is twisted by applying moments at its ends, what will be the angle of twist when the maximum shearing stress is 10,000 lb per sq in.? (Refer to Table 1.) *Ans.* $\theta = 0.12$ radian $= 6.86°$

109. The principle employed in the torque stabilizer is illustrated in Fig. 109. M is a body mounted on springs, such as the body of an automobile. $ABEF$ is a

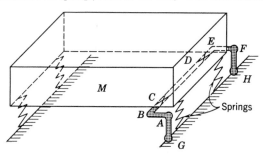

Fig. 109. A torque stabilizer—a principle used in automobiles.

continuous cylindrical bar made of high-strength steel. C and D are bearings attached to M in which $ABEF$ can turn. A and F are frictionless joints. AG and FH are rigid bars that can turn slightly about G and H, respectively. In an automobile, G and H would be points on the wheel axle. If the body M moves (vibrates) up and down without lateral rotation, no resistance to vibration is offered by the bar $ABEF$. But, if body M rotates about an axis perpendicular to plane $AGHF$ (clockwise, say), B will move up and E will move down, and the portion of the bar BE will be subjected to equal (and opposite) twisting moments at its ends; the accompanying forces exerted by the bearings C and D will resist the rotation of M. If BE is 8 ft long and has a diameter of 1 in., and AB is 2 ft, what is the maximum torsional shearing stress in the bar when M rotates 5°? If the distance between C and D is 5 ft, what is the magnitude of the moment resisting the rotation of M? Assume that the proportional limit is not exceeded.

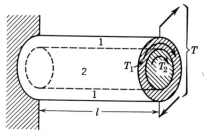

Fig. 110. A two-material torsion member.

110. Figure 110 represents a torsional member made of two bodies of different materials; the two bodies act elastically as a unit (as one torsional member). If T is the twisting moment applied to the composite body, T_1 is the part of T that is transmitted by body 1, and T_2 the part of T transmitted by body 2, show that

$$T_1 = \frac{T}{1 + G_2J_2/G_1J_1} \quad \text{and} \quad T_2 = \frac{T}{1 + G_1J_1/G_2J_2}$$

in which G refers to the shearing modulus of elasticity and J to the polar moment of inertia of the transverse cross-sectional area (see Art. 12 for a similar expression for central loads).

111. A steel pipe having a wall thickness of $\frac{1}{4}$ in. and an inside diameter of 8 in. encases a solid cylindrical bar of aluminum alloy (see Table 1). The aluminum bar and the steel casing form a composite cylinder. The composite body is used as a torsional member. If the torsional moment applied to the composite member is 800,000 lb-in., calculate the maximum shearing stress in the aluminum bar, assuming that the proportional limits of the materials are not exceeded. (See Table 1 and Prob. 110.) *Ans.* 4330 lb/in.²

112. A steel tube with a wall thickness of $\frac{1}{15}$ in. is shrunk on a steel shaft having enlarged ends as shown in Fig. 111. The shaft is held twisted by couples of

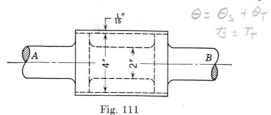

$$\theta = \theta_s + \theta_T$$
$$T_s = T_T$$

Fig. 111

80 lb-ft applied at the ends of the shaft while the tube is being shrunk on. After the tube has become firmly attached to the shaft, the twisting couples are removed. Calculate the twisting couple still left on the shaft between the enlarged ends. Assume that the shearing proportional limit of the material is not exceeded; assume that the radius of tube is 2 in. in calculating J. *Ans.* 54.4 lb-ft.

29. Elastic-shearing-stress concentration in torsion. As previously noted, the maximum elastic shearing stress in a torsional bar is given by the expression $\tau = Tc/J$, provided that the bar has a constant circular cross section, although the expression gives a satisfactory value for τ if a gradual variation in the diameter occurs. If, however, an abrupt change in diameter takes place as in a so-called stepped

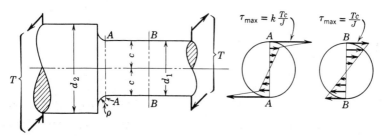

Fig. 112. Torsional shearing-stress concentration at a fillet.

shaft indicated in Fig. 112, a shearing-stress concentration $\tau_{\max}$ occurs which may be expressed by use of a stress concentration factor k in the expression

$$\tau_{\max} = k\,\frac{Tc}{J} \tag{64}$$

The approximate stress distribution on a section at the abrupt change in section is shown in section AA, Fig. 112, and that at a section in the small part of the shaft a short distance from the abrupt change in section in section BB, Fig. 112.

Abrupt changes in cross section of cylindrical shafts caused by oil holes, keyways, grooves, etc.,* may also be expressed by Eq. 64. The theoretical value for k (for elastic stresses) depends on the geometry of the abrupt change in section. For a stepped shaft it depends on the two ratios ρ/d_1 and d_2/d_1, as indicated in Table 2. The influence of

TABLE 2

THEORETICAL VALUES FOR SHEARING-STRESS-CONCENTRATION FACTORS IN A
STEPPED SHAFT

Values of k in $\tau = k\dfrac{Tc}{J}$

$\dfrac{\rho}{d_1} =$	0.02	0.04	0.08	0.12	0.20
$d_2/d_1 = 1.10$	1.85	1.54	1.30	1.20	1.15
$d_2/d_1 = 1.20$	2.40	1.96	1.63	1.47	1.32
$d_2/d_1 = 2.00$	2.90	2.25	1.83	1.63	1.44

small inelastic strains on the value of stress concentrations is discussed in the next article.

Other Conditions Causing Elastic-stress Concentrations. Torsional-shearing-stress concentrations frequently arise by virtue of the fact that elastic strains (and hence stresses) cannot be transmitted to some portion of another member until excessively large (often inelastic) strains first occur in another part of the member. This fact is often neglected in the analysis, resulting in wrong conclusions concerning the load-carrying capacity of the member. For example, Fig. 113 represents a heavy hub A that has been pressed on or shrunk on a shaft. The assumption is frequently made that the shearing elastic stresses (and strains) are distributed uniformly on the contact surface between the hub and shaft as the twisting moment is transferred from the shaft to

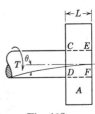

Fig. 113

* See our book, *Advanced Mechanics of Materials*, John Wiley & Sons, 1952.

the hub (or vice versa). But it is evident that the torsional elastic strains (and corresponding shearing stresses) cannot be transmitted to those sections within the hub that are near to section EF until strains first are developed in the portion near to section CD of the shaft. Thus the strains are distributed nonuniformly, giving rise to a stress concentration at or near section CD, unless the shaft slips in the hub (acting somewhat like a friction clutch), and thus transferring the torque part way, at least, along the length L of the hub. This action tends to loosen the fit of the two members, especially under repeated loading.

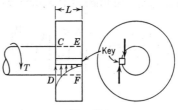

Fig. 114

The same reasoning applies in showing that, if the two members are connected by a key as in Fig. 114, the pressure on the side of the key cannot, for elastic behavior, be constant along the key as frequently is assumed, but instead there must be an elastic-stress concentration at or near to section CD. This undesirable action may be reduced somewhat by using more than one key which leads to the idea of a splined shaft as utilized in automobiles, etc.

The influence on the behavior of members of small inelastic deformations at the points of stress concentrations is discussed in the next article.

§ 2 Inelastic Behavior

30. Introduction. As previously noted, the *minimum* static torsional load (twisting moment) that is likely to cause damage to a cylindrical bar or shaft of constant diameter made of ductile material having a yield point is usually considered to be the value of T in the torsion formula $(T = \tau J/c)$ that causes in the most stressed fiber a shearing stress τ equal to the shearing proportional limit or yield point τ_y. $(T_y = \tau_y J/c$, Fig. 115a.)

In many service conditions the maximum useful load-carrying capacity of such a member will not be reached until some inelastic (plastic) deformation has occurred. And the *maximum* static twisting moment that can be applied without destroying the load-resisting function of the member is usually considered to be the fully plastic twisting moment, which is the value of the moment that causes the plastic deformation at one or more sections to penetrate nearly to the center of the shaft. Since the material has a yield point, the stress in the plastically deformed material at the section will be equal to the yield point, and hence will be uniformly distributed on nearly the whole area as indicated in Fig. 115b.   The fully plastic twisting moment $T_{fp} = \frac{4}{3}\tau_y J/c$ is derived in the next article.

Influence of Localized Inelastic Deformation on Stress Concentration. If the shaft is a stepped shaft containing an abrupt change of section as indicated in Fig. 115c and d, inelastic deformation will start at the most stressed fiber at the abrupt change in section and progress toward

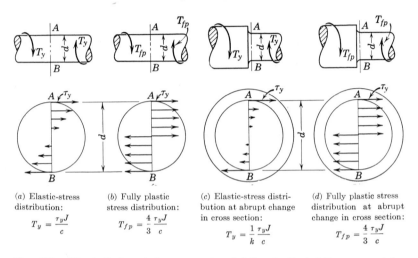

(a) Elastic-stress distribution:

$$T_y = \frac{\tau_y J}{c}$$

(b) Fully plastic stress distribution:

$$T_{fp} = \frac{4}{3}\frac{\tau_y J}{c}$$

(c) Elastic-stress distribution at abrupt change in cross section:

$$T_y = \frac{1}{k}\frac{\tau_y J}{c}$$

(d) Fully plastic stress distribution at abrupt change in cross section:

$$T_{fp} = \frac{4}{3}\frac{\tau_y J}{c}$$

Fig. 115.   Elastic-limit twisting moment and fully plastic twisting moment for each of two shafts.

the center of the shaft as the twisting moment is increased, in much the same manner that it does in a similar member subjected to a static *central* load as explained in Art. 17.   The shaft, as a whole, gives only slight evidence of inelastic behavior until inelastic strains penetrate to all parts of the section at the abrupt change in section, after which a small increase in twisting moment causes appreciable inelastic twisting of the shaft.   The inelastic strains which start at the points of high stress concentration cause a change in the stress distribution on the section by reducing the elastic-stress concentration and tending to produce a uniform stress, equal to the yield point, on the whole section, as indicated in Fig. 115d.

The fully plastic twisting moment for a stepped shaft is, therefore, substantially the same as that for one of constant diameter equal to the minimum diameter of the stepped shaft.

31. The fully plastic twisting moment.   The static fully plastic twisting moment T_{fp} for a cylindrical shaft may thus be found by calculating the resisting torsional moment T_r corresponding to the uniform distribution of stress shown in Fig. 116 and equating it to T_{fp}. Hence,

$$T_{fp} = T_r = \int \tau_y \, da \cdot \rho = \int \tau_y 2\pi\rho \, d\rho \cdot \rho$$

$$= 2\pi\tau_y \int_0^c \rho^2 \, d\rho = 2\pi\tau_y \frac{c^3}{3} = \frac{4}{3} \frac{\tau_y}{c} \frac{\pi c^4}{2}$$

MUST:

Hence

$$T_{fp} = \frac{4}{3} \frac{\tau_y J}{c} \tag{65}$$

1 YIELD POINT

2 RIGHT CYCLINDER

3 NOT A HOLLOW SHAFT

Therefore, the limiting value of the static twisting moment that can be applied to a cylindrical shaft of constant radius c made of material

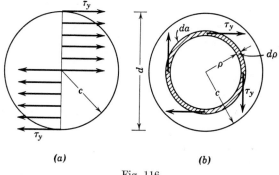

(a)   (b)

Fig. 116

having a shearing yield point τ_y will usually lie between $T_y = \tau_y J/c$ and $T_{fp} = 1.33\tau_y J/c$, depending on service conditions.

Ultimate Twisting Moment. The ultimate static twisting moment T_u that is required to twist the shaft in two (fracture it in shear) is greater than the fully plastic twisting moment T_{fp}, and is obtained from Fig. 116 and Eq. 65 by replacing τ_y with the ultimate shearing strength τ_u of the material (see Table 1) as follows

$$T_u = \frac{4}{3} \frac{\tau_u J}{c} \tag{66}$$

Ductile material

Justification for Assumption of Uniformly Distributed Shearing Stress in Inelastically Twisted Shaft. The assumption of a uniformly distributed shearing stress as shown in Fig. 115b and d and in Fig. 116a that is used in deriving Eqs. 65 and 66 may be justified from a consideration of the shearing stress-strain diagrams in Fig. 117 as follows: Fig. 117a shows that, when the shearing yield point τ_y in steel is reached, the shearing stress does not become larger than τ_y as the twisting moment is increased until the shearing strain γ has increased to 10 to 30 times the value at which inelastic shearing strain begins. Figure 117a and b also show that for steel and the nonferrous alloy the shearing resistance of the material increases as the inelastic shearing strains become relatively large, and at the maximum * value of the strain the corresponding value of the stress τ_u of the resisting stress again remains constant for a rather wide range of values of shearing strain.

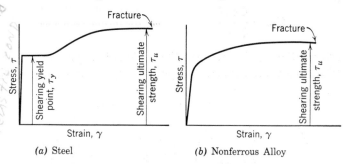

Fig. 117.   Typical torsional shearing-stress diagrams for two metals with emphasis on inelastic strains.

Inelastic Angle of Twist.   An analysis giving a relationship between twisting moment and angle of twist for a shaft subjected to inelastic torsional deformation will not here be made; if inelastic deformations are permissible in the shaft, the fully plastic moment usually will be the maximum moment that can be applied rather than the moment causing a given angle of twist.

§ 3   Design of Torsional Member

32. Introduction.   The foregoing analyses of elastic and inelastic behaviors of the restricted types of torsional members considered may now be used in the design of such members, since the analyses involve

---

* The value of τ_u may be determined from a torsion test of a solid cylindrical specimen of the material to its ultimate twisting moment T_u. From Eq. 65 the value of $\tau_u = T_u c / 1.33 J$ is found by substituting the test value of T_u. Sometimes a hollow cylindrical (tubular) specimen is used in the test. Usually the wall thickness is made equal to one-tenth the outer diameter, and under these conditions the derivation of Eq. 65 leads to the equation $T_u = 1.04 \tau_u J / c$, and hence the ultimate strength as obtained from such a test is $\tau_u = T_u c / 1.04 J$. A quantity called the modulus of rupture, denoted by τ_r, is found by substituting for T in the expression $\tau = T c / J$ the ultimate value of the twisting moment as obtained from a torsional test of the bar. The value of τ_r, however, is not a stress and has little physical significance except for brittle material.

the main conditions in the member that are commonly considered to limit the loads (twisting moment) that can be applied to such a load-resisting member in a structure or machine (see Art. 22 under Modes of Failure for a list of these conditions). It will be recalled that thin-walled cylindrical tubes for which the load-carrying capacity is limited by buckling are not here considered (see Chap. VI).

33. Design for elastic strength. *Ductile Material with a Yield Point.* As suggested in Art. 23, the design equation for the working load T_w for these conditions is obtained from the equation $T = \tau J/c$ by giving τ a working value τ_w. Hence, for either transverse or longitudinal elastic shearing stress, we may write

$$T_w = \frac{\tau_w J}{c} = \frac{\tau_y}{N} \frac{J}{c} \tag{67}$$

in which τ_w is obtained by applying a factor of safety N to τ_y, since τ_y for the conditions specified is the value of either the transverse or longitudinal shearing stress that causes the member to cease to function satisfactorily as a load-resisting member.

Brittle Material. The material is assumed to be elastic until it fractures. The limiting twisting moment is reached when the diagonal tensile stress σ_t reaches the tensile proportional limit (which is also the ultimate tensile strength σ_u). But, as shown in Art. 26, $\sigma_t = \tau = Tc/J$. Hence, the design formula is

$$T_w = \frac{\sigma_w J}{c} = \frac{\sigma_e}{N} \frac{J}{c} = \frac{\sigma_u}{N} \frac{J}{c} \tag{68}$$

34. Design for elastic stiffness. *Working Value of Angle of Twist.* The limiting twisting moment occurs when a specified angle of twist θ_s is reached. But, as shown in Art. 28, $T = GJ\theta/l$. Hence, the design formula is

$$T_w = \frac{T}{N} = \frac{GJ}{l} \frac{\theta_s}{N} \tag{69}$$

An alternative method is to use a working stress as follows.

Working Value of Stress. The stress τ_s corresponding to θ_s as obtained from the elastic stress-strain diagram is expressed by the equation

$$\tau_s = G\gamma_s = G \frac{c\theta_s}{l} \tag{70}$$

The working value of τ is obtained by dividing both sides of Eq. 70 by N, which gives

$$\tau_w = \frac{\tau_s}{N} = \frac{\theta_s}{N}\frac{cG}{l} \tag{71}$$

The working value of the twisting moment is now obtained from

$$T_w = \frac{\tau_w J}{c} \tag{72}$$

in which τ_w from Eq. 71 is used.

35. Design based on fully plastic twisting moment. If the limiting twisting moment is considered to be the fully plastic moment T_{fp} as given in Art. 31, the working moment T_w is found by applying a factor of safety N to the stress τ_y in Eq. 65 as follows:

$$T_w = \frac{T_{fp}}{N} = \frac{4}{3}\frac{\tau_y J}{N\,c} = \frac{4}{3}\frac{\tau_w J}{c} \tag{73}$$

36. Design based on ultimate or fracture twisting moment. If the limiting twisting moment is considered to be the ultimate or fracture twisting moment T_u for a ductile member (Eq. 66), the working load T_w is found by applying a factor of safety N to the ultimate shearing strength τ_u. We may write the design equation as follows:

$$T_w = \frac{4}{3}\cdot\frac{\tau_u}{N}\frac{J}{c} = \frac{4}{3}\frac{\tau_w J}{c} \tag{74}$$

Illustrative Problem

Problem 113. A solid cylindrical shaft is required in service to resist a static twisting moment of 100,000 lb-in. The shaft is made of steel having a stress-strain diagram shown in Fig. 117a, the value of the yield point (and proportional limit) being $\tau_y = 20,000$ lb/in.^{2} Under the service conditions the shaft would fulfill its load-resisting function satisfactorily until some inelastic deformation occurred in the shaft. Determine the diameter for the shaft based on a factor of safety of $N = 2$.

Solution. Upper Limit for Diameter. First it will be assumed that the shaft fails when inelastic deformation *begins* in the most stressed (outer) fibers: that is, when the stress in the outer fibers reaches the value τ_y. The working value of the twisting moment is $T_w = 100,000$ lb-in., and the working value of the stress is $\tau_w = 20,000/2 = 10,000$ lb/in.^{2} Hence, from Eq. 67 we have

$$T_w = \frac{\tau_w J}{c} = \frac{\tau_y}{N}\cdot\frac{J}{c}, \qquad 100,000 = 10,000\,\frac{\pi d^3}{16}$$

$$d^3 = \frac{160}{\pi} = 51.0 \text{ in.}^3 \qquad d = 3.7 \text{ in.}$$

Lower Limit for Diameter.   Second, it will be assumed that inelastic deformation sufficient to develop the fully plastic resisting moment may occur without causing failure of the member.   The working stress is the same as in the preceding solution, $\tau_w = 10,000$ lb/in.[2]   Hence, from Eq. 73, we have

$$T_w = \frac{4}{3} \frac{\tau_w J}{c}$$

$$100,000 = \frac{4}{3} 10,000 \frac{\pi d^3}{16}$$

$$d = 3.38 \text{ in.}$$

Thus, to satisfy the requirements for static strength the diameter should have a value between these two limiting values (3.70 in. and 3.38 in.) depending on the amount of inelastic deformation that is considered to be permissible before the member is said to have failed.

Problems

114. A cylindrical bar, 2.5 in. in diameter, is made of brittle material whose stress-strain diagram is a straight line until the bar fractures by diagonal tension as in Fig. 89.   The tensile ultimate strength (and proportional limit) of the material is $\sigma_u = 30,000$ lb/in.[2]   Calculate the allowable or working value of the twisting moment for a factor of safety of 3.   *Ans.* $T_w = 30,800$ lb-in.

115. A stepped shaft (see Art. 29) is made of steel having a shearing yield point of 40,000 lb/in.[2]   The theoretical or elastic shearing-stress-concentration factor at the abrupt change in section is 1.8.   (See Table 2.)   The shaft ceases to fulfill its function as a load-resisting member (fails) when only a very small inelastic strain occurs in the most stressed fibers.   Calculate the value of the allowable or working static twist moment if the smaller of the two diameters is 4 in. and a factor of safety of $N = 2$ is used.   *Ans.* $T_w = 140,000$ lb-in.

116. A steel plate (Fig. 118) is riveted to a fixed member by means of 4 steel $\frac{3}{4}$-in. rivets, as shown in the figure.   Failure of the riveted joint does not

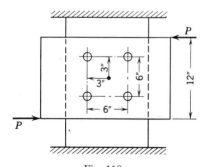

Fig. 118

occur until the rivets are sheared in two.   The ultimate strength of the rivet material is $\tau_u = 45,000$ lb/in.[2]   Calculate the forces P of the applied twisting moment that will cause failure of the joint or connection by fracturing all of the rivets.

117. An aluminum-alloy plate (Fig. 119) is fastened to a member by means of four aluminum-alloy rivets. Determine the diameter of the rivets that are required to resist the loads if a factor of safety of 3 based on the shearing ultimate or fracture load is specified. The ultimate shearing strength of the rivet material is $\tau_u = 36,000$ lb/in.^{2} (See Table 1.) The plate is assumed to be sufficiently thick to prevent failure caused by the bearing stress. Let $P = 15,000$ lb.

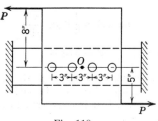

Fig. 119

118. A steel shaft, 10 ft long, is to be used to transmit a working load (torque) of 500,000 lb-in. from a turbine to a generator. For satisfactory functioning of the unit, the elastic angle of twist of the shaft must not exceed a limiting value of 1 degree per 20 diameters of length. Compute the value of the diameter of the shaft that will allow the angle of twist of the shaft when resisting the working torque to be only one half of the limiting angle of twist.   *Ans.* 10 in.

Chapter III

BENDING LOADS.   STRESSES IN BEAMS

37. Preliminary considerations. *Definitions.* Beams are very important load-resisting members in many engineering structures and machines. A *beam* is a bar or member that is bent by forces acting perpendicular to the axis of the bar.* Such forces are called *transverse* or *cross-bending* loads. It will be assumed that the cross-bending loads acting on a beam lie in one plane containing the central longitudinal axis of the beam and that this plane is a plane of symmetry of the beam. Many beams satisfy, approximately, these conditions. The bending loads cause, in general, normal and shearing stresses on any transverse cross section of the beam and also cause the beam to deflect. The deflection of beams is discussed in Chapter IV. The main purpose of the present chapter is to obtain a relationship between the loads and the stresses caused by the loads. Several common types of beams are described as follows.

A *simple* beam is one that rests on two supports at the ends of the beam; the distance between the supports is called the *span* of the beam.

---

* If the beam acts as it is assumed to act, in this and the following chapters, its length must be at least several times its depth. Furthermore, the thickness or width of the beam must be sufficient to prevent collapse by wrinkling or twisting (buckling); thus, extremely deep thin rectangular beams and I beams with very wide thin flanges, etc., are excluded from consideration in this chapter.

Figure 120 shows a horizontal simple beam subjected to two equal concentrated loads at the third points. The curve assumed by the central longitudinal axis of the deflected beam is called the *elastic curve* of the beam, provided that the maximum stress in the beam does not exceed the elastic limit of the material. The elastic deflections of beams of the usual relative dimensions when stressed to the elastic limit of the

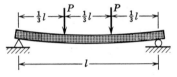

Fig. 120.   Simple beam.   Fig. 121.   Fixed-ended beam.

material are small, although the elastic deflections depend on the stiffness (modulus of elasticity) of the material of which the beam is made as well as on the relative dimensions. For example, the elastic deflection of a beam made of an aluminum alloy (see Table 1) would be about three times as much as that of a similar beam made of steel. The deflections shown in Figs. 120 to 125 are exaggerated in order to show the form assumed by the beams in response to the loads.

A *fixed* or *fixed-ended* beam is one so restrained at its end that the slope of the elastic curve of the beam at the restrained end does not change when the load is applied. Figure 121 shows a beam fixed at both ends, and subjected to a uniformly distributed load of w per unit length; Fig. 122 represents a beam fixed at one end and supported at

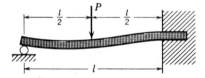

Fig. 122.   Beam fixed at one end, supported at other end.   Fig. 123.   Cantilever beam.

the other, and subjected to a concentrated load at midspan. The end connections of beams in structures and machines frequently offer considerable restraint but not sufficient to establish the conditions required for fixed-ended beams; such beams are then intermediate between simply supported beams and fixed-ended beams.

A *cantilever* beam is one that is fixed at one end and free at the other end. Figure 123 shows a cantilever beam subjected to a uniformly distributed load over its entire length and to a concentrated load at its end.

Figure 124 shows an overhanging beam that overhangs both supports and that carries concentrated loads at the end of the beam and a uniformly distributed load over the span between supports.

A *continuous* beam is one that rests on more than two supports. Figure 125 shows a continuous beam with three equal spans carrying a uniformly distributed load of w_1 per unit of length over two spans

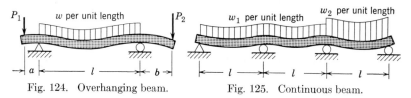

Fig. 124.   Overhanging beam.   Fig. 125.   Continuous beam.

and a uniformly distributed load of w_2 per unit of length over the third span.

Fibers of a Beam. It is frequently convenient to consider that a beam is composed of a large number of longitudinal rods or filaments called fibers whose cross sections are very small (differential areas). Some of these very slender elements or fibers shorten when the loads are applied (are in compression), and others stretch (are in tension). The student should study Figs. 120 to 125 and determine whether the fibers stretch or shorten in the upper and lower portions of the beams at various sections along the beams, in order to permit the beams to deflect as shown.   Such a qualitative analysis of beam behavior will be very useful later in this chapter.

Pure bending is bending caused by couples. Thus the middle third of the beam in Fig. 120 is subjected to pure bending.   Bending produced by forces that do not form couples is called *ordinary* bending. As shown later, a beam subjected to pure bending has no transverse shearing stresses developed in it—the stresses on any transverse section are normal (tensile or compressive) stresses, whereas in *ordinary* bending the loads develop shearing stresses as well as normal stresses on a transverse section.

It should be observed that in pure bending the stresses on any transverse section of the beam constitute a uniaxial system of stresses, but these stresses are not distributed uniformly on the section; it will be found later that the stress is zero at the center of any section and increases directly with the distance from the center (see Fig. 129).

Reactions. For convenience the forces exerted on a beam by the supports are called reactions, and the other forces are called loads, but both loads and reactions are merely external forces that act on the beam and hold the beam in equilibrium.

Statically Determinate and Statically Indeterminate Beams. If the loads are known, the reactions can be found by use of the equations of equilibrium, *provided that there are not more than two unknown reactions.* For the forces that hold the beam in equilibrium constitute a parallel-force system in a plane, and for such a force system there are only two independent equations of equilibrium: namely,

$$\begin{cases} \Sigma F = 0 \\ \Sigma M = 0 \end{cases} \quad \text{or} \quad \begin{cases} \Sigma M_A = 0 \\ \Sigma M_B = 0 \end{cases}$$

which state that the algebraic sum of the forces and the algebraic sum of the moments of the forces about any point are equal to zero. Or the algebraic sum of the moments of the forces about each of two points A or B, not in a line parallel to the forces, is equal to zero.

Beams for which the reactions can be found from the equations of equilibrium are called *statically determinate* beams, and those for which the number of unknown reactions is greater than the number of equilibrium equations are called *statically indeterminate beams*. Simple and cantilever beams and overhanging beams that rest on two supports are *statically determinate* beams. Fixed-ended beams and continuous beams are *statically indeterminate*, and hence equations in addition to the equilibrium equations are required for determining the reactions, as will be discussed later.

In this chapter we deal mainly with the problem of determining the relation between the external forces acting on statically determinate beams and the normal and shearing stresses that the forces develop in the beams. Statically indeterminate members are discussed in Chapter V.

Problems

119. Find the reactions of the supports for the beam shown in Fig. 126; neglect the weight of the beam.

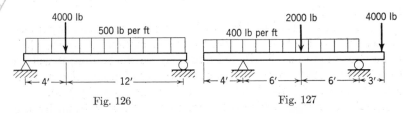

Fig. 126   Fig. 127

120. Determine the reactions of the supports for the beam shown in Fig. 127; neglect the weight of the beam.   *Ans.* $R_1 = 4267$ lb; $R_2 = 8133$ lb.

121. Calculate the reactions of the supports for the beam shown in Fig. 135.

122. In Fig. 124, let $P_1 = 1000$ lb, $P_2 = 2000$ lb, $w = 200$ lb per ft, $a = 3$ ft, $b = 6$ ft, and $l = 20$ ft. Calculate the reactions of the supports.

123. The floor in a room supports a uniformly distributed load of 300 lb per sq ft. The room is 30 ft wide, and the floor rests on simple beams having supports directly beneath the walls; that is, the span of the beams is 30 ft. If the beams are spaced 2 ft apart, what are the reactions at the ends of the beams?

Ans. $R_1 = R_2 = 9000$ lb.

124. In Fig. 123, let $P = 2000$ lb, $w = 300$ lb per ft, and $l = 12$ ft. Calculate the reactions (couple and vertical force) exerted by the wall on the beam.

125. Calculate the reactions on the beam shown in Fig. 136; neglect the weight of the beam.

126. Calculate the reactions on the beam shown in Fig. 145.

127. Calculate the reactions on the beam shown in Fig. 167. Assume that $P = 200$ lb, $Q = 100$ lb, $W = 360$ lb, $d = 10$ in., $l = 50$ in.

Ans. $R_A = 160$ lb; $R_B = 200$ lb.

38. Internal forces at any section.

As previously noted, the main problem considered in this chapter is to obtain relationships between the external forces acting on a beam and the normal and shearing stresses at any point on a transverse cross section of the beam. These stresses are considered to be the significant stresses since the failure of a beam often occurs when these stresses reach certain values depending on the properties of the material of which the beam is made.

In obtaining the desired relationship in accordance with the method outlined in Art. 8, we shall first express the internal forces on any transverse cross section in terms of the external forces by use of the equations of equilibrium (see Art. 4), and then (in the following articles) the internal forces will be expressed in terms of the stresses on the section, and thus the desired relationship will be obtained.

In Fig. 128a is shown a simple beam subjected to two concentrated loads, the weight of the beam being negligible. As previously noted,

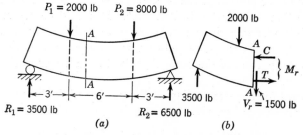

Fig. 128. Internal forces at any section of beam.

when a horizontal beam is deflected by vertical loads, the longitudinal (horizontal) fibers in the upper portion of the beam shorten, and those in the lower portion stretch; thus the normal stresses in the upper portion are compressive stresses, and those in the lower portion are tensile stresses.   The reactions R_1 and R_2 are found to be 3500 and 6500 lb, respectively.   Let it be required to determine the character of the internal forces that must occur on any section of the beam, such as section AA.

It is important to have a definite and correct concept of the expression "internal forces at a section of a beam" as used in this and the following articles.   In visualizing these internal forces it is convenient to consider the beam to be composed of fibers, a fiber being an elementary part (rod) of the beam having a cross-sectional area da and extending the length of the beam.   The internal forces at a section of a beam, then, are the forces exerted on the areas of these fibers at the section considered, and the force on each fiber is the product of the stress on the area of the fiber and the area da of the fiber; that is, the normal internal force on any fiber is $\sigma\, da$, and the shearing internal force on any fiber is $\tau\, da$.   The normal stress σ (sometimes called the fiber stress) and the shearing stress τ vary with the position of the fiber in the beam, but are assumed to be constant over the small area da of any fiber.

If the portion of the beam to the right of section AA is removed, forces equivalent to those that the right portion exerted on the left portion must be applied on section AA in order to hold the left portion in equilibrium, since it was in equilibrium before the right portion was removed.   The problem, therefore, is to determine the internal forces that must act on section AA in order to hold the forces R_1 and P_1 in equilibrium.

It may now be shown that these internal forces must be equivalent to a vertical force V_r and a couple M_r composed of a compressive force C on the upper portion of the section AA and a tensile force T on the lower portion as indicated in Fig. 128b.   It should be observed that, although the forces acting on any cross section of the beam are *internal* forces with respect to the *whole* beam, they are *external* forces with respect to the portion of the beam that lies to the left or to the right of the section.

The total force system acting on the portion of the beam to the left of AA as shown in Fig. 128b must satisfy the equilibrium equations:

Algebraic sum of horizontal forces $= 0$
Algebraic sum of vertical forces $= 0$
Algebraic sum of moments of forces $= 0$

But, since it is only the unbalanced part, or resultant, of the external forces that must be held in equilibrium by the forces on the section of the beam, it is convenient to have names and symbols for the components of the resultant, or stress-producing part, of the loads and to use them in the equations of equilibrium rather than the external forces themselves. Thus,

The *vertical shear* for a section of a beam is the magnitude of the resultant of the external forces (loads and reactions) that lie on one side of the section. Or, in other words, it is the algebraic sum of the forces that lie on one side of the section.

The symbol V will be used to denote vertical shear and, for convenience, the forces that lie on the *left* of the section will here be used.

The vertical shear is resisted by a shearing force on the section AA which is called the resisting shear and is denoted by V_r. Hence:

The *resisting shear* at a section of a beam is the shearing force on the section.

Thus, the second of the preceding equilibrium equations may be written

$$\text{Vertical shear} = \text{resisting shear} \quad \text{or} \quad V = V_r$$

For the beam shown in Fig. 128a the vertical shear V for section AA is an upward force equal to 3500 lb − 2000 lb, or 1500 lb, and hence the resisting shear V_r on section AA (Fig. 128b) is a downward force of 1500 lb. It should be noted that the vertical shear for a section does not act at the section; the resisting shear, however, acts at, or on, the section.

Similarly:

The *bending moment* for (or with respect to) a section of a beam is the moment, about the section, of the resultant of the external forces and couples that lie on one side of the section; that is, it is the algebraic sum of the moments, about the section, of the external forces and couples that lie on one side of the section.

The bending moment will be denoted by the symbol M, and the forces that lie to the *left* of the section will be used. The bending moment at section AA (5 ft from R_1) is

$$M = +3500 \times 5 - 2000 \times 2 = +13{,}500 \text{ lb-ft}$$

The bending moment about the section AA is resisted by the moment of the tensile and compressive internal forces at or on the section. This latter moment is called the *resisting moment*. Hence:

The resisting moment at a section of a beam is defined to be the algebraic sum of the moments of the forces acting on the section, about a line in the section.   It will be denoted by the symbol M_r.

Thus, the third of the preceding equilibrium equations may be written

Bending moment = resisting moment   or $M = M_r$

The first of the equilibrium equations may be written

Total tensile force = total compressive force   or $T = C$

To summarize: Since any portion of the beam (Fig. 128b) is in equilibrium, the forces acting on the portion must satisfy the equations

Algebraic sum of horizontal forces $= 0$ or $T = C$ (75)
Algebraic sum of vertical forces $= 0$ or $V = V_r$ (76)
Algebraic sum of moments of forces $= 0$ or $M = M_r$ (77)

For pure bending, Eq. 76 would not exist, but, even for ordinary bending, the influence of shearing stresses on the normal stresses on the section can usually be neglected.

Sign Conventions.   The sign of the *bending* moment for (or about) a given section is considered to be positive if the top (upper) fibers in a horizontal beam are in compression and the bottom (lower) fibers are in tension, as shown in Fig. 128b.   It should be noted that the bending moment for section AA in Fig. 128b is positive, regardless of the portion (left or right) of the beam that is considered in computing the moment; the fact that the bending moment would be clockwise if the left portion were used and counterclockwise if the right-hand portion were used does not influence the sign of the bending moment.   It should be noted also that the resisting moment at or on the section is always opposite in direction to the bending moment for or about the section.

The vertical shear for a section of a beam is considered to be positive when it is directed upward for the left-hand portion of a horizontal beam (the resisting shear on the section directed downward) as in Fig. 128b (see Fig. 139); similarly the vertical shear is negative if it is directed downward for the portion of the beam to the left of the section.

§ 1   Elastic Behavior of Beam

39. The flexure formula.   Elastic normal stress.   The problem stated at the beginning of Art. 38 will be solved first on the assumption that the behavior of the beam is purely elastic; inelastic behavior will be considered later.   By expressing M_r at any section of the beam in terms of the normal stress on any fiber and the dimensions of the section, and then substituting this expression in Eq. 77, the flexure formula is obtained. This formula gives the desired relation between the external forces acting on the beam and the normal elastic stress at any point on the cross section of the beam and the dimensions of the cross section.

In order to find the expression for M_r at any section, the manner in which the elastic fiber stress varies with the position of the fiber in the beam must be known. It is found that on one line in the section per-

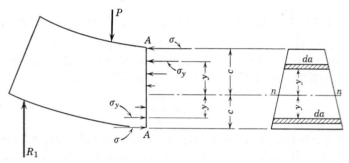

Fig. 129.   Stress distribution on the cross section of beam.

pendicular to the plane of the loads (see nn in Fig. 129) the fiber stress is zero; this line is called the *neutral axis*. Furthermore it is found that

> The normal (tensile or compressive) elastic stress on a fiber at any section of the beam is directly proportional to the distance of the fiber from the neutral axis; the justification for this assumption is given in the next article. (See Art. 45 for a discussion of other assumptions and limitations.)

Thus, if σ_y and σ (Fig. 129) denote the elastic stresses on fibers at the distances y and c, respectively, from the neutral axis, the foregoing statement is expressed mathematically as follows:

$$\frac{\sigma_y}{\sigma} = \frac{y}{c} \quad \text{or} \quad \frac{\sigma_y}{y} = \frac{\sigma}{c} = \text{a constant} \tag{78}$$

Expression for Resisting Moment. An expression may now be found for the resisting moment in terms of the normal stress on any fiber and the dimensions of the cross section of the beam as follows:

The stress σ_y on a fiber at the distance y from the neutral axis (Fig. 129) may be assumed to be constant over the cross-sectional area da of the fiber, and, hence,

Normal force on area of one fiber $= \sigma_y\, da$
Moment of normal force on one fiber $= \sigma_y y\, da$

Sum of moments of normal forces on all fibers $= M_r = \int \sigma_y y\, da$

This may be written $M_r = \int \dfrac{\sigma_y}{y} y^2\, da$, but, from Eq. 78, $\dfrac{\sigma_y}{y} = \dfrac{\sigma}{c} = a$

constant, and, hence,

$$M_r = \frac{\sigma}{c} \int y^2\, da = \frac{\sigma I}{c}$$

in which $I = \int y^2\, da$ is the moment of inertia of the cross section of the beam with respect to the neutral axis, since y is measured from the neutral axis (see Appendix I for discussion of moments of inertia).

But equilibrium requires that $M = M_r$.   Therefore,

$$M = \frac{\sigma I}{c} \tag{79}$$

in which σ is the normal stress on any fiber at the distance c from the neutral axis, but, since the maximum value of σ usually is desired, the distance c usually will be taken as the distance to the most remote fiber.   This formula is known as the *flexure formula*.   If σ is expressed in pounds per square inch, as is customary in the United States, then M must be expressed in pound-inches, I in inches to the fourth power, and c in inches.   Furthermore, I/c is called the *section modulus* of the beam and is expressed in inches to the third power (in.^{3}).   The values of the section modulus for steel rolled sections are given in Appendix II.   If Z is used to denote the section modulus, the flexure formula may be written

$$\sigma = \frac{M}{Z} \tag{80}$$

Position of the Neutral Axis.   The value of I in the flexure formula cannot be found unless the position of the neutral axis in the area is known.   As noted in Eq. 75, the algebraic sum of all the horizontal forces at any section must be equal to zero; this condition determines the position of the neutral axis, which may be shown as follows:

$$\int \sigma_y\, da = 0 \quad \text{or} \quad \int \frac{\sigma_y}{y} y\, da = 0$$

and, hence,

$$\frac{\sigma_y}{y} \int y\, da = 0 \quad \text{since} \quad \frac{\sigma_y}{y} = \text{a constant}$$

But σ_y/y is not equal to zero. Therefore, $\int y\,da = 0$, in which y is measured from the neutral axis; but $\int y\,da$ is, by definition, the moment (often called the first or statical moment) of the cross-sectional area of the beam with respect to the neutral axis (see Fig. 130), and may be written $a\bar{y}$, in which a is the total area of the cross section and $\bar{y}$ is the distance of the centroidal axis of the cross section from the neutral axis. Thus,

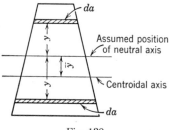

$$\int y\,da = a\bar{y} = 0$$

But a is not equal to zero. Therefore, $\bar{y} = 0$ which states that the distance from the centroidal axis to the neutral axis is zero, and, hence, for pure bend-

Fig. 130

ing of an elastically stressed straight beam, the neutral axis at any cross section is coincident with the centroidal axis of the section, and this statement may be assumed to apply also to ordinary bending.

It is assumed that the student is familiar with the methods of locating the centroids of areas; this topic, however, is treated in Appendix I. The methods for determining the moment of inertia of an area with respect to an axis also are discussed in Appendix I.

Illustrative Problems

Problem 128. A simple beam having a rectangular cross section (Fig. 131) is subjected to a uniformly distributed load of 400 lb per ft (including the weight of

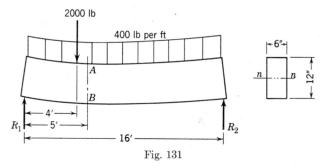

Fig. 131

the beam) over the whole span, and a concentrated load of 2000 lb at a distance of 4 ft from the left support. Find the tensile stress on the outer fiber of the beam at the section AB, 5 ft from the left support.

Solution.   First Method.   The reactions are found to be

$$R_1 = 4700 \text{ lb}, \qquad R_2 = 3700 \text{ lb}$$

The bending moment M at the section AB is

$$M = 4700 \times 5 - 400 \times 5 \times 2.5 - 2000 \times 1$$

$$= 16{,}500 \text{ lb-ft} = 198{,}000 \text{ lb-in.}$$

The centroidal axis (and hence the neutral axis) of the cross section is the central horizontal axis XX, and the moment of inertia of the cross section about the neutral axis is (see Prob. 428, Appendix I)

$$\bar{I} = \tfrac{1}{12}bd^3 = \tfrac{1}{12} \times 6(12)^3 = 864 \text{ in.}^4$$

The tensile stress on the bottom fiber at the section AB, then, is

$$\sigma = \frac{Mc}{I} = \frac{198{,}000 \times 6}{864} = 1370 \text{ lb per sq in.}$$

provided that this stress is not greater than the proportional limit of the material. A compressive stress of the same magnitude occurs on the top fiber.

Second Method.   Instead of expressing the resisting moment as the algebraic sum of the moments of the forces on the fibers of the cross section, which leads to the expression $\sigma I/c$, we may express the resisting moment as the moment of the couple formed by the resultants of the tensile and compressive internal forces on the two parts of the section.   Thus, as shown in Fig. 132, the action line of the

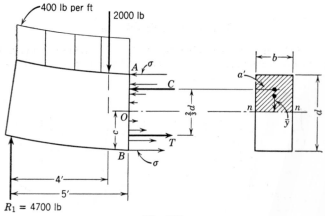

Fig. 132

resultant C of the compressive forces is $\tfrac{2}{3}$ of OA from O, and similarly the resultant T acts at a distance of $\tfrac{2}{3}OB$ from O.   Hence, the resisting moment is $C \times \tfrac{2}{3}d$ or $T \times \tfrac{2}{3}d$.   The magnitude of C (and T) is the product of the average stress, $\tfrac{1}{2}\sigma$, on the area above (or below) the neutral axis and that area. Hence,

$$C = T = \tfrac{1}{2}\sigma \times \tfrac{1}{2}bd$$

and this may be written

$$C = T = \frac{\sigma}{c} \times \frac{1}{8}bd^2$$

$$Z = \frac{bd^2}{6} \quad \text{for } \square$$

Therefore the resisting moment is

$$M_r = \frac{\sigma}{c} \times \frac{1}{8}bd^2 \times \frac{2}{3}d = \frac{\sigma}{c}\frac{bd^3}{12}$$

and, hence,

$$M = \frac{\sigma}{c}\frac{bd^3}{12} = \frac{\sigma I}{c}$$

which is the same equation as that used in the first method of solution. It is important to note that the resultants T and C do not act at a distance of $\tfrac{2}{3}$ of c from O unless the section of the beam is of constant width.

Problem 129. A T beam (Fig. 133) is subjected to a concentrated load of 4000 lb at the center of the span. The beam is made of material having a tensile

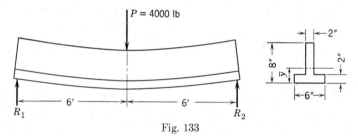

$P = 4000$ lb

R_1 6'   6' R_2

Fig. 133

proportional limit of 4000 lb per sq in. and a compressive proportional limit of 8000 lb per sq in. Find the maximum tensile and compressive stresses at the midspan section.

Solution. Each stress is obtained by use of the flexure formula $\sigma = Mc/I$. But, in order to determine c and I, the neutral axis must be located. The distance $\bar{y}$ of the centroidal axis (and hence of the neutral axis) from the bottom line of the section is found as follows to be 3 in. (see Art. 154):

$$a\bar{y} = \Sigma a_0 y_0$$

$$\bar{y} = \frac{12 \times 5 + 12 \times 1}{12 + 12} = 3 \text{ in.}$$

The moment of inertia of the cross section with respect to the neutral axis is found as follows (see Art. 155 for another solution):

$$\bar{I}_x = \tfrac{1}{12} \times 2(6)^3 + 12 \times (2)^2 + \tfrac{1}{12} \times 6(2)^3 + 12 \times (2)^2 = 136 \text{ in.}^4$$

The bending moment about the midsection is

$$M = R_1 \times \frac{l}{2} = 2000 \times 72 = 144{,}000 \text{ lb-in.}$$

Therefore, the maximum tensile stress (on the bottom fiber of the beam) at the midsection is

$$\sigma_t = \frac{Mc}{I} = \frac{144{,}000 \times 3}{136} = 3180 \text{ lb per sq in.}$$

and the maximum compressive stress (on the top fiber) is

$$\sigma_c = \tfrac{5}{3}\sigma_t = \tfrac{5}{3} \times 3180 = 5300 \text{ lb per sq in.}$$

These stresses are less than the corresponding proportional limits and hence they are valid.

Problems

130. Calculate the fiber elastic stress at a point on the section AB (Fig. 131) at a distance of 1 in. from the top face of the beam.   *Ans.* $\sigma = 1150$ lb per sq in.

131. Find the elastic stress on the bottom fiber of the beam in Fig. 131 on a section 6 ft from the left support.

132. Calculate the maximum compressive elastic stress on a section of the beam in Fig. 133 at a distance of 3 ft from the left end.

133. If each load P in Fig. 120 is 1000 lb and l is 12 ft, and the cross section of the beam is a rectangle 4 in. wide by 8 in. deep, what is the maximum tensile and compressive stress at any section between the loads if it is assumed that the proportional limit of the material is not exceeded?   *Ans.* $\sigma = 1125$ lb per sq in.

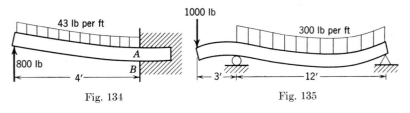

Fig. 134   Fig. 135

134. A steel shaft, 4 in. in diameter, is used as a cantilever beam and loaded as shown in Fig. 134; the uniformly distributed load is the weight of the shaft. Find the maximum elastic fiber stress in the section AB at the wall.

Ans. $\sigma = 5450$ lb per sq in.

135. Find the maximum tensile fiber elastic stress on the section above the left support of the beam shown in Fig. 135. The beam is a rolled-steel 4-in. 10.5-lb I beam. Find also the maximum tensile fiber stress on a section midway between the supports. State in each instance whether the fiber on which the stress occurs is on the top or bottom of the beam. (Consult Table B in Appendix II.)

136. A vertical timber beam having a square cross section 8 in. by 8 in. is loaded as shown in Fig. 136. Compute the maximum elastic tensile fiber stress on the section at the 3000-lb load.

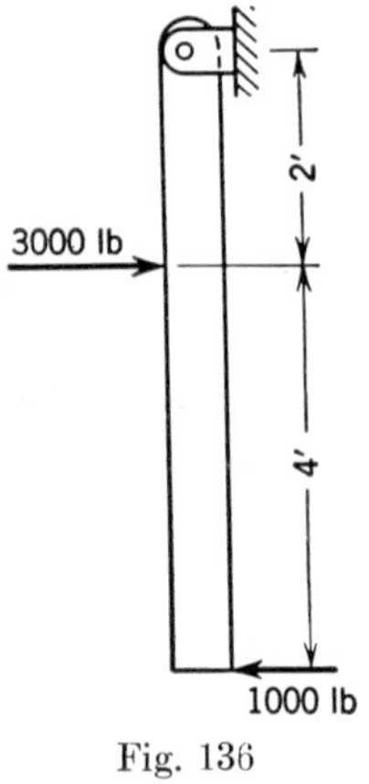

Fig. 136

Ans. $\sigma = 560$ lb per sq in.

40. Justification of assumed stress distribution. In the preceding derivation of the flexure formula, it was assumed that the fiber stress on any cross section of the beam varies directly with the distance from the neutral axis. As pointed out in Art. 39, in order to justify this assumption there is required a knowledge of

(*a*) The way in which the strain of a fiber varies with the position of the fiber in the beam when the beam is bent; strains can be seen and measured directly, whereas stress cannot.

(*b*) The relation, for the material of which the beam is made, of the stress in a fiber to the strain of the fiber.

Information concerning these points comes mainly from the results of experiments:

(*a*) When a simple horizontal beam is bent (Fig. 137), the fibers on the top side shorten and those on the bottom elongate, and the fibers in one plane within the beam do not deform. This plane is called the *neutral surface,* and the line of intersection of the neutral surface and a cross section of the beam is called the *neutral axis* for the section. Furthermore, when a beam is subjected to bending, experiments show that, if two straight lines, *DE* and *FG* (Fig. 137) are drawn, before the beam is bent, on the side of the beam a

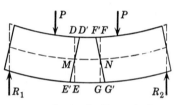

Fig. 137.   Strains in fibers of a beam at any cross section vary directly with their distances from the neutral axis of the section.

short distance *MN* apart, these lines still will be approximately straight lines, *D'E'* and *F'G'*, after the beam is bent. Thus, one fiber *MN*, in the neutral surface, remains constant in length and, if the beam is subjected to pure bending:

> The total deformation of any fiber is directly proportional to the distance of the fiber from the neutral surface. Further, since the original lengths of all the fibers are equal, the strain of any fiber is also proportional to the distance of the fiber from the neutral surface.

(*b*) If one of the fibers were removed from the beam and subjected to an axial load in a testing machine so that the stress (equal to P/a) and the strain (equal to e/l) could be measured, it would be found, as stated in Art. 16, that the stress in the fiber is proportional to the strain of the fiber, *provided that the proportional limit of the material is not exceeded;* it is assumed that the fiber when in the beam acts according to the same law as when tested alone.

Therefore, since the strain of a fiber is directly proportional to the distance of the fiber from the neutral surface, and since the stress on a fiber is directly proportional to the strain of the fiber, it follows that:

The normal stress on a fiber at any transverse section of the beam is directly proportional to the distance of the fiber from the neutral axis of the section.

41. Section of maximum bending moment. If a beam has a constant cross section throughout its length, the values of I/c (section modulus) for all sections are equal, and hence the maximum value of σ in the flexure formula, $M = \sigma I/c$, occurs in the section at which the bending moment M is a maximum. It is important, therefore, to obtain a method of locating the section at which the bending moment is a maximum. This section is called the *dangerous section* of the beam and may be located in accordance with the following statement:

If a beam is subjected to concentrated loads or to distributed loads or to combinations of such loads, the section of the beam at which the bending moment is a maximum is the section for which the vertical shear either is equal to zero or changes sign.

Proof. In Fig. 138a is represented a simply supported beam subjected to a concentrated and a uniformly distributed load. The bending moment M at the distance x from the left support is

$$M = R_1 x - P(x - a) - \frac{wx^2}{2}$$

The moment M will have its maximum value at some section, such as AA in Fig. 138a; the values of M at distance x from the left end is shown by ordinates to the curve $OA'C$ in Fig. 138c. The value of x that will make M a maximum is the value that will make the first derivative of M with respect to x equal to zero. The first derivative of M with respect to x is

$$\frac{dM}{dx} = R_1 - P - wx$$

Therefore, the value of x that will make M a maximum, denoted in Fig. 138c where the tangent $A'B$ is horizontal, may be found from the equation

$$R_1 - P - wx = 0$$

But $R_1 - P - wx$ is the vertical shear for the section at the distance x from the left support; that is, $dM/dx = V$. Therefore, the section at which the moment has its maximum value is the section for which the vertical shear is zero (A' in Fig. 138b).

A convenient method of locating the section for which the vertical shear is zero (dangerous section) is to draw a shear diagram as shown in Fig. 138b where the shear at any distance x from the left end is shown

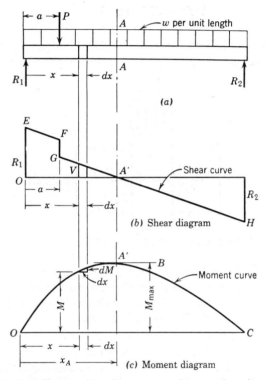

Fig. 138. Shear and bending-moment diagrams for a beam.

as ordinates to the line $EFGA'H$. The methods of plotting the shear diagram and moment diagram are discussed in the next article.

Alternative Method of Proof. An alternative method of deriving the equation $V = dM/dx$ is as follows: In Fig. 139 is shown a part of a beam included between two sections, one being at the distance x (Fig. 138) from the left end of the beam and the other at the distance $x + dx$. All the forces acting on this element of the beam are shown in Fig. 139; the moment and shear on the first section are M and V, and on the second section $M + dM$ and $V - dV$, and the load is $w\,dx$. These forces hold the element in equilibrium; hence, the algebraic sum of their moments is equal to zero. Thus, by taking moments about O, the following equation is found:

$$M + V\,dx - w\,dx \times \tfrac{1}{2}\,dx - (M + dM) = 0$$

and, since products of differentials may be neglected, this equation reduces to

$$V\,dx = dM \quad \text{or} \quad V = \frac{dM}{dx} \tag{81}$$

Equation 81 may be interpreted in the following manner: The change dM in moment between two sections a distance dx apart is equal to

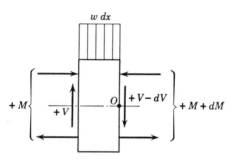

Fig. 139.   Relation between vertical shear and bending moment at a section.

$V\,dx$. But, as shown by the element of area in Fig. 138b, the product $V\,dx$ is the area under the shear diagram in the distance dx. The use of this interpretation of Eq. 81 for determining bending moments from a shear diagram is discussed in Art. 43.

42. Shear and moment diagrams. *Shear Diagram.* As was indicated in Art. 41, a shear diagram for a beam is a curve in which the abscissas represent distances along the beam and the ordinates represent the vertical shears for the sections at which the ordinates are drawn.

For example, let it be required to draw a shear diagram for the beam shown in Fig. 140a. The reactions are found to be

$$R_1 = 7000 \text{ lb} \quad \text{and} \quad R_2 = 5000 \text{ lb}$$

The vertical shear for section A (just to the right of the left support) is $V_A = R_1 = 7000$ lb upward, and the resisting shear just to the right of A is downward. V_A is positive and is represented as shown in Fig. 140b plotted above the base line. The vertical shear for section C (just to the left of the load P) is

$$V_C = 7000 - 4 \times 500 = +5000 \text{ lb}$$

The vertical shear for any section between A and C at the distance x, say, from A is

$$V = 7000 - 500x \tag{82}$$

and hence the vertical shear decreases with x at the constant rate of 500 lb per ft of length of the beam from 7000 lb at A $(x = 0)$ to 5000 lb at C $(x = 4)$, as shown in Fig. 140b.

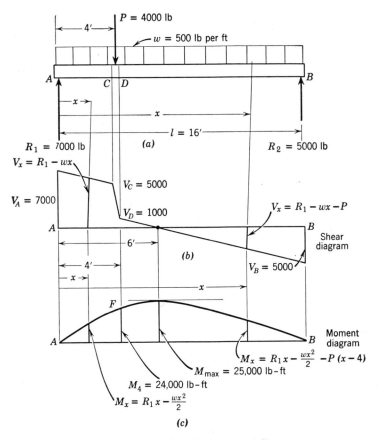

Fig. 140. Shear and bending-moment diagrams.

The vertical shear at section D (just to the right of the concentrated load) is

$$V_D = 7000 - 500 \times 4 - 4000 = +1000 \text{ lb}$$

Thus, there is an abrupt change in the vertical shear in passing from section C to D due to the concentrated load, but the shear (in this particular problem) does not pass through zero under the load; the shear, therefore, must be equal to zero for some section to the *right* of the concentrated load. The vertical shear for any section between D and B at a distance x from the left support is

$$V = 7000 - 4000 - 500x \qquad (83)$$

and hence the vertical shear decreases at the constant rate of 500 lb per ft of length of the beam from 1000 lb at D to -5000 lb for a section just to the left of the right reaction. At 6 ft from the left support the vertical shear is zero, and hence the maximum value of the bending moment occurs at this section.

It is important to note that, if a concentrated load acts on a beam in addition to a distributed load, the shear may pass through zero under the load. If it does, the location of the dangerous section cannot be found by equating any expression such as Eq. 82 and Eq. 83 to zero and solving for x. It is desirable, therefore, in finding the dangerous section, to plot a shear diagram. If a beam is acted on by concentrated loads only, the dangerous sections *always* occur under one of the loads, since the shear changes only at the sections where the loads act.

Moment Diagram. A *moment diagram* for a beam is a curve in which the abscissas represent distances along the beam and the ordinates represent the bending moments for the sections at which the ordinates are drawn.

Let it be required to draw a moment diagram for the beam shown in Fig. 140a. The bending moment at the section A is equal to zero since the moment arm of R_1 about A is zero. The bending moment at any section between A and C, at a distance x from the left support, is

$$M = R_1 x - \frac{wx^2}{2} \qquad (84)$$

in which x cannot have a value greater than 4. The bending moment at any section between D and B (x greater than 4), at a distance x from the left support, is

$$M = R_1 x - \frac{wx^2}{2} - P(x - 4) \qquad (85)$$

in which x cannot have a value less than 4. The value of the bending moment at the section beneath the load ($x = 4$) may be found from either equation by making x equal to 4.

If various values of x from 0 to 4 be substituted in Eq. 84 and the resulting values of the bending moments plotted, the moment diagram obtained is AF (Fig. 140c), and, if values of x from 4 to 16 be substituted in Eq. 85, the resulting diagram is FB.

It may be noted that the maximum ordinate to the moment curve occurs at the section for which the shear is zero. It is also important to observe that the moment diagram is composed of two *distinct* curves, AF and FB, which have only one point F in common, and that the maximum bending moment can be found from the equation of only one of these curves. Thus, in the beam of Fig. 140a, the value of x for which the bending moment is a maximum cannot be substituted in Eq. 84, since 4 is the greatest value x can have in this equation. If values of x greater than 4 are substituted in Eq. 84, the corresponding values of M will have no physical meaning; and, if values of x less than 4 are substituted in Eq. 85, the corresponding values of M will have no physical meaning.

Moment Diagram by Superposition of Parts. An alternate method of constructing the bending-moment diagram for a beam is to plot a separate moment diagram for each load and reaction on the beam, and then add, algebraically, the ordinates of these diagrams. An ordinate of each of these separate diagrams represents the bending moment that would exist for any section if the particular load or reaction being considered were the only force lying to one side of the section. The procedure for constructing the bending-moment diagram by this method will be illustrated for the same beam as that shown in Fig. 140a for which the bending-moment diagram is given in Fig. 140c.

Let the left reaction R_1 (Fig. 141a) be considered first. In Fig. 141b the ordinates to AB are equal to $+R_1x$, which is the bending moment at any section whose distance from the left end is x if R_1 is considered to be the only force acting on the beam to the left of the section. Similarly, in Fig. 141c the ordinate to the curve CD is equal to $-wx^2/2$, which is the bending moment at any section whose distance from the left end is x if the distributed load w is considered to be the only load acting on the beam to the left of the section. In like manner, in Fig. 141d the ordinate to EF is $-P(x - 4)$, which is the bending moment at any section whose distance is x from the left end, if the load P is considered to be the only load acting on the beam to the left of the section.

The complete bending-moment diagram is shown in Fig. 141e and is constructed by adding algebraically, for each value of x, the ordinates in Fig. 141b, c, and d. For example, at section nn, the bending moment is $M = R_1x - wx^2/2$, which is the same as Eq. 84, and, at section mm, $M = R_1x - wx^2/2 - P(x - 4)$, which is the same as Eq. 85. The bending-moment diagram as found from its several parts is especially convenient to use in solving certain problems, such as in computing the deflection of a beam (Chap. IV) or in solving for the reactions on statically indeterminate beams (Chap. V).

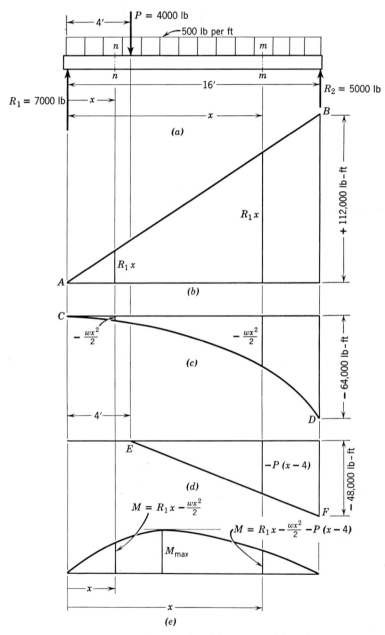

Fig. 141. Moment diagram found by superposition of parts.

Overhanging Beam. It should be noted that the bending moment at a section in an overhanging beam may be negative, and there are two maximum moments to be considered: the maximum positive moment and the maximum negative moment. In other words, the vertical shear passes through zero at two or more sections of the beam. Furthermore, since the moment changes along the beam from a positive to a negative value, it must be zero (or pass through zero) at some section; the section in the beam at which the bending moment is zero is called the *point of inflection* on the elastic curve of the beam. These facts are illustrated in the solution of Prob. 139.

do by part

Illustrative Problems

Problem 137. A solid cylindrical steel shaft is used as a simple beam over a span of 12 ft. It acts elastically when loaded as shown in Fig. 142*a.* Draw the

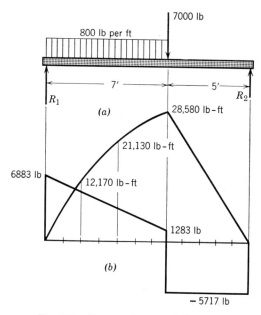

Fig. 142. Shear and moment diagrams.

shear and moment diagrams, and calculate the diameter of the shaft if the maximum (bending) fiber stress is 16,000 lb per sq in.

Solution. The reactions are found to be $R_1 = 6883$ lb and $R_2 = 5717$ lb. The shear and moment diagrams are shown in Fig. 142*b.* The dangerous section is under the concentrated load, and the maximum bending moment is

$$M = 6883 \times 7 - 800 \times 7 \times \tfrac{7}{2} = 28,580 \text{ lb-ft}$$

The maximum fiber stress is

$$\sigma = \frac{Mc}{I} = \frac{28{,}580 \times 12 \times d/2}{\pi d^4/64}$$

Hence,

$$d^3 = \frac{28{,}580 \times 12 \times 32}{16{,}000 \times \pi} = 218 \text{ in.}^3 \quad \text{and} \quad d = 6.02 \text{ in.}$$

Problem 138. The bar CAB in Fig. 143a is supported at A and B and loaded as shown. By making use of the method of superposition of parts, draw the bending-moment diagram for the portion of the bar extending from A to B.

Solution. A free-body diagram of the portion from A to B is shown in Fig. 143b, and the unknown reactions R_1, R_2, and M_A on this part of the beam are found from the equilibrium equations to have the values given in the figure; the couple $M_A = -8000$ lb-ft acting at the left end of the beam is produced by the force P and the equal and opposite horizontal force exerted by the pin at A.

The moment diagram for the 2000-lb reaction, for the 8000-lb-ft couple, and for the 5000-lb load, are shown in Fig. 143c, d, and e, respectively, each diagram representing the bending-moment for any section as if the respective reaction R_1, couple M_A, or load Q were the only force (or couple) acting on the beam to the left of the section for which the bending moment is calculated. Finally, the ordinates of Fig. 143c, d, and e are added algebraically at each section of the beam, giving the diagram in Fig. 143f, which is the complete bending-moment diagram of the beam from A to B.

Problem 139. A 6-in.-by-12-in.-by-14-ft timber beam acts elastically when supported and loaded as shown in Fig. 144a. (a) Draw the shear and moment diagrams. (b) Locate the dangerous section. (c) Find the maximum positive moment. (d) Find the maximum negative moment. (e) Locate the point of inflection. (f) Calculate the maximum fiber stress.

Solution. The reactions are found to be $R_1 = 4600$ lb and $R_2 = 7400$ lb.

(a) The shear and moment diagrams are shown in Fig. 144b. The vertical shear is equal to zero for a section 3.25 ft from the left support and passes through zero at the section above the right support. These two sections, then, are the dangerous sections. The bending moment at any section to the left of the first concentrated load P_1, at a distance x from the left support, is

$$M = 4600x - 800\,\frac{x^2}{2} \tag{1}$$

in which x has any value from 0 to 3. The bending moment at any section between P_1 and the right reaction is

$$M = 4600x - 800\,\frac{x^2}{2} - 2000(x - 3) \tag{2}$$

in which x cannot have a value less than 3 ft or greater than 10 ft. The bending moment at any section between the right reaction and the right end of the beam is

$$M = 4600x + 7400(x - 10) - 2000(x - 3) - 8000(x - 5) \tag{3}$$

in which x cannot be less than 10 or greater than 14 ft. Or, if x is measured from the right end of the beam instead of the left end, then the bending moment at any section between R_2 and P_2 is

$$M_x = -2000x \tag{4}$$

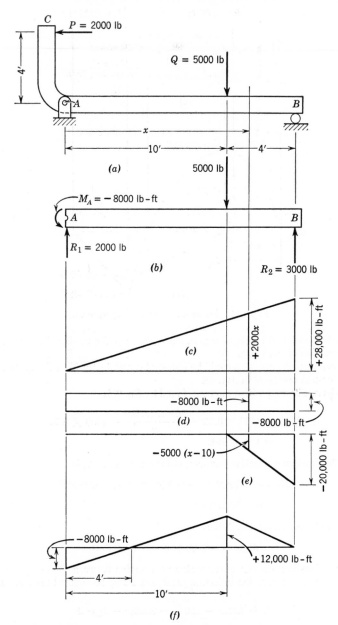

Fig. 143. Moment diagram found by superposition of parts.

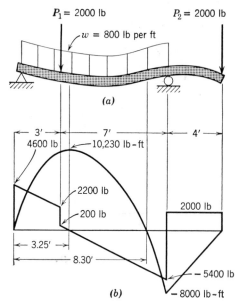

Fig. 144. Shear and moment diagrams.

Equations 3 and 4 will give, of course, the same value for the bending moment at a given section of the beam.

The moment diagram also could be obtained conveniently from the shear curve by the method discussed in Art. 43.

(b) The maximum positive moment, found by Eq. 2, is

$$M_{pos} = 4600 \times 3.25 - \frac{800 \times (3.25)^2}{2} - 2000 \times 0.25$$
$$= 10,230 \text{ lb-ft}$$

(c) The maximum negative moment, obtained from Eq. 2, is

$$M_{neg} = 4600 \times 10 - 800 \times 10 \times 5 - 2000 \times 7$$
$$= -8000 \text{ lb-ft}$$

Or, when obtained from Eq. 4, it is

$$M_{neg} = -2000 \times 4 = -8000 \text{ lb-ft}$$

(d) The bending moment changes sign at a section between the dangerous sections. Hence, to locate the inflection point, Eq. 2 may be equated to zero. Thus,

$$M = 4600x - 800\frac{x^2}{2} - 2000(x - 3) = 0$$

Therefore,

$$x = 8.30 \text{ ft}$$

and hence the inflection point is 8.30 ft from the left support.

(e) Since the maximum positive moment is larger than the maximum negative moment, the maximum fiber stress is

$$\sigma = \frac{Mc}{I} = \frac{10{,}230 \times 12 \times 6}{\frac{1}{12} \times 6 \times (12)^3} = 852 \text{ lb per sq in.}$$

Problems

140. Plot a shear diagram, and locate the dangerous section for the beam shown in Fig. 145. Find also the maximum bending moment and the maximum fiber elastic stress in the beam.

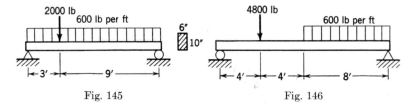

Fig. 145   Fig. 146

141. Draw to scale a shear and a moment diagram for the beam shown in Fig. 146. If the beam is a cylindrical bar, what diameter should it have if the maximum elastic fiber stress is 18,000 lb per sq in.?   *Ans.* $d = 5.07$ in.

142. The cast-iron frame shown in Fig. 147 is subjected to a load P of 4000 lb. Find the maximum tensile and compressive fiber stresses at the section AB. As-

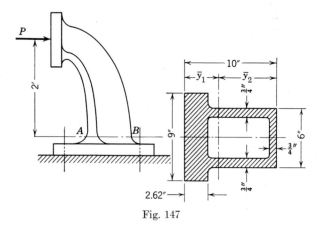

Fig. 147

sume that the material acts elastically. The dimensions of the area at the section AB are shown in the figure.   *Ans.* $\bar{y}_1 = 3.5$ in.; $\bar{I} = 391$ in.^{4}; $\sigma_t = 858$ lb per sq in.; $\sigma_c = 1590$ lb per sq in.

143. Two equal loads P are applied to the L-shaped beam supported as shown in Fig. 148. What value of the loads P will cause a maximum elastic fiber stress of 20,000 lb per sq in. in the I beam?   The dimensions of the cross section are shown in the figure.   *Hint.*   Plot the bending-moment diagram of the beam from B to D by superposition of parts (see Prob. 138).

$$I = \frac{4 \times 8^3}{12} - \frac{3.75 \times 6^3}{12} =$$

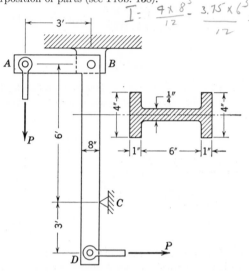

Fig. 148

144. A beam having a rectangular cross section 6 in. wide by 12 in. deep has the same section modulus as another beam whose cross section is circular.   What is the diameter of the circular cross section?   Assume that both beams act elastically.   *Ans.* $d = 11.4$ in.

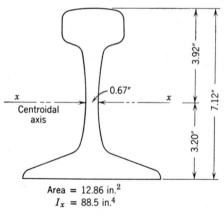

Area = 12.86 in.^{2}
I_x = 88.5 in.^{4}

Fig. 149

145. The railroad rail having the cross-sectional area shown in Fig. 149 is used as a simple beam on a span of 20 ft.   What concentrated load at midspan will cause a maximum tensile elastic stress in the rail of 20,000 lb/in.^{2}?

146. Calculate all the forces acting on the vertical beam AD in Fig. 150, and draw a moment diagram for AD resulting from the cross-bending components of the forces acting on the member. Assume $P = 2000$ lb.

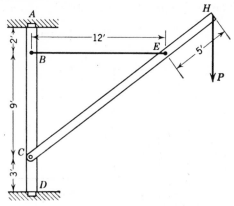

Fig. 150

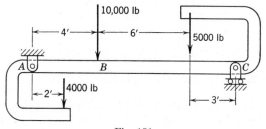

147. A simple beam having a span of 18 ft carries a total uniformly distributed load of W lb and a concentrated load equal to $W/2$ at the center of the span. If the cross section of the beam is rectangular, 6 in. wide by 12 in. deep, and the maximum fiber elastic stress is 1000 lb per sq in., find the value of W.

148. The beam ABC shown in Fig. 151 extends beyond its supports at A and C, but the ends are curved and are loaded as shown in the figure, so that the beam

Fig. 151

as a whole is acted on by three concentrated loads and the reactions of the supports. Plot the bending-moment diagram for the beam from A to C, and determine the magnitude and location of the maximum bending moment.

Ans. $M_{\max} = +37,800$ lb-ft located at B.

43. Shear-area method of obtaining moment diagram.

Frequently it is convenient to obtain the moment diagram for a beam from the shear diagram. This may be done as follows: In Art. 41 it was shown that $V = dM/dx$, which states that the vertical shear for a section of a beam is equal to the rate, with respect to the distance along the beam, at which the bending moment is changing at the section.   Or the equation may be written $dM = V\,dx$ which means that the difference dM (Figs. 138 and 152) between the bending moments at two sections that are the distance dx apart is represented by the area $V\,dx$ under

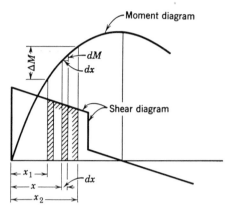

Fig. 152.   Relation between bending moment and vertical shear at a section of a beam.

the shear curve between the two sections.   Therefore, the difference $(M_2 - M_1$ or $\Delta M)$ between the bending moments at the sections x_2 and x_1 (Fig. 152) is

$$\Delta M = \int_{M_1}^{M_2} dM = \int_{x_1}^{x_2} V\,dx \qquad (86)$$

Since $\int_{x_1}^{x_2} V\,dx$ represents the area under the shear curve between the ordinates at the sections x_1 and x_2, it follows that

$\Delta M = M_2 - M_1 =$ area under the shear curve between ordi-nates at the sections x_1 and x_2.   Therefore, the difference between the bending moments at two sections of a beam is represented by the area under the shear curve between ordinates at the two sec-tions.

It is evident, therefore, that the bending moment at a given section of a simple beam is represented by the area under the shear curve be-tween the end of the beam $(M = 0)$ and the given section.   For exam-ple, let it be required to find the maximum bending moment for a simple beam subjected to a total load W, uniformly distributed over the entire span l.   The shear diagram is shown in Fig. 153.   According to the preceding proposition, the difference between the bending moments at the center and end is represented by the area under the shear curve between these two sections. But the moment at the end is zero, and hence the moment at the center is

$$M_c = \frac{1}{2} \text{base} \times \text{altitude} = \frac{1}{2}\frac{W}{2} \times \frac{l}{2} = \frac{1}{8} Wl$$

Frequently this proposition may be used conveniently to obtain the moment diagram for a beam from the shear curve, by calculating the

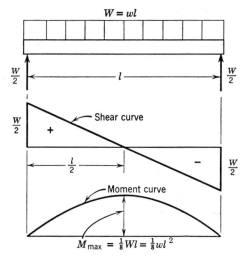

Fig. 153. Moment at a section is represented by area under the shear curve.

areas under the shear curve between as many sections as are necessary to plot satisfactorily the moment curve. The following problems are to be solved by this method.

Problems

149. Draw a shear diagram and a bending-moment diagram for the beam shown in Fig. 154.

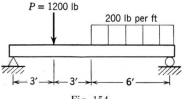

Fig. 154

150. Figure 155 represents the shear diagram for a simply supported beam. Draw a diagram of the beam and the forces acting on the beam. Also draw a bending-moment diagram for the beam.

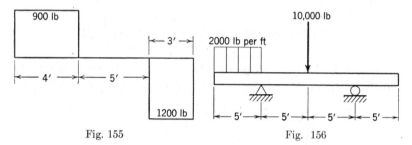

Fig. 155   Fig. 156

151. Draw the shear and bending-moment diagrams for the beam shown in Fig. 156, neglecting the weight of the beam. If the beam is made of an aluminum alloy having an elastic limit of 35,000 lb per sq in. and the cross section of the beam has a section modulus of 18 in.³, what is the maximum bending stress in the beam?

152. Calculate the maximum bending moment for the beam shown in Fig. 157. Assume $P = 2000$ lb.   *Ans.*   6400 lb-ft.

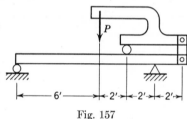

Fig. 157

153–155. For each of the beams described in the following three problems obtain (a) the shear and moment diagrams, (b) the maximum positive and negative bending moments, (c) the points of inflection, and (d) the maximum fiber stress in the beam. The weight of each beam may be neglected, and the assumption may be made that each beam acts elastically.

153. The beam shown in Fig. 158 has the following dimensions: $b = 8$ in., $d = 10$ in., and the loads are $P = 2000$ lb and $w = 200$ lb per ft.

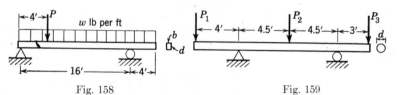

Fig. 158   Fig. 159

154. The diameter d of the beam shown in Fig. 159 is 4 in., and the loads are $P_1 = 2000$ lb, $P_2 = 6000$ lb, and $P_3 = 4000$ lb.

155. In Fig. 127 let the beam have a rectangular cross section 3 in. wide and 12 in. deep.

44. Bending moments determined graphically.   *Culmann's Method.*   The bending moment of the forces acting on a beam about any section may be found by use of the force and string polygons as follows: In Fig. 160a is shown a beam acted on by four vertical loads P_1 to P_4. By drawing the force and string polygons in the usual way, the reactions R_1 and R_2 are found, as indicated in Fig. 160b. Let it be required to find the bending moment about the section A. By definition, this moment is the algebraic sum of the moments of R_1 and P_1

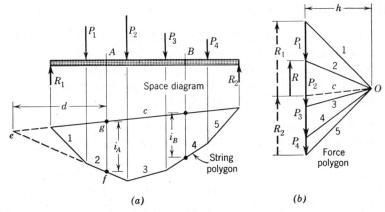

Fig. 160.   Graphical determination of bending moment.

about A, or the moment of the resultant of R_1 and P_1 about A. The magnitude and direction of this resultant is given in the force polygon, denoted by R, and one point on its action line is the intersection of the strings c and 2, denoted by e in the space diagram; the perpendicular distance from A to this resultant is denoted by d. Therefore the bending moment for the section A is

$$M_A = Rd$$

If now a line is drawn through A parallel to the resultant R intersecting the strings c and 2 at g and f, the resulting triangle efg in the string polygon has its sides parallel to the sides of the triangle formed by R, c, and 2 in the force polygon. These triangles, therefore, are similar, and their altitudes and sides are proportional. Let h denote the perpendicular distance from R to the pole O in the force polygon, and let the intercept gf in the string polygon be denoted by i_A. Then, from similar triangles the following equation is found:

$$\frac{d}{h} = \frac{i_A}{R} \quad \text{or} \quad Rd = hi_A$$

Therefore,

$$M_A = hi_A \quad \text{and similarly} \quad M_B = hi_B$$

in which h is called the pole distance and i the intercept. This relation is not restricted to a parallel system of forces but applies to any coplanar-force system. It states that the moment of any set of coplanar forces, about a point A, is equal to the product of the pole distance of the resultant of the forces and the intercept which the strings that represent the two components of the resultant cut from a line drawn through A parallel to the resultant. Or, stated in a different way:

> Ordinates in the bending-moment diagram may be found by multiplying the corresponding ordinates (intercepts) in the string polygon by h. Thus, by choosing proper scales (for example, by choosing h equal to unity), the string polygon may be made to represent the bending-moment diagram.

It should be remembered that h represents a force and must be measured to the scale of the force polygon, and that i is a length and must be measured to the scale of the space diagram.

For distributed loads (either uniform or varying) this graphical method may be used by dividing the length of the beam over which the load is distributed into short lengths, and assuming the load on each short length to be a concentrated load acting at the center of the length.

Review Problems for Articles 39 to 44

156. A simple beam having a span of 12 ft is made of yellow pine. The beam carries concentrated loads of 1000, 2000, and 4000 lb at distances of 3, 6, and 7 ft, respectively, from the left support, and also a total uniformly distributed load of 2400 lb. If the width of the beam is 8 in. and the depth is 16 in., compute the maximum bending stress.   *Ans.*   800 lb per sq in.

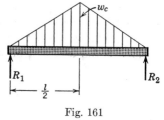

Fig. 161

157. Show that the maximum bending moment for a simple beam loaded as shown in Fig. 161 is

$$M = \tfrac{1}{6}Wl$$

in which W is the total load on the beam, and l is the span of the beam.

158. Draw the shear and bending-moment diagrams for the beam loaded and supported as shown in Fig. 162. Determine the magnitude and location of the maximum vertical shear and the maximum bending moment; also locate the point of inflection.

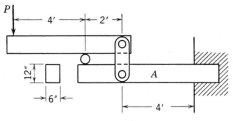

Fig. 162

159. The load P in Fig. 163 is 800 lb. Compute the maximum bending stress in the timber beam A; the beam acts elastically.   *Ans.* 670 lb per sq in.

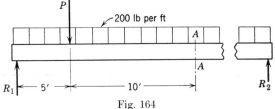

Fig. 163

160. For the beam shown in Fig. 164 it is known that the bending moment for section AA is positive and equal to 10,000 lb-ft and that the vertical shear for the

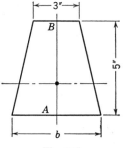

Fig. 164

same section is negative and equal to 2600 lb. Calculate the bending moment for the section beneath the concentrated load. *Hint.* Pass a plane through the beam at section AA, remove the portion to the right of the section and replace it by the forces it exerts on the remaining portion of the beam, and then use the definition of the bending moment for any section of a beam.   *Ans.* 26,000 lb-ft.

161. The cross section of a beam is a trapezoidal section as shown in Fig. 165. On any section the flexural stress at any point A on the bottom of the section is two thirds of that at any point B on the top face of the beam, all stresses on the section being less than the proportional limit of the material. What is the width b of the base of the area?   *Ans.* $b = 12$ in.

Fig. 165

162. A small barge floats in water when loaded as shown in Fig. 166. Draw the shear and moment diagrams for the barge. Neglect the weight of the barge, and assume that the loads are concentrated forces and are applied in a longitudinal plane of symmetry.

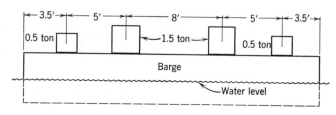

Fig. 166

163. Calculate the maximum bending stress in the steel beam shown in Fig. 167. Assume $P = 200$ lb, $Q = 100$ lb, $W = 360$ lb, $d = 10$ in., $t = 0.5$ in., $l = 50$ in., and $b = 6$ in. Also assume that the proportional limit of the material is 60,000 lb per sq in.   *Ans.* $\sigma = 24,000$ lb per sq in.

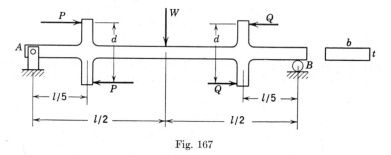

Fig. 167

164. Sand is piled on a floor so that the load on the beams supporting the floor varies from zero pressure at one end to a pressure of w lb per ft at the other end (Fig. 168). Show that the vertical shear is zero for a section at a distance of $0.577l$ from the left support, and that the maximum bending moment is $0.0642wl^2$.

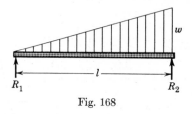

Fig. 168

165. Draw the shear and moment diagrams for the beam shown in Fig. 169; hinges exist at B and C which can resist shear but not bending. Compute the maximum bending stress in the beam if the cross section of the beam is 4 in. wide by 10 in. deep. The proportional limit of the material (timber) is 2000 lb per sq in. *Ans.* 1800 lb per sq in.

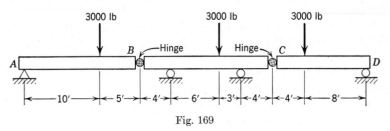

Fig. 169

166. A beam 16 ft long is supported at its left end and at the section 6 ft from its right end. It carries a uniform load of 1000 lb per ft over the 10-ft length lying between points 4 ft and 14 ft, respectively, from the left end of the beam. Draw the shear and moment diagrams, and give the location of the point of inflection.

167. A simply supported beam having a span of 16 ft carries a uniformly distributed load of 500 lb per ft of length on one half of the span and a uniformly distributed load of 1000 lb per ft over the other half. The beam has a hollow rectangular cross section, the outside dimensions being 6 in. wide and 10 in. deep. The sides, top, and bottom are each 1 in. thick. Compute the maximum bending stress in the beam. *Ans.* 4460 lb per sq in.

168. A beam 15 ft long is partially restrained at both ends and carries a uniform load of 160 lb per ft over the entire span. There is a negative bending moment of 2000 lb-ft at each end of the beam. Draw the shear and moment diagrams, and determine the maximum bending moment for the beam.

169. A horizontal beam 20 ft long is simply supported at each end and is subjected to a downward concentrated load P at a point 4 ft from the left end and to an upward concentrated load Q at a point 9 ft from the left end. The bending moment for a section 6 ft from the left end is known to have a negative value of 4500 lb-ft, and at a section 5 ft from the right end the bending moment has a negative value of 7500 lb-ft. Determine the values of the loads P and Q and of the reactions.

45. Assumptions and limitations involved in the flexure formula. In the derivation of the flexure formula, several assumptions were made which impose limitations on the use of the formula. Each assumption made falls under one of the following two headings: (a) The properties of the material of which the beam is made, and (b) geometrical conditions, including the shape of the beam and the location and direction of the forces (loads and reactions) acting on the beam. These assumptions and limitations may be summarized as follows:

1. The stress on any fiber of the beam is proportional to the strain of the fiber, and hence the maximum fiber stress in the beam does not exceed the proportional limit. In other words, the beam acts elastically and the strains are small. This assumption of proportionality of

stress and strain is a reasonably close approximation to the law of elastic behavior of most engineering materials for working or design stresses.

2. The beam is composed of material for which the modulus of elasticity in tension is the same as that in compression. This assumption is a reasonably close approximation to the results of experiments for most engineering materials, except gray (cast) iron, but the error involved is not as a rule serious at working or design stresses. The flexure formula, of course, does not apply directly to a beam made of two or more different materials such as a reinforced-concrete beam, but can be made to apply to such a beam by the use of an equivalent or transformed homogeneous section (see Chap. XI).

3. The axial deformation (stretch or shortening) of any fiber in the beam is proportional to the distance of the fiber from the neutral surface. This involves the further assumption that the effect of shearing strain (discussed in Art. 48) on the axial strain is negligible; which, except for very short deep beams, introduces little error, particularly since the maximum longitudinal (tensile or compressive) fiber stress occurs at the section on which the shearing stress is zero. This also involves the further assumption that there is no sudden change in cross section such as a hole, fillet, etc., in the beam (see next article).

4. The strain, as well as the total deformation of any fiber of the beam, is proportional to the distance of the fiber from the neutral axis. This assumption requires that all fibers shall have the same length before bending; that is, the beam shall be straight, and hence the flexure formula does not apply to sharply curved beams.

5. The loads act in one plane which contains the centroidal axis of the beam; the loads are perpendicular to the centroidal axis of the beam; and the neutral surface is perpendicular to the plane of the loads. These assumptions require that the plane of the loads shall contain an axis of symmetry of each cross section, in which case the neutral axis of any section is the other axis of symmetry (or the other principal axis of inertia of the cross section). The flexure formula does not apply, therefore, to a beam loaded unsymmetrically.

6. The proportions of the beam are such that the beam fails (is structurally damaged) by bending and not by twisting, lateral collapse, local wrinkling, etc. For example, a rectangular beam $\frac{1}{4}$ in. wide by 12 in. deep probably would fail by twisting, and an I beam having very wide and thin flanges probably would fail by local wrinkling (buckling) of the flange, etc.

Most of the metal, timber, and other one-material beams that occur in so-called heavy structures and machines subjected to static loads conform approximately to the conditions (properties of the material and shape of the beam, direction and location of loads) on which the flexure formula is based. Furthermore, the flexure formula is applied frequently to beams (such as curved beams, unsymmetrically loaded beams, flat plates) that do not satisfy the conditions required to make its application valid; this practice often is justified if the amount of the error is known approximately, and if allowance is made for the error in some way as, for example, by introducing a correction factor in the formula.

46. Elastic-stress concentration in a beam. If a beam has an abrupt change in cross section such as a fillet or a groove, as shown in

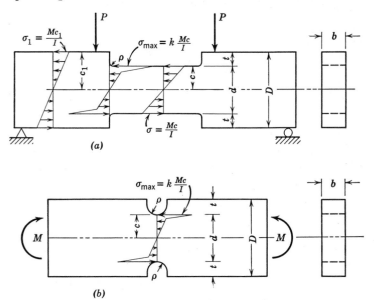

Fig. 170. Stress concentration at abrupt change in section in a beam.

Fig. 170, the section at the abrupt change in area does not remain plane when the loads are applied and hence the bending-(normal-)stress distribution at the section is not linear. The elastic-strain, and hence the elastic-stress, distribution is represented in Fig. 170a and b, in which the maximum bending stress is given by the expression

$$\sigma_{max} = k\frac{Mc}{I} \tag{87}$$

where k is the elastic (theoretical or ideal) stress-concentration factor (for a similar expression for axial loads, see Art. 15).

Values for k in Eq. 87, as found by the photoelastic (polarized-light) method, are given in Table 3 for a beam with a fillet (Fig. 170a). For values of k for other abrupt changes in section (such as the groove in Fig. 170b) see our book, *Advanced Mechanics of Materials*.

TABLE 3

Values of Stress-concentration Factor k for Beam with Fillet (Fig. 170a)

Values of ρ/d	Values of t/ρ					
	0.25	0.5	1.0	2.0	4	8
0.5	1.15	1.20	1.22	1.22	1.22	1.22
0.2	1.27	1.37	1.46	1.50	1.52	1.55
0.1	1.32	1.50	1.67	1.72	1.75	1.89
0.05	1.35	1.62	1.90	2.05	2.23	2.30

The maximum bending (normal) stress as given by Eq. 87 is the significant stress in the beam under certain conditions, as, for example, when the material is brittle, or when the loads are applied and released repeatedly for many times (see Chap. IX for further discussion of repeated loads). However, when the material is ductile and when the loads are not repeated many times, we usually ignore the effects of the stress concentration and compute the stress by the ordinary flexure formula ($k = 1$ in Eq. 87). This fact is discussed in Art. 58.

§2 Elastic Shearing Stresses in Beams

47. Significance of the shearing stresses in beams. In Art. 39 it was shown that, for elastic behavior of a beam, the tensile (or compressive) stress σ in the outer fibers at a transverse cross section of a beam is given by the expression $\sigma = Mc/I$, as indicated at section AB in Fig. 171. An elastic shearing stress also occurs at the same point on any diagonal plane passing through the point; the maximum value τ_{max} of the shearing stress occurs on diagonal planes making angles of 45° with the transverse cross section as shown at B in Fig. 171. Furthermore, $\tau_{max} = \frac{1}{2}\sigma$ (see Art. 10).

Even though τ_{max} is only one-half the value of σ, nevertheless it may be the cause of failure of beams that are made of a material that is relatively weak in shear.

At a section of a beam that is subjected to vertical shear in addition to bending, as at section CD in Fig. 171, there are also shearing stresses τ_V and τ_H in the transverse (vertical) and longitudinal (horizontal) planes, respectively, at the point. Furthermore, as indicated in Fig. 171, these shearing stresses have the value zero at the outer fibers and have their maximum values at the neutral axis; this statement will be

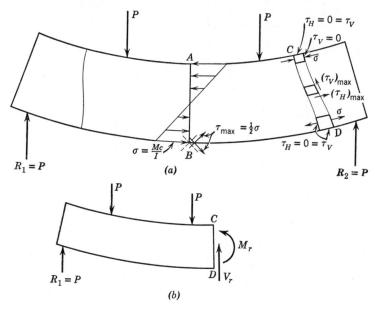

Fig. 171. Shearing stresses in a beam.

proved in the next article. The fact that $\tau_V = \tau_H$ at any point follows from Art. 25.

The Problem Defined. The problem now to be considered is to express the elastic shearing stress τ_H or τ_V at any point in the beam in terms of the external forces acting on the beam and the dimensions of the cross section of the beam. The shearing stress is of special importance in timber beams (see Fig. 181), in concrete beams, and in certain built-up metal beams that are used in airplane structures, bridges, etc. Physical evidence that vertical and horizontal shearing stresses are present in a beam (except for pure bending) is obtained from a study of the behavior of a beam composed of two parts as shown in Fig. 186; if the two parts act as a unit (as a single beam) as in Fig. 186b, shearing stresses must exist between the two parts.

If the method outlined in Art. 8 were used in solving the foregoing problem, we would proceed as follows in obtaining an expression for

τ_V: The vertical shear V for the section CD in Fig. 171b is $V = P$, and the condition of equilibrium requires that $V_r = V = P$. If now V_r can be expressed in terms of τ_V at any point on the section CD and the

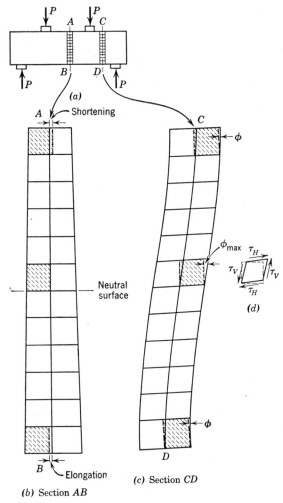

Fig. 172. Actual strains in a rubber beam when subjected to pure bending as in (b), and when subjected to ordinary bending as in (c).

dimensions of the area, our problem will be solved; this step, of course, requires that the shearing-stress distribution be known. But, in order to determine the shearing-stress distribution, the shearing-strain distribution must first be found. Unfortunately the distribution of shearing strains over the area is unknown and is difficult to determine quantitatively by an experimental method; this is in marked contrast to the satisfactory method of determining the strains normal to the area. Therefore, the method outlined in Art. 8 and used for determining the expression $\sigma = Mc/I$ *cannot* be used in obtaining the expression for τ_V (or τ_H) in terms of the loads acting on the beam.

It is possible and desirable, however, to determine, qualitatively, the distribution of elastic shearing strains (and elastic shearing stresses τ_V) as indicated in Fig. 172c. The beam in Fig. 172a was made of rubber which permitted strains to be produced that were sufficiently large to be observed with the naked eye. Before the beam was loaded, squares $\frac{1}{2}$ in. on a side were ruled on the vertical face of the beam, and, after the loads were applied, these squares were deformed as shown in Fig. 172b and c.

It will be observed that, in the central portion of the beam where pure bending occurs, and hence where no vertical shear exists, the tensile and compressive (longitudinal) strains of the fibers vary directly with the distances of the fibers from the neutral surface, as shown in Fig. 172b. However, at a section, such as CD, for which vertical shear exists in addition to some bending, plane sections do not remain plane, and the deformations of the squares in Fig. 172c show that shearing deformation, and therefore the shearing stresses τ_V and τ_H occur, in addition to normal (tensile and compressive) strains.

The shearing strains are represented by the angle ϕ (see Art. 6); its value increases from zero at the outer fibers to a maximum at the neutral axis, but it is difficult to determine, quantitatively, the law of variation, and furthermore the law of variation depends on the shape of the cross section. Since, for elastic behavior of the beam, the elastic shearing stresses are proportional to the elastic shearing strains, it follows that the values of the horizontal and vertical shearing stresses are equal to zero at the outer fibers, and their maximum values occur at the neutral axis. A quantitative expression for τ_H (and τ_V) will now be obtained by use of the equation $V = dM/dx$ (see Art. 41).

48. Relation of loads and horizontal shearing stress. The horizontal shearing stress τ_H at any point in the beam may be expressed in terms of the external forces and dimensions of the beam as follows: Since $V_r = V$ (Fig. 171b), it can be anticipated that the external forces in the final expression for τ_H (or τ_V) will be represented by the vertical shear V for the section considered.

Let a block B having a small width dx (Fig. 173b) be removed from the beam and replaced by the forces that the block exerted on the beam. These forces must have been exerted, of course, on the faces that were in contact with the beam.   As shown in Art. 40, the compressive (or tensile) stress at any point on any cross section of the beam varies directly as the distance of the point from the neutral axis, being zero at the neutral axis.   Thus, the block B must have pushed horizontally on its two end faces, and in addition exerted vertical shearing forces on the beam, downward at its left end and upward at its right end.   Fig. 173b is a free body diagram of B.

But, since the bending moments at the two sections are not, in general, equal, the sum of the compressive forces H and H' on the two

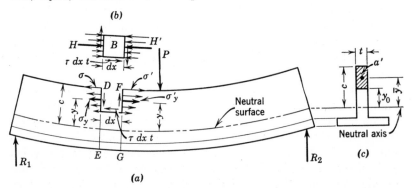

Fig. 173.   Method of determining expression for longitudinal shearing stress in beam.

faces of the block (Fig. 173b) are not equal, and hence there must be shearing forces on the bottom face of the block and also on the left and right faces of the block.   A free-body diagram (Fig. 173b) of the block B shows that these forces constitute two couples of equal magnitude and opposite sense which hold the block in equilibrium.

If H' and H represent the total force on the right and left faces, respectively, the total shearing force on the bottom face is equal to $H' - H$ (Fig. 173b).   Furthermore, since the area $dx \cdot t$ on which the shearing stress occurs is small, the shearing stress τ_H may be assumed to be constant over the area, and hence the total shearing force is $\tau_H \cdot dx \cdot t$.   Therefore,

$$\tau_H \, dx \cdot t = H' - H \tag{88}$$

But $H' = \displaystyle\int_{y_0}^{c} \sigma'_y \, da$, in which σ'_y is the normal stress on the plane FG on a fiber at the distance y from the neutral axis (Fig. 173a).   But $\sigma'_y/y = \sigma'/c = $ a constant (Art. 40), and hence

$$H' = \frac{\sigma'}{c} \int_{y_0}^{c} y \, da \quad \text{and similarly} \quad H = \frac{\sigma}{c} \int_{y_0}^{c} y \, da$$

Thus,

$$\tau_H \, dx \cdot t = \frac{\sigma' - \sigma}{c} \int_{y_0}^{c} y \, da$$

But $\sigma' = M'c/I$ and $\sigma = Mc/I$, in which M' and M are the bending moments at the sections FG and DE, respectively. Therefore,

$$\tau_H \, dx \cdot t = \frac{M' - M}{I} \int_{y_0}^{c} y \, da$$

But $M' - M = dM$ since the two sections are the small distance dx apart. Hence,

$$\tau_H = \frac{dM}{dx} \cdot \frac{1}{It} \int_{y_0}^{c} y \, da$$

and, from Art. 41, $dM/dx = V$. Therefore,

$$\tau_H = \frac{V}{It} \int_{y_0}^{c} y \, da \tag{89}$$

in which τ_H is the horizontal shearing stress (and also the vertical shearing stress τ_V) in a cross section for which the vertical shear is V, and at a point whose distance from the neutral axis is y_0; the thickness of the beam at the distance y_0 from the neutral axis is t, and I is the moment of inertia of the whole cross section of the beam about the neutral axis. The expression $\int_{y_0}^{c} y \, da$ is the first moment (often called the statical moment), about the neutral axis, of that part of the cross-sectional area of the beam between the plane on which the horizontal shearing stress τ_H occurs and the outer face of the beam (that is, between y_0 and c). This area is the cross-hatched area a' in the end view in Fig. 173a. Furthermore, if the distance $\bar{y}$ of the centroid of the area a' from the neutral axis is known, the moment of this area may be found from the product $a'\bar{y}$ since $\int_{y_0}^{c} y \, da = a'\bar{y}$ (Art. 153). Hence, the foregoing equation may be written

$Q \to p.420$

$$\tau_H = \frac{V}{It} \cdot a'\bar{y} = \frac{VQ}{It} \tag{90}$$

in which $Q = \int_{y_c}^{c} y \, da' = a'\bar{y}$ and, as already noted, is called the statical moment of that portion of the whole area between $y = y_0$ and $y = c$ about the central axis.

Equation 90 is valid only when the flexure formula is valid since the flexure formula was used in the derivation of Eq. 90.

Maximum Value of τ_H. It is important, next, to locate the point in a beam at which the shearing stress τ_H is a maximum. If the beam has a constant cross section, I and t are constant, and, hence, the maximum value of τ_H in Eqs. 89 and 90 will occur in the section of the beam for which V is maximum; for a *simple* beam subjected to a uniform load, V is maximum close to one support. Furthermore, in any section of constant thickness, τ_H will be maximum when $\int_{y_0}^{c} y\,da$ or $a'\bar{y}$ is maximum, which occurs when y_0 is zero; that is, τ_H is maximum at the neutral surface. Thus, in a *simple* beam of *constant thickness,*

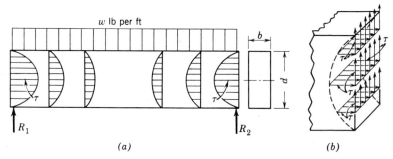

Fig. 174. Variation of shearing stress in beam.

subjected to a uniform load, the horizontal shearing stress varies throughout the beam as shown in Fig. 174, and, at any point in a section, the horizontal and vertical shearing stresses are equal, as indicated in Fig. 174*b*.

Thus, the maximum horizontal or vertical shearing stress in any section of a beam having a *rectangular* cross section *bd* (Fig. 174) is

$$\tau = \frac{V}{It}\,a'\bar{y} = \frac{V}{\frac{1}{12}bd^3 \cdot b} \cdot b\,\frac{d}{2} \times \frac{d}{4} = \frac{3}{2}\frac{V}{bd} = \frac{3}{2}\frac{V}{a}$$

in which a is the area of the whole cross section. Hence, the maximum value of τ in any section of a rectangular beam is 50 per cent greater than the average shearing stress in the section. If a beam has a *circular* cross section, the maximum value of τ is $33\frac{1}{3}$ per cent greater than V/a; that is, $\tau = \frac{4}{3}V/a$. If the beam is a thin circular tube the maximum value is $\tau = 2V/a$.

49. Vertical and horizontal shear in flanged-type beams. In a beam having relatively thin flanges such as channel and I sections, and certain shapes used in airplane construction, it is frequently assumed that the flanges offer no resistance to the vertical shear V; all the resistance to shear is assumed to be offered by the web of the I section, etc. Furthermore, the vertical shearing stress on the area of the web is considered to be constant, the web being regarded as extending the entire depth of the beam. The justification for the foregoing simplifying assumption about an I section may be found in a study of Fig. 175.

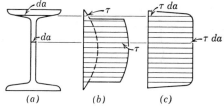

Fig. 175. Variation of shearing stress on cross section of I beam.

In any section of an I beam, τ, according to Eq. 89, will be large where t is small, and small where t is large, the effect on τ of the term $\int_{y_0}^{c} y\, da$ being relatively small in the case of an I section; furthermore, τ will change abruptly where t changes abruptly. Hence, the horizontal (and vertical) shearing stress at a section in an I beam varies approximately as shown in Fig. 175b, and the total shearing force ($\tau\, da$) on the elementary strips of the section (the total force per unit of depth) is approximately constant for the whole depth of the section as shown in Fig. 175c.

50. Lateral shear in flanges of channel or I section. Let Fig. 176a represent a rolled channel used as a horizontal cantilever

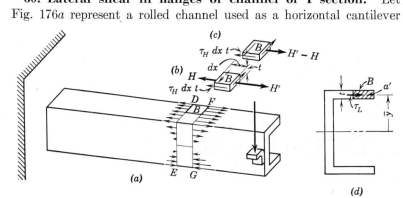

Fig. 176. Lateral shearing stress in flanges of channel beam.

beam subjected to a vertical concentrated load at its free end. Let a small block B (Fig. 176b) be removed from the upper flange of the beam between sections DE and FG. The forces that hold the block B in equilibrium are shown in Fig. 176c. These forces represent two couples equal in magnitude but opposite in sense lying in the horizontal central plane of the flange. This fact shows that the horizontal shear τ_H is equal to a lateral shear τ_L that acts laterally along the center line of the flange as shown in the cross section (enlarged) in Fig. 176d. Furthermore, the magnitude of τ_H and of τ_L is computed by Eq. 90 in which the quantities t, a', and $\bar{y}$ are as shown in Fig. 176d.

Significance of Lateral Shear in Flanges. The lateral shearing forces in the flanges of I and channel sections are as shown in Fig. 177a and b.

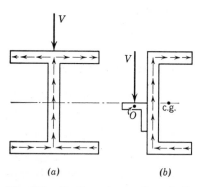

(a)   (b)

Fig. 177. Load must pass through the shear center O to prevent twisting of beam as it bends.

It will be noted that, in an I section, these lateral shearing forces act to the right and left in each flange and are balanced because of the symmetry of the section. However, in the channel section the lateral shearing forces act to the left in the lower flange and to the right in the upper flange, and therefore create an unbalanced twisting couple, which must be balanced by locating the load to the left of the centroid, if the beam is prevented from twisting as it bends. The location of the action line of the load V is through the shear center O. The shear center is discussed further in Chapter IV of our book, *Advanced Mechanics of Materials*.

51. Shear flow. The shearing force along a horizontal or longitudinal surface in a beam varies along the beam. This shearing force

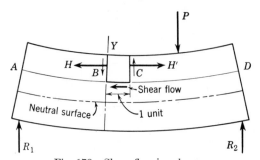

Fig. 178. Shear flow in a beam.

per unit length along the beam is called the shear flow for the horizontal or longitudinal surface considered, and is usually designated by q. For example, in Fig. 178 the shear flow along the surface $ABCD$ is

$(H' - H)/dx$ where H and H' are the longitudinal forces exerted in the beam by the rectangular block. If we let $H' - H = dH$ at the section YY in Fig. 178, then $q = dH/dx$. Hence, by making use of the foregoing expressions for H' and H as developed in the derivation of Eq. 89, we obtain

$$q = \frac{VQ}{I} \qquad (91)$$

In some types of problems it is convenient to calculate the shear flow and then obtain the shearing stress by dividing the shear flow by the area on which it acts, which is $t \times 1$. Hence,

$$\tau = \frac{q}{t} = \frac{VQ}{It} \qquad (92)$$

Illustrative Problem

Problem 170. Compute the maximum shearing stress in a simple beam composed of two 15-in. 45-lb channels placed back to back and covered with two $12'' \times \frac{1}{2}''$ steel plates fastened to the channels by $\frac{7}{8}''$ rivets (Fig. 179a) and used

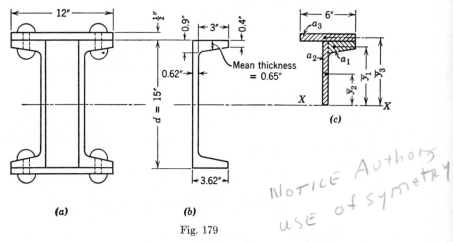

(a)   **(b)**   **(c)**

Fig. 179

on a 12-ft span. The beam is subjected to a concentrated load of 100,000 lb at the center of the span. (Neglect the weight of the beam.) The dimensions of each channel are shown in Fig. 179b. Also compute the spacing of the $\frac{7}{8}''$ rivets if each rivet is allowed to resist a 9000-lb shearing force between the plate and the channel.

Solution. A steelmaker's handbook gives the following values for each channel in addition to those shown in Fig. 179b.

$$I_x = 375 \text{ in.}^4, \qquad a = 13.2 \text{ sq in.}$$

$$I_x \text{ for the two cover plates} = 2(12 \times \tfrac{1}{2} \times 7.75^2) = 720 \text{ in.}^4$$

Thus I_z for two channels and two cover plates is 1470 in.[4] The maximum shearing stress is $\tau = \dfrac{V}{It} a'\bar{y}$.

$$V = 50,000 \text{ lb}, \qquad I = 1470 \text{ in.}^4, \qquad t = 1.24 \text{ in.}$$

The value of $a'\bar{y}$ is most easily found as the sum of the moments of the areas a_1, a_2, and a_3 (Fig. 179c) for both channel sections and plates. Thus,

$$a'\bar{y} = 2a_1\bar{y}_1 + 2a_2\bar{y}_2 + 2a_3\bar{y}_3$$

$$= 2(3 \times 0.65) \times \left(7.5 - \frac{0.65}{2}\right) + 2(0.62 \times 7.5) \times 3.75$$

$$+ 2 \times 6 \times 0.5 \times 7.75 = 109.5 \text{ in.}^{\text{3}}$$

Therefore,

$$\text{Max } \tau = \frac{50,000 \times 109.5}{1470 \times 1.24} = 3000 \text{ lb/in.}^2$$

The maximum bending stress ($\sigma = Mc/I$) is found to be 19,400 lb/in.[2] Thus the maximum shearing stress is small in this section (and in nearly all other rolled-steel sections, except when used on very short spans), even though the bending (normal) stress is the full allowable value.

The average shearing stress over the entire cross section is

$$\tau_{\text{avg}} = \frac{V}{a} = \frac{50,000}{38.4} = 1300 \text{ lb/in.}^2$$

and, hence, the maximum shearing stress is 2.3 times the average.

The average shearing stress over the web area of the two channels is

$$\tau_{\text{avg}} = \frac{V}{a_w} = \frac{50,000}{15 \times 2 \times 0.62} = 2690 \text{ lb/in.}^2$$

The rivet spacing is obtained from the shear flow q between one half of one plate and one of the channels; i.e., the spacing is $9000/q$. But $q = VQ/I$, where Q is the first moment of a_3 in Fig. 179c.

Therefore,

$$Q = a_3\bar{y}_3 = 6 \times 0.5 \times 7.75 = 23.25 \text{ in.}^3$$

and

$$q = \frac{50,000 \times 23.25}{1470} = 780 \text{ lb per in. of length}$$

Rivet spacing $= \frac{9000}{780} = 11.5$ in.

Problems for Arts. 48 to 51

171. A simply supported horizontal beam is made of wood and has a cross-sectional area 6 in. wide by 10 in. deep. A concentrated vertical load of 18,000 lb acts at the midspan section, and the span is 10 ft. (a) Calculate the maximum horizontal and vertical shearing stress in the beam. (b) Calculate also the shearing stress at a point 3 in. from the top of the beam at a section 2 ft from the left support.

172. A simply supported horizontal timber beam that has a hollow square cross section is made by fastening together four 2-in.-by-8-in. planks with screws as shown in Fig. 180. The span of the beam is 10 ft, and the beam is subjected

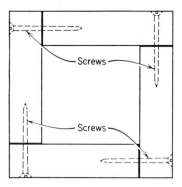

Fig. 180

to a concentrated vertical load of 6000 lb that acts 3 ft from the left end. (*a*) Calculate the maximum shearing stress, and state where in the beam this stress occurs. (*b*) Determine the spacing of the screws along the beam between the left support and the load if each screw is capable of resisting a direct shearing force of 460 lb.   *Ans.*   2 in.

173. A Douglas-fir beam (Fig. 181) having a rectangular cross section 1 in. by 2 in. when tested as a cantilever beam with a concentrated load at the free end failed by horizontal shear (as shown in Fig. 181) when the total load on the beam

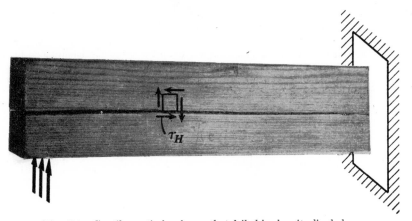

Fig. 181. Cantilever timber beam that failed by longitudinal shear.

was 381 lb. Calculate the maximum horizontal shearing stress when the failure occurred. Assume that shearing stress is proportional to shearing strain (elastic behavior) until rupture occurs; this assumption will give approximate but useful results.   *Ans.* $\tau = 286$ lb/in^2

174. A simply supported horizontal beam is subjected to two equal concentrated vertical loads $P = 115,000$ lb that are applied at the quarter points of the beam. The beam span is $l = 10$ ft, and the cross section consists of an I beam with four hollow tubular cylinders welded continuously longitudinally along the edges of the four flanges as shown in Fig. 182. Determine the magnitude of the

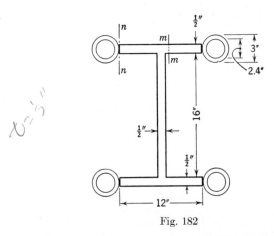

Fig. 182

longitudinal shearing stress on each of the following longitudinal planes: (a) the plane nn through the throat of weld joining a tube to a flange edge, (b) the plane mm at the juncture of the flange and web, (c) the maximum longitudinal (or transverse) shearing stress.   *Ans.* $\tau_{nn} = 2880$ lb/in.^{2}; $\tau_{mm} = 6120$ lb/in.^{2};
$$\tau_{max} = 14,700 \text{ lb/in.}^2$$

175. A horizontal cantilever beam of length $l = 6$ ft is loaded by a vertical load $P = 560$ lb at its free end. The beam consists of three 2"-by-4" pieces of timber glued together with their longitudinal axes parallel as indicated by the cross-sectional view shown in Fig. 183. Compute the maximum longitudinal (or transverse) shear in the beam, and determine its location in the beam.

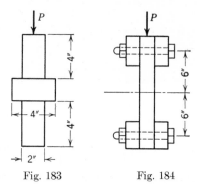

Fig. 183   Fig. 184

176. A horizontal simply supported beam is 10 ft in length and is loaded at its center by a concentrated load $P = 6000$ lb. The beam is made by fastening four 2"-by-4" timbers to a 2"-by-16" timber as shown in Fig. 184 by steel bolts

$\frac{1}{2}$ in. in diameter spaced 8 in. apart along the length. The longitudinal axes of all the timbers are parallel. Compute the following stresses: (a) the maximum bending stress, (b) the maximum longitudinal shearing stress in the beam, (c) the shearing stress in the steel bolts, (d) the bearing stress between the steel bolts and the 2″-by-16″ timber. *Ans.* (a) $\sigma = 870$ lb/in.^{2}; (b) $\tau_{\max} = 145$ lb/in.^{2}; (c) $\tau = 3530$ lb/in.^{2}; (d) $\sigma = 1390$ lb/in.^{2}

177. A horizontal cantilever beam of length $l = 6$ ft supports a vertical load $P = 2000$ lb at its free end. The load causes the beam to bend without twisting. The beam (Fig. 185a) consists of a flat plate of steel bent into a semicircular cylindrical shape that is stiffened by 1″ × 1″ × $\frac{1}{4}$″ steel angles which are riveted to the inside of the cylindrical shape in the longitudinal direction at 45° intervals as shown in the cross-sectional view (enlarged) in Fig. 185b. Such beams occur in

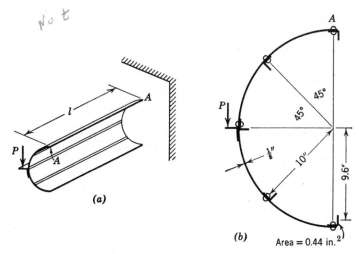

(a)

(b)

Area = 0.44 in.^{2}

Fig. 185. A cantilever beam with stiffeners.

aircraft structures. Compute the following: (a) the shearing stress in the rivets connecting the angle to the semicircular plate along the outermost part of the beam AA if the rivets are $\frac{1}{4}$ in. in diameter and are spaced 10 in. apart, (b) the maximum shearing stress in the beam. *Ans.* (a) 5440 lb/in.^{2}; (b) 1000 lb/in.^{2}

178. Compare the flexural strengths of the two beams illustrated in Fig. 186; the beams have rectangular cross sections. In (a) the beam is composed of two

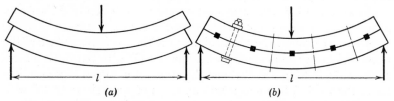

(a)

(b)

Fig. 186. Effect of shearing resistance in a beam composed of two parts.

equal parts of the same material; one part slides over the other, if no shearing resistance is developed on the surfaces of contact, and hence the bending resistance of the beam is the sum of the resistances of the two beams acting independently. In (b) shearing resistance is exerted by the keys and bolts, and hence the two parts of the beam act as one beam.

179. A railroad rail having the cross section shown in Fig. 149 is used as a simple beam. If a concentrated load of 40,000 lb is applied at the center of the span, what is the maximum horizontal shearing stress in the rail. The moment about the centroidal axis of the area of cross section on either side of the centroidal axis is found to be 16.0 in.[3] If the maximum tensile fiber stress in the rail is 24,000 lb/in.[2], what is the span of the beam?   *Ans.* $\tau = 5400$ lb/in.[2]; span = 5.53 ft.

§3   Inelastic Stresses in Beams

52. Manner in which inelastic strains develop in beams of ductile metal. An experimental study of the formation of inelastic strain markings (Luder's lines or bands) in beams of ductile steel shows

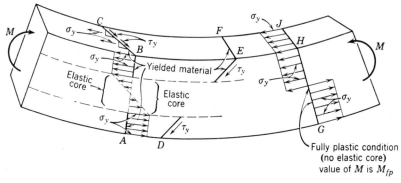

Fig. 187.   Manner in which inelastic deformation (yielding) develops in a beam leading to the fully plastic condition.

that inelastic strains occur on either or both of two sets of planes as illustrated in Fig. 187.

These strain markings are evidence of early inelastic strains that are of the same order of magnitude as that of the strain at the elastic limit, and hence do not cause appreciable inelastic behavior of the beam as a whole until the inelastic strains penetrate the full depth of the beam at one or more sections and then spread along the beam.

One set of planes is perpendicular to the top (or bottom) face of the beam and makes an angle of approximately 45° with the vertical faces as shown at *ABC* in Fig. 187, and the other set of planes is perpendicular to the vertical face and makes an angle of approximately 45° with the top (or bottom) face, as indicated by *DEF* in Fig. 187.

These 45° planes are the planes on which the maximum shearing stresses occur, and the shearing stress in the yielded material is the shearing yield point τ_y of the material, as indicated on the top face along the line BC ($\tau_y = \frac{1}{2}\sigma_y$). It is more convenient, however, to deal with the accompanying *normal* yield-point stress σ_y on a transverse plane at each point along BC as shown in Fig. 187, and to consider that these normal yield-point stresses σ_y act on one transverse plane such as *GHJ* in Fig. 187.

53. Fully plastic bending moment. Ultimate or fracture moment. When the loads on the beam have increased sufficiently to cause one or more of the yielded portions (wedges), such as *CB* or *EF* in Fig. 187, to penetrate from the outer surfaces through the entire depth of the beam, the value of the bending moment is called the fully plastic bending moment and is denoted by M_{fp}. Thus, when this bending moment is acting, there is no elastic core of material remaining at the section to restrain the yielding, and hence the beam is said to have a plastic hinge at this section. This condition means that the beam will continue to deflect approximately at a constant value of M_{fp} as the yielding spreads along the beam if a portion of the beam is subjected to a constant bending moment. Thus the beam will fail by general (unrestrained) yielding, provided that the material has a yield point. Hence, for a statically determinate beam, the fully plastic bending moment is also the ultimate bending moment for the beam; inelastic behavior of statically *indeterminate* beams is discussed briefly in Chapter VII.

The value of the fully plastic moment for the *rectangular* beam shown in Fig. 187 may be found as follows: The forces acting on the

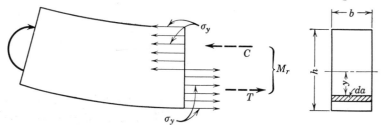

Fig. 188. Method of determining the fully plastic bending moment.

portion of the beam that lies to one side (left side) of the section *GHJ* in Fig. 187 are shown in Fig. 188. The equations of equilibrium applied to these forces give

$$\Sigma F_x = 0 \cdot \qquad \int \sigma \, da = 0 \quad \text{or} \quad T = C = \sigma_y \frac{bh}{2} \qquad (93)$$

$$\Sigma M = 0; \qquad M_{fp} = \int y\sigma_y \, da = \sigma_y \frac{bh^2}{4} \qquad (94)$$

Hence the fully plastic moment is given by the expression

$$M_{fp} = \sigma_y \frac{bh^2}{4} \tag{95}$$

Since the bending moment M_y that would cause the stress in the outer fibers just to reach the value σ_y is

$$M_y = \frac{\sigma_y I}{c} = \sigma_y \frac{bh^2}{6} \tag{96}$$

We may write

$$M_{fp} = \mathbf{1.5} M_y \tag{97}$$

The moment M_y is often called the elastic-limit moment. Hence, the fully plastic (and ultimate) bending moment for this beam is 50 per cent greater than the elastic-limit bending moment, provided that the beam has a rectangular cross section and is made of material having a yield point that has the same value for tension and compression.

Influence of Shape of Cross Section. It should be noted that the shape of the cross section has an important influence on the value of the fully plastic bending moment. We note that in Eq. 97 one and a half times M_y is equal to M_{fp} for a rectangular cross section. This factor, which is designated by K, to be multiplied into M_y to obtain M_{fp} is given in Table 4 for several cross sections. (For other cross sections, see our book, *Advanced Mechanics of Materials*). Hence, Eq. 97 for any cross section may be written

$$M_{fp} = K M_y \quad \text{or} \quad M_{fp} = K \cdot \frac{\sigma_y I}{c} \tag{98}$$

The values of K in Table 4 reveal two very important facts: (1) If

TABLE 4

Cross Section	Values of K in Fully Plastic Bending Moment: $M_{fp} = K M_y$
Rectangular	1.5
Circular	1.7
Circular tube (inner diam. $\frac{3}{4}$ outer diam.)	1.4
I or [sections	1.1 to 1.2

a beam has certain common types of cross sections, such as rectangular or circular cross sections, and is used where small inelastic strains are permissible, the maximum static loads that the beam can resist are much larger than those found by restricting the loads to values that produce stresses and strains within the elastic limit. Thus, by taking advantage of the greater moment resulting from small inelastic strains in the beam, the maximum moment that can be applied to the beam without causing structural failure is greatly increased. (2) But the strength of beams having I and channel cross sections can be increased very little by permitting small inelastic strains to occur.

In the usual method of design of beams made of ductile metals and used in so-called heavy structures for resisting static loads at ordinary temperatures, the moment M_y that causes a maximum stress in the outer fibers equal to the elastic limit σ_y is assumed to be the moment that causes failure of the beam, even though the beams in such structures would usually function satisfactorily if subjected to small inelastic strains.

In this method of design, some beams (with rectangular, circular, etc., cross sections) will have excessive reserve strength whereas beams with some other types of cross sections (I sections, etc.) will have very little excessive reserve strength.

Ductile Material without a Yield Point. Throughout the discussion in § 3, it was assumed that the material was ideally plastic; that is, the material had a yield point and the stress-strain diagram in tension was the same as that for compression. If, however, the stress-strain diagrams in tension and compression are not identical, and the material does not have a yield point, there is no fully plastic bending moment since there is no yield point; when there is no yield point, the resisting moment will continue to increase with increase in the external fiber strain until fracture occurs. Fortunately, an approximate and useful value for the resisting moment corresponding to any small inelastic strain can be obtained by replacing the two stress-strain diagrams with an approximately equivalent single curve having no yield point (see our *Advanced Mechanics of Materials* for discussion of this approximate method).

Brittle Material. Ultimate or Fracture Moment. Modulus of Rupture. For beams made of brittle material it is usually assumed that the material behaves elastically up to the load that causes fracture of the beam, and hence the bending moment corresponding to fracture would be

$$M_{\mathrm{ult}} = \frac{\sigma_{\mathrm{ult}}I}{C} \tag{99}$$

where σ_{ult} is the ultimate tensile strength of the material. However, when such beams are tested to fracture in bending, it is found that the value of M_{ult} from tests is 20 to 100 per cent greater than that given by Eq. 99.   This fact is explained by the change in the stress distribution in bending which occurs as a result of the inelastic behavior that takes place beyond the proportional limit of the material.   Consequently, when beams of brittle material such as gray iron, terra cotta, building stone, timber are used, a fictitious value σ_r of the stress, known as the modulus of rupture, is employed in Eq. 99.   The value of σ_r is obtained from bending tests of beams of the material from the formula

$$\sigma_r = \frac{M_{\text{ult}} \cdot c}{I} \tag{100}$$

Values of σ_r are greater than the ultimate tensile strength σ_u.   The value of σ_r will depend on the shape of the cross section of the beam used in the tests; for example, values of σ_r obtained from tests of beams of circular cross section are greater than those obtained from tests of beams with an I section.

Illustrative Problem

Problem 180.   A simply supported horizontal beam has a span of $l = 50$ in. and is loaded by two equal vertical forces P applied at equal distances of 10 in. from each end.   The cross section of the beam is an area in the shape of a T whose dimensions are as shown in Fig. 189a.   The loads P lie in the plane of symmetry

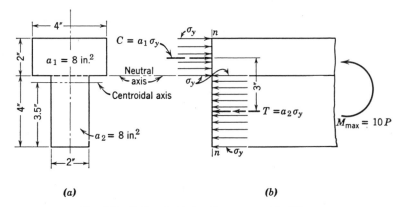

(a)   (b)

Fig. 189.   Fully plastic bending moment in T beam.

of the T section.   Compute the value of the ultimate loads P for the beam if it is made of a structural-grade steel having a yield point σ_y in tension and compression of 35,000 lb per sq in.   The resisting moment in the beam is the fully plastic moment when the ultimate load is reached, as explained in Art. 53.

Solution.   The maximum bending moment in the beam is $M_{\max} = 10P$.   This bending moment is resisted by the fully plastic moment M_{fp}, as indicated in Fig.

189b. The stress distribution on any cross section nn between the loads is indicated in Fig. 189a and b, where the neutral axis is located so as to divide the cross section into two equal areas a_1 and a_2 and is *not* the centroidal axis as in the case of elastic bending. The proof of this latter fact is as follows: From equilibrium conditions:

$$\text{Sum of the horizontal forces on the beam} = 0$$

· Therefore,

$$C = T \quad \text{or} \quad a_1\sigma_y = a_2\sigma_y \tag{1}$$

But, since σ_y in compression is equal to σ_y in tension, it follows from Fig. 189a that $a_1 = a_2$.

Also, from equilibrium conditions,

$$M_{\max} = M_{fp} \tag{2}$$

The value of M_{fp} is equal to the moment of the couple which consists of the forces T and C, each of which passes through the centroid of the areas a_1 and a_2, respectively, since the stress is uniformly distributed on these areas. Therefore, $M_{fp} = a_1\sigma_y \times 3 = 8 \times 35,000 \times 3 = 840,000$ lb-in. Hence, from Eq. 2,

$$M_{\max} = 10P_{\text{ult}} = 840,000 \text{ lb-in.}$$

$$P_{\text{ult}} = 84,000 \text{ lb}$$

Comparison with Elastic-limit Load. The load P_y at which the extreme fiber stress first reaches the yield point σ_y is obtained as follows:

$$M_y = M_{\max} = 10P_y = \frac{\sigma_y I}{c_1} \tag{3}$$

in which I is the moment of inertia with respect to the centroidal axis (which is also the neutral axis for elastic conditions in bending). The value of $I = 49.0$ in.[4] Therefore, from Eq. 43,

$$10P_y = \frac{35,000 \times 49.0}{3.5} = 490,000$$

$$P_y = 49,000 \text{ lb}$$

Hence, the ultimate load P_{ult} is 1.71 times the elastic-limit load P_y. The fact that $M_{fp} = 1.71M_y$ for the cross section given in this problem could be added to the data in Table 4.

Problems

181. A beam made of a ductile material having a yield point in tension and in compression of $\sigma_y = 40,000$ lb per sq in. has a trapezoidal cross section (Fig. 190). If the beam is subjected to pure bending by loads that lie in the plane of symmetry of the cross section, compute the values of the elastic-limit moment M_y and the fully plastic moment M_{fp} for the beam.

Ans. $M_y = 377,000$ lb-in.; $M_{fp} = 677,000$ lb-in.

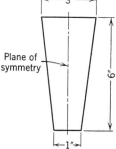

Fig. 190

182. Calculate the load P acting on the steel beam shown in Fig. 191 when the fully plastic moment is developed in the beam. Assume that the yield point of the steel is $\sigma_y = 35,000$ lb per sq in.   *Ans.* 26,250 lb.

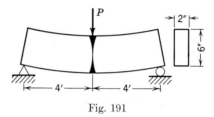

Fig. 191

183. Calculate the maximum bending moment that can be applied to the beam shown in Fig. 192 if it is specified that an elastic core must exist in the middle half of the depth of the beam. The yield point of the material is σ_y, and the cross section has the dimensions b and h.

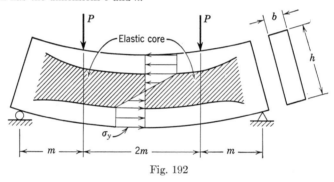

Fig. 192

184. Show that the expression for the fully plastic bending moment for a simply supported beam having a circular cross section is $1.7M_y$ as given in Table 4.

185. Let the beam in Fig. 191 be made of dry yellow pine whose modulus of rupture is $\sigma_r = 11,000$ lb per sq in. Compute the ultimate or fracture load for the beam.

§ 4   Design of Beam for Static Strength

54. Design for static strength. Design of a statically determinate beam for static loads and ordinary temperature, only, is considered in § 4. Design for stiffness and for buckling under static loading is discussed in Chapters IV and VI, respectively. Design for strength under repeated loading (fatigue) is considered in Chapter IX, and design for strength under dynamic (impact or energy loading) is treated in Chapter X.

Failure of the beam under static loading and ordinary temperature will be assumed to occur when either of two conditions prevails: (1) For certain service conditions, failure is assumed to occur when the maximum stress in the outer fibers first reaches the elastic limit (or yield point) of the material or when the maximum longitudinal or transverse shearing stress τ reaches the shearing yield point τ_y; this is called design for *elastic strength*. (2) For certain other uses of beams, particularly beams made of ductile metal, failure is assumed to occur when the fully plastic condition (plastic hinge) is developed which destroys the elastic core in the beam at the given section and permits unrestricted yielding, which leads to collapse of the beam by large deflection under nearly constant load, as explained in Arts. 52 and 53. If, however, the material is made of brittle material, the failure occurs by fracture of the beam.

As previously pointed out, (1) a rational method for the design of a load-resisting member is based on a knowledge of the mode of failure and (2) if the design is for strength (rather than stiffness, buckling, etc.) a relation must be found between the external forces and the stresses developed in the member *at failure;* a factor of safety applied to this relationship gives a design equation. For each of the two modes of failure of a beam described in the foregoing paragraph this relationship between loads and stresses at failure has already been obtained. The maximum stress developed at failure is the yield point σ_y in each case of failure, but in the first case this stress occurs only on the outer fibers of the beam (see Fig. 196), whereas in the second case it occurs on all fibers of the beam at the section of the plastic hinge (Fig. 197).

Thus the bending moment at failure for the first mode of failure is M_y and for the second mode of failure is M_{fp} for ductile materials having a yield point, and M_{ult} for materials that are not ductile. Design equations for beams that will fail under these conditions can now be written by referring to § 1, § 2, and § 3 of this chapter.

55. Design for static elastic strength. From § 1, $\sigma_y = \dfrac{M_y}{I/c}$, and, if a factor of safety N_y is applied to this equation, we obtain

$$\frac{\sigma_y}{N_y} = \frac{M_y/N_y}{I/c} \quad \text{or} \quad \sigma_{wy} = \frac{M_{wy}}{I/c} \tag{101}$$

in which σ_{wy} is the allowable or working stress and M_{wy} is the corresponding allowable bending moment.

Also, from § 2, $\tau_y = V_y Q/It$ (see Eq. 90). If the factor of safety N_y is applied, we obtain

$$\frac{\tau_y}{N_y} = \frac{(V_y/N)Q}{It} \quad \text{or} \quad \tau_{wy} = \frac{V_{wy}Q}{It} \tag{102}$$

in which τ_{wy} and V_{wy} are the allowable or working values of τ and V.

56. Economical sections of beams for elastic strength. The efficient use of material in a force-resisting member involves (1) the selection of available material that is well suited to the use of the member, and (2) the distribution of the material in the member so that it can best resist the forces acting on the member. The use of material, however, always must be considered in relation to the cost involved.

The main point here considered is the effect of the distribution of the material in a beam on the resistance of the beam to external loads; this involves (a) the effect of the shape of cross section and (b) the effect of a variation of size of cross section along the beam.

Effect of Shape of Cross Section. If a beam having a constant cross section safely resists static loads, the maximum fiber stress at the dangerous section must not exceed the allowable or working stress that experiments and experience have shown to be permissible. That is, σ in the flexure formula $\sigma = Mc/I$ must not be greater than the working stress when M is the maximum bending moment.

The flexure formula shows that, when a given stress σ is developed in the beam, the bending moment M required to develop this stress is

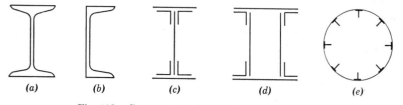

(a)   (b)   (c)   (d)   (e)

Fig. 193.   Cross sections having large values of I/c.

large when I/c is large. Furthermore, I/c is made large by forming the cross section so that the greater part of the area is as far from the neutral axis as is practicable, for, although both I and c are increased by this procedure, I is increased much more than c. Thus, metal beams made of steel, aluminum, etc., are rolled in the form of I sections (Fig. 193a), channel sections (Fig. 193b), etc. Built-up metal beams of various shapes (Fig. 193c and d), are made to conform to this principle. Steel beams are made with the two flanges equal in area, since the proportional limits in compression and tension are approximately equal. Gray-iron beams, however, frequently are cast with the tensile flanges larger in area than the compressive flange (see Fig. 147), since the compressive strength of gray iron is much (about four times) larger than the tensile strength. Although gray-iron beams rarely are used in buildings or bridges, they frequently are

used in machine frames that are subjected to bending. The influence
of the shape of cross section is shown in another way in Fig. 194 by
comparing the values of I/c for four different shapes of sections all

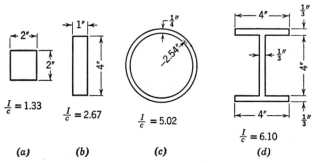

Fig. 194. Cross sections having the same areas but widely different values of I/c.

having the same area. It will be noted that the value of the section
modulus I/c varies from 1.33 in.[3] to 6.10 in.[3]

Effect of Varying Section along the Beam. As discussed in Art. 41,
the bending moment, in general, varies along a beam and is maximum
at one section of the beam. If, then, a beam has a constant cross section ($I/c =$ a constant), the maximum fiber stress will occur on the

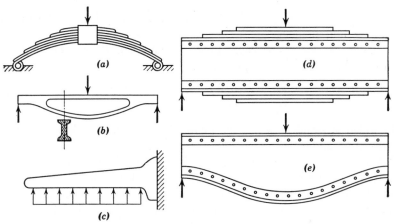

Fig. 195. Form of beams that approach the condition of uniform strength in
which I/c varies approximately as M varies.

outer fiber of the section at which the bending moment is maximum,
and the stress in the outer fibers at all other sections will be less than
that at the dangerous section. Therefore, when the beam is carrying
the load that causes the allowable fiber stress in the beam, there is

much material in the beam on either side of the dangerous section that is understressed, and hence this understressed material could be saved by varying the cross section of the beam so that the I/c would vary as the bending moment M varies. This would cause the stresses in the outer fibers of all sections to be equal, since $\sigma = \dfrac{M}{I/c}$.

Rolled-steel beams nearly always are beams of constant cross section, since the cost of rolling a beam of variable cross section would offset the saving in material. Built-up beams, such as leaf springs (Fig. 195a) and plate girders (Fig. 195d), frames of cars (Fig. 195e), forged axles (Fig. 195b), and tapered wing of an airplane (Fig. 195c), frequently are made with a variable section so that the beam approximates a beam of uniform strength.

57. Design for inelastic strength; fully plastic condition. From § 3, Eq. 98, we obtain $\sigma_y = \dfrac{M_{fp}/K}{I/c}$. If a factor of safety N_p is applied to this equation, we obtain

$$\frac{\sigma_y}{N_p} = \frac{(M_{fp}/K)\dfrac{1}{N_p}}{I/c} \quad \text{or} \quad \sigma_{wp} = \frac{M_{wp}/K}{I/c} \tag{103}$$

in which σ_{wp} and M_{wp} are the allowable or working values of the stress and bending moment.

Brittle Fracture Condition. From § 3 and Eq. 100 we obtain, by introducing a factor of safety N_f,

$$\frac{\sigma_r}{N_f} = \frac{M_{\text{ult}}/N_f}{I/c} \quad \text{or} \quad \sigma_{wf} = \frac{M_{wf}}{I/c} \tag{104}$$

in which σ_{wf} and M_{wf} are the allowable or working values of these quantities, and σ_r is the modulus of rupture.

58. Values of factor of safety. In general, the values of N_y, N_p, and N_f will be different. Usually N_y is smaller than N_p, and N_p is smaller than N_f. This fact arises from the difference in the damaging effects that may result to the member as a consequence of actual failure; for example, a very small permanent set accompanying a stress slightly greater than the elastic limit of the material may not be so damaging as would be collapse of the member resulting from the fully plastic condition (or fracture if the material is brittle). Furthermore, it should be noted that the working values of stresses σ_{wy}, τ_{wy}, σ_{wp}, and σ_{wf} corresponding to the factors of safety N_y, N_p, and N_f are usually substantially less than the elastic limit of the material, and also that the values of M_{wy}, M_{wp}, and M_{wf} are usually less than the value of $M = \sigma_y I/c$ where σ_y is the elastic limit of the material. This fact is sometimes misinterpreted to mean that an analysis of elastic behavior of the member is all that is needed for design.

Effect of Stress Concentration. If the beam has an abrupt change in section giving rise to a stress-concentration factor k as indicated by a comparison of the stress distribution in Fig. 196a and Fig. 196b, the

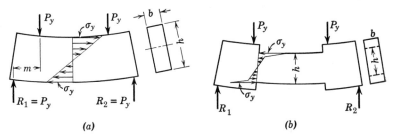

Fig. 196. Effect of stress concentration in the design of the beam.

failure of the beam, in the design for *elastic* strength, would be considered to occur when the maximum (localized) stress at the abrupt change in section reached the elastic limit (or yield point) σ_y, and hence the design equation becomes

$$\sigma_w = \frac{\sigma_y}{N} = \frac{kM_y/N}{I/c} = \frac{kM_{wy}}{I/c} \qquad (105)$$

But in the design of the beam that does not fail until the fully plastic moment M_{fp} is developed at an abrupt change in section (Fig. 197b),

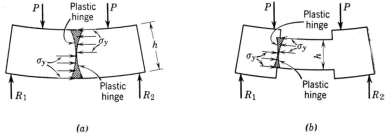

Fig. 197. Fully plastic bending moment not affected by stress concentration.

the concentrated stress is considered to have *no effect* on the value of M_{fp}; its only effect is to determine the section at which a plastic hinge first develops. The stress distribution on the section where the plastic hinge first occurs will be the same as in Fig. 197a.

It should be emphasized that the foregoing equations apply only when the beam satisfies the assumptions made concerning properties of material and nature of loading.

Illustrative Problems

Problem 186. Determine the depth h required for strength of the beam shown in Fig. 198 for each of the following two conditions: (1) The failure of the beam is considered to occur when the maximum stress reaches the yield point (or elastic limit) of the material; and (2) the failure occurs when a plastic hinge forms (fully

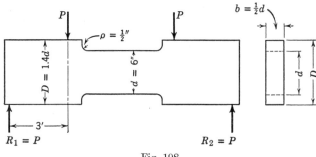

Fig. 198

plastic condition develops as discussed in Art. 53) which destroys the elastic core of material and permits general (unrestrained) yielding to start. Assume the yield point to be $\sigma_y = 36,000$ lb/in.^{2} Use factors of $N_y = 1.5$ and $N_p = 1.8$.

Solution. (*a*) *Design for Elastic Strength.* The stresses at failure are shown in Fig. 196*b*. The equation for the failure condition is $\sigma_y = \dfrac{kM_y}{I/c}$ and the design formula is $\sigma_w = \dfrac{kM_{wy}}{I/c}$. But $\sigma_w = \dfrac{\sigma_y}{N_y} = \dfrac{36,000}{1.5} = 24,000$ and $M_{wy} = 36 \times P_{wy}$. Also $\dfrac{I}{c} = \dfrac{\frac{1}{12}bd^3}{d/2} = \dfrac{bd^2}{6} = 18$ in.^{3} From Table 3 (p. 160), $k = 1.70$. Therefore,

$$24,000 = \frac{1.70 \times 36P_y}{18} \quad \text{and} \quad P_{wy} = 7000 \text{ lb}$$

(*b*) *Design for Inelastic Strength.* The stress distribution at failure is shown in Fig. 197*b*. The equation for the failure condition is (Eq. 103)

$$\sigma_{wp} = \frac{M_{wp}/K}{I/c}$$

in which $K = 1.5$ from Table 4 (p. 176), $M_{wp} = 36P_{wp}$, and $I/c = 18$. But $\sigma_{wp} = \sigma_y/N_p = 36,000/1.8 = 20,000$ lb per sq in. Hence,

$$20,000 = \frac{36P_{wp}/1.5}{18} \quad \text{and therefore} \quad P_{wp} = \frac{20,000 \times 18 \times 1.5}{36} = 15,000 \text{ lb}$$

Problem 187. The rolled-steel I beam shown in Fig. 199 rests at A on a soft material which distributes the pressure on the beam uniformly over the surface of contact. The rectangular tank and water B weigh 4000 lb. Draw the shear diagram for the beam, and calculate the maximum bending moment. Assume a working fiber stress of 20,000 lb/in.², and calculate the section modulus required. From a steel designer's handbook (or from the tables in Appendix II) select a rolled-steel I beam.

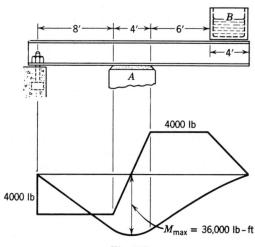

Fig. 199

Solution. In the design of beams that are made from steel rolled sections such as I beams, channels, etc., and that are subjected to loading conditions as in this problem, the failure of the beam will be by general yielding which occurs when the fully plastic bending moment M_{fp} is reached, provided that the beam is supported laterally to prevent overturning or twisting (in Fig. 199 there is no lateral support shown for the end that supports the water tank, but it is assumed to exist in this solution of this problem).

For Resisting Maximum Elastic-bending Moment. $\sigma_w = \dfrac{M_{wy}/K}{I/c}$. From Table 4, the value of K for rolled sections is 1.1 to 1.2, but, since its value is approximately 1.0 and since commercial sizes of the beam are to be used, the value of K is usually chosen as 1.0. Hence, we use the equation $\sigma_w = \dfrac{M_{wy}/1}{I/c}$ and

$$\frac{I}{c} = \frac{M_{wy}}{\sigma_w} = \frac{36,000 \times 12}{20,000} = 21.6$$

From Table A in Appendix II a 10″ 22.4-lb I beam will provide an $I/c = 22.7$ in.³

Check for Shear Stress. The average shearing stress is $\tau_{avg} = V_{max}/a_{web} = 4000/10 \times 0.252 = 1590$ lb per sq in., which is much below the allowable shear.

Problems

188. Find the diameter needed for a structural-steel beam having a circular cross section if the beam is used under conditions in which it does not fail until

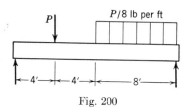

Fig. 200

general yielding starts.   The beam is shown in Fig. 200 in which $P = 3200$ lb. Consult Table 1.   Let the factor of safety $N_p = 1.8$.   *Ans.* $d = 3.63$ in.

189. Find the length t_1 of each side of the square cross section for the right half of the beam shown in Fig. 201 if the structural nickel-steel beam (see Table 1) does not fail until general yielding starts.   Assume the material has a yield point.

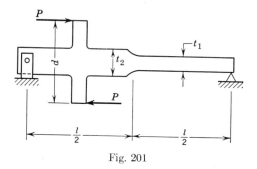

Fig. 201

Let $P = 400$ lb, $d = 10$ in., $l = 4$ ft, $t_2 = 2t_1$, radius of fillet $\rho = \frac{1}{8}$ in.   Let the factor of safety $N_p = 1.8$.

190. In Prob. 189 calculate the value for t_1 if the assumption is made that the beam is used under conditions in which failure would occur if the maximum stress in the outer fiber exceeded the elastic limit (or yield point).   Consult Tables 1 and 3.   Let the factor of safety $N_y = 1.5$.   *Ans.* $t_1 = 0.8$ in.

191. Let the beam shown in Fig. 200 be made of mild steel having a tensile and compressive yield point of 36,000 lb/in.^{2} The beam consists of a hollow cylinder with an outer diameter of 4 in. and an inner diameter of 3 in.   For this cross section the value of K in Table 4 is 1.4.   If the mode of failure of the beam would be by general yielding, find the working value of the load P for a factor of safety of $N_p = 1.8$.

192. The beam shown in Fig. 202 is made of ductile brass having a yield strength of 40,000 lb/in.^{2} (See Table 1.)   Assume $d = 3$ in., and $t = 1$ in.   Let the stress-concentration factor $k = 2.0$ for the point at the root of the groove whose radius is ρ.   Determine the maximum value for P (a) if the beam would fail when the maximum stress exceeded the yield strength, (b) if the beam would not fail until general yielding started. Consult Table 4.

Ans. (a) $P = 620$ lb; (b) $P = 1860$ lb.

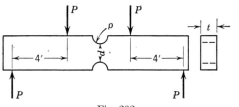

Fig. 202

193. Draw the shear and moment diagrams for the beam shown in Fig. 203. If the beam is made of timber for which the modulus of rupture is 5000 lb/in.², what should be the dimensions of the rectangular cross section, if it is assumed that the depth is twice the width. Use a factor of safety of $N_f = 5$.

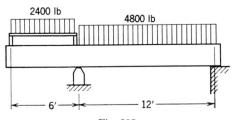

Fig. 203

194. The beam shown in Fig. 204 contains a hole 4 in. in diameter as shown, the center line of the hole lying on the neutral surface of the beam. Assume $b = 4$ in. and $h = 12$ in. If the beam is made of brittle material that fractures when the maximum tensile stress is equal to 30,000 lb/in.², which section of the beam

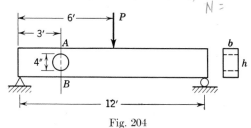

Fig. 204

is the dangerous section? Calculate the allowable or working value for P. A stress-concentration factor of $k = 2.3$ for the hole may be used.

Chapter IV

DEFLECTION OF BEAMS

59. Introduction. As noted in Art. 37, the maximum load that can be applied to a beam sometimes may be limited by an elastic deflection, beyond which the beam would not function satisfactorily under the given service conditions. This means that the stiffness, rather than the strength, of the beam is the governing condition that the beam must satisfy. Thus it is important that we find a relationship between the loads acting on a beam and the elastic deformation or deflection caused by the loads; this relationship will also include the stiffness of the material of which the beam is made (as indicated by the modulus of elasticity) and the dimensions of the beam. The general form of this relationship is expressed by the elastic-curve equation for the beam.

The Main Problem. In this chapter the main purpose is to derive the equation of the elastic curve for a beam (see Fig. 205a) and to use the equation for determining the deflection at any point of the elastic curve (especially the maximum elastic deflection) of beams of various types.

Elastic Curve Defined. The elastic curve of an originally straight beam is the curve of the longitudinal centroidal axis of the stressed beam, provided that the maximum stress in the beam does not exceed the proportional limit of the material; for beams of usual proportions and materials, this means that the deflections are small; the deflections in the subsequent figures are greatly exaggerated in order to indicate the form of the elastic curve. Since the elastic curve lies in the neutral surface of the beam, it does not change its length as the beam is bent. Furthermore, since the elastic deformations are small a differential length dl along the elastic curve of an originally horizontal straight

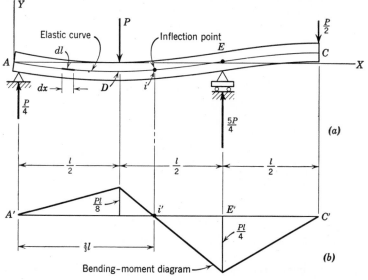

Fig. 205. General characteristics of elastic curve of beam.

beam usually may be assumed to be equal to the horizontal differential length dx (see Figs. 205, 206, and 207); and the change in slope at two points on the curve the distance dl apart may be assumed to be equal to the change in the angle $d\theta$ itself ($\tan \theta = \theta = dy/dx$). The deflection y of any point of the elastic curve and especially the maximum deflection y_{max} (Fig. 207) will be found in later articles of this chapter.

60. General features of elastic behavior of a beam. The general shape of the elastic curve of a definite beam can be determined from the bending-moment diagram. For example, let Fig. 205a represent a horizontal simply supported beam that overhangs its right-hand support; the bending-moment diagram is shown in Fig. 205b. The elastic curve of the beam is represented in Fig. 205a; the curve from A to i is concave upward since the bending moment is positive at all sections of the beam from A to i, whereas the curve is concave downward from i to C since the bending moment at all sections from i to C is negative. The point of the elastic curve at which the curvature changes from concave upward to concave downward is called the _inflection point_, and it occurs at the section of the beam for which the bending moment is equal to zero, as indicated in Fig. 205 (see Eq. 110).

Angle Change. In the solution of the main problem previously stated, it will be convenient to consider the beam to be made up of elements consisting of thin slices of length $dl = dx$. One such element is shown as $GHFE$ in Fig. 206. The bending moments M and

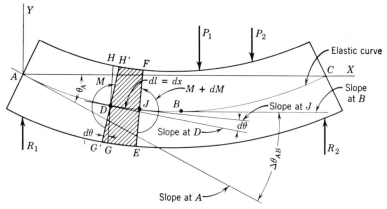

Fig. 206. Change of slope to elastic curve of beam.

$M + dM$ acting on the vertical faces of any element cause one face of the element to rotate with respect to the other face through an angle $d\theta$; the value of M, of course, varies with the position of the element in the beam. The angle change $d\theta$ is equal to the change of slope of the elastic curve in the length dl, and the change of slope $\Delta\theta$ over a finite length of the curve, as from A to B, is the summation of the angle changes in all the elements from A to B. Thus,

$$\Delta\theta_{AB} = \int_A^B d\theta \tag{106}$$

In order to determine the elastic curve of the beam we now need to find an expression for $d\theta$ in terms of M, E, I, and dx so that the integral in Eq. 106 can be evaluated.

61. Equation of elastic curve in terms of angle change. In Fig. 207 is shown a deflected beam similar to that in Fig. 206. The line HG is drawn parallel to $F'E'$ to show the angle change $d\theta$ through which $H'G'$ has rotated relative to $E'F'$. In the triangle DGG' let the elongation GG' of the extreme fiber GE' be denoted by de. Since GG' is small in comparison with the distance $c(DG)$ from the neutral axis to the extreme fiber, the angle GDG' may be obtained from the following equation

$$\text{Angle } GDG' = d\theta = de/c \qquad (107)$$

But the elongation de of the extreme fiber is equal to $\epsilon\, dl$ in which ϵ is the strain in the fiber and dl the fiber length. Furthermore, as previ-

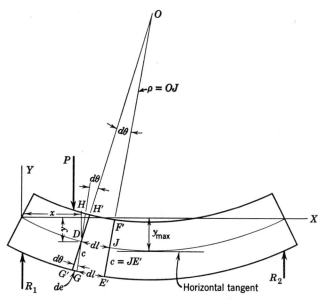

Fig. 207. Analysis of strains in beam for determining deflection of beam.

ously shown $\epsilon = \sigma/E$ and $\sigma = Mc/I$, where σ is the stress in the extreme fiber. By making these substitutions in Eq. 107, we have

$$d\theta = \frac{\epsilon\, dl}{c} = \frac{\sigma\, dl}{Ec} = \frac{\dfrac{Mc}{I}\, dl}{Ec} = \frac{M\, dl}{EI} \qquad (108)$$

in which M is the bending moment (the change dM is neglected) in the element of length dl for which the angle change is $d\theta$, I is the moment of inertia of the cross section, and E is the modulus of elasticity of the material. Equation 108 is the elastic-curve equation for the beam expressed in terms of the change in slope $d\theta$ between two tangents drawn at the ends of the element of length dl of the curve in terms of M, E, I, and dl. The expression for $d\theta$ from Eq. 108 is substituted in Eq. 106, which gives

$$\Delta\theta = \int \frac{M}{EI}\, dl \; = \; \int \frac{M}{EI}\, dx \tag{109}$$

This equation may be used to great advantage in determining the deflection of a beam, as will be seen later in this chapter; the student should become familiar with its derivation and use.

Illustrative Problems

Problem 195. A cantilever beam (Fig. 208) of length l is fixed at its right end and supports a concentrated load P at its free end. Let E be the modulus of elas-

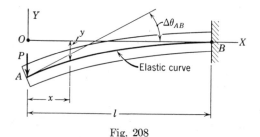

Fig. 208

ticity of the material and I the moment of inertia of the cross section. Compute the change in slope $\Delta\theta$ between the fixed end and the free end in terms of P, l, E, and I.

Solution. From Eq. 106,

$$\Delta\theta_{AB} = \int_A^B \frac{M}{EI}\, dl = \int_0^l \frac{M}{EI}\, dx$$

Since the changes in slope are assumed to be small (greatly exaggerated in Fig. 208), $dl = dx$, and the bending moment $M = -Px$. Hence,

$$\Delta\theta_{AB} = \int_0^l -\frac{Px\, dx}{EI} = -\left[\frac{Px^2}{2EI}\right]_0^l = -\frac{Pl^2}{2EI}$$

It should be noted that the slope of the beam at its fixed end does not change when the beam is loaded. For this reason the value of $\Delta\theta_{AB}$ in the foregoing equation is the actual slope at the free end of the beam.

Problem 196. A beam of constant cross section is made of an aluminum alloy (see Table 1) and is supported and loaded as shown in Fig. 209. The cross section of the beam is 2 in. wide and 8 in. deep. By making use of the sketch of the elastic curve of the beam and the bending-moment diagram, compute the following values: (a) maximum bending stress in the beam; (b) change in slope from A to B; (c) change in slope from C to B; (d) change in slope from A to C.

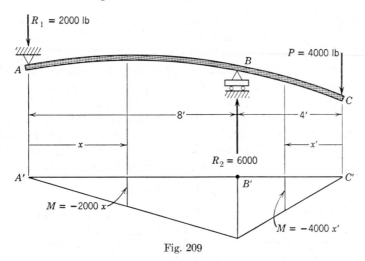

Fig. 209

Solution. (a) $I = \frac{1}{12} \times 2 \times 8^3 = 85.33$ in.^{4}

$$\therefore \quad \sigma_{\max} = \frac{M_{\max}\,c}{I} = \frac{192{,}000 \times 4}{85.33} = 9000 \text{ psi}$$

This stress is less than the proportional limit.

(b) $\quad \Delta\theta_{AB} = \int_A^B \frac{M}{EI}\,dx = \int_0^{96} -\frac{2000x}{EI}\,dx$

$$= \left[-\frac{1000\,x^2}{EI}\right]_0^{96} = \frac{-1000 \times \overline{96}^2}{10^7 \times 85.33} = -0.0108 \text{ radian}$$

(c) $\quad \Delta\theta_{CB} = \int_C^B \frac{M\,dx'}{EI} = \int_0^{48} \frac{-4000x'}{EI}\,dx$

$$= \left[\frac{-2000x'^2}{EI}\right]_0^{48} = \frac{-2000 \times \overline{48}^2}{10^7 \times 85.33} = -0.0054 \text{ radian}$$

(d) $\quad \Delta\theta_{AC} = \Delta\theta_{AB} + \Delta\theta_{CB} = -0.0162 \text{ radian}$

Problems

197. A simply supported beam carries a uniformly distributed load of w lb per unit length of the beam. Determine the change in slope of the elastic curve between the left end and the midpoint of the span, in terms of w, l, E, and I.

198. A simply supported beam with a span of 12 ft supports equal concentrated loads of 4000 lb at the third points. If the beam is made of an aluminum alloy (see Table 1) and has a rectangular cross section 3 in. wide and 6 in. deep, compute the change in slope $\Delta\theta$ between the left end and the midpoint of the span. Justify the assumption that the beam acts elastically.   *Ans.* 0.017 radian.

199. In Fig. 205 determine the change in slope between tangents drawn at the points A and D of the elastic curve in terms of P, l, E, and I.

200. In Fig. 205 determine the change in slope between tangents drawn at the points C and E of the elastic curve in terms of P, l, E, and I.

62. Elastic-curve equation in terms of radius of curvature.

Equation 108 may be interpreted in a slightly different way to derive a relationship between the radius of curvature at any point of the elastic curve and the values of M, E, and I. In Fig. 207 let O be the center of curvature of the elastic curve at section $E'F'$, and let ρ be the radius of curvature (which is assumed to be constant at each point of the length dl). From triangle OJD we may state that $dl = \rho\, d\theta$. If this value of dl is substituted in the right member of Eq. 108, we obtain

$$1/\rho = M/EI \quad \text{or} \quad \rho = EI/M \qquad (110)$$

in which ρ is the radius of curvature of the elastic curve at a section, and M, E, and I have the same meaning as in Eq. 108.

It should be recalled that, by definition, $1/\rho$ represents the curvature of the beam at the cross section where the radius of curvature is ρ. Thus Eq. 110 indicates a very important fact: namely, that the bending moment at any section of a beam (and hence also the maximum stress at the section) is directly related to the curvature at that section.

We should note also from Eq. 110 that, if a beam of constant cross section is so loaded that the bending moment M is constant over a portion of the beam, the radius of curvature of the elastic curve of this portion also will be constant (since E and I are constant), and hence the elastic curve for this portion is an arc of a circle. Conversely, if a beam is bent in an arc of a circle, the bending moments for all sections of the beam are equal. Further, the preceding equation also shows that, when M is equal to zero, ρ is equal to infinity; thus, at the inflection point (Art. 60) the center of curvature is at an infinite distance from the beam.

Problems

201. In Fig. 210 is shown a thin strip of brass (see Table 1) bent around a portion AB of a stationary cylindrical surface of radius $R = 20$ in. The dimensions

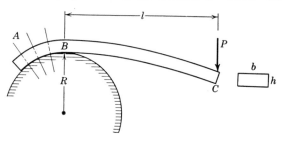

Fig. 210

of the cross section are $b = 0.5$ in. and $h = 0.05$ in. Calculate the bending moment at section B (and at all sections between A and B), and then calculate the value of P if $l = 12$ in.

202. A simple beam (Fig. 211) is composed of two rectangular bars of the same width and of the same material. The depth of the top bar is $\frac{1}{2}$ in., and that of the bottom bar is 1 in. The beam is subjected to loads causing no stress greater

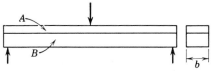

Fig. 211

than the proportional limit of the material. Compare the maximum bending stresses in the two bars. *Hint.* The radii of curvature of the two beams at any section are equal. Not EXACTLY TRUE

203. In Prob. 202 let the two bars have the same cross-sectional dimensions, but let the top beam be made of steel and the other of an aluminum alloy (see Table 1). Compare the maximum bending stresses in the two bars.

63. Elastic-curve equation in terms of rectangular coordinates.

An expression for the elastic-curve equation in terms of the rectangular coordinates x and y, where the x and y axes are as shown in Fig. 207, is obtained from Eq. 110 by expressing the radius of curvature in terms of the rectangular coordinates. This equation is (see any book on calculus)

$$\frac{1}{\rho} = \frac{d^2y/dx^2}{[1 + (dy/dx)^2]^{3/2}} \tag{111}$$

The denominator of the right side of Eq. 111 may be assumed with negligible error to be equal to unity for beams that are straight before being loaded and that are given only small deflections. For such beams the value of the slope dy/dx to the elastic curve at any point is always small compared to unity, and hence $(dy/dx)^2$ is sufficiently small to be neglected without introducing serious errors. Thus the expression in Eq. 111 becomes

$$1/\rho = d^2y/dx^2 \tag{112}$$

If the quantity $1/\rho$ is eliminated from Eqs. 110 and 112, the following equation is found

$$d^2y/dx^2 = M/EI \tag{113}$$

64. Use of elastic-curve equation for determining deflection.

Equations 108, 110, and 113 are three different expressions of the elastic-curve equation for a beam. They are alike in that each contains the term M/EI, and they differ only in the fact that this quantity M/EI is related to different variables in each equation. To summarize these facts, note that, from Eq. 108, $M/EI = d\theta/dl$; from Eq. 110, $M/EI = 1/\rho$; and, from Eq. 113, $M/EI = d^2y/dx^2$. The quantity M/EI, therefore, has special physical significance and deserves further consideration. It is, in fact, the curvature of the elastic curve (see any book on calculus), or, to state it in terms of the slope dy/dx of the elastic curve, it is the rate of change in slope of the elastic curve of the beam at the section where the bending moment is M.

We may solve Eq. 113 by using a method known as the double-integration method or by the conjugate beam method. These methods are treated in Chapters XIII and XIV, respectively, and will not be considered further in this chapter. We may solve Eqs. 108 and 110 by making use of definite integrals instead of obtaining the general solution of a differential equation. This method has the advantage of having a rather easy physical interpretation which makes possible the computation of the definite integrals by using semigraphical means. One method based on the use of Eqs. 108 and 110 is widely used and is called the moment-area method. It is derived in the following article and is used later in solving problems in this chapter.

65. Moment-area method. A convenient semigraphical interpretation and procedure, called the moment-area method,* leads to two theorems for determining the slope and deflection at any point of the elastic curve of a beam. The first step in the method involves an interpretation of Eq. 109, $\Delta\theta = \displaystyle\int \frac{M}{EI}\, dx$. For example, Fig. 212a represents a beam subjected to a distributed load; Fig. 212b represents the M/EI (curvature) diagram for the beam, any ordinate in which is the bending moment at the section where the ordinate is erected divided by EI; that is, the ordinate represents the curvature of the beam at the section if the beam is homogeneous and has a constant cross section; EI is a constant, and hence the M/EI diagram has the same form as the moment diagram.

In Fig. 212c, $CAEFBD$ represents the elastic curve of the beam, with deflections greatly exaggerated. As indicated in Fig. 212b, $M/EI\, dx$ is represented by a differential area under the M/EI diagram, as shown between the ordinates at E' and F'. But, from Eq. 108, the angle $d\theta$

---

* Sometimes this method is called the slope-deviation method. We suggest that the name *curvature-area method* be given to it, since the area referred to is always the area under the curve whose ordinate represents the curvature of the beam at the section.

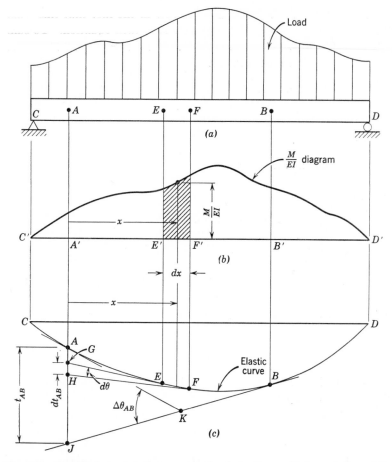

Fig. 212. Graphical constructions used in the derivation and interpretation of the moment-area method for determining deflections of beams.

between any two tangent lines GE and HF in Fig. 212c drawn at points E and F on the elastic curve, a differential distance dx apart, is equal to the quantity $(M/EI)\, dx$. Let the total change in slope between tangent lines drawn to the elastic curve at any two points such as A and B be $\Delta\theta_{AB}$. Then,

$$\Delta\theta_{AB} = \int_A^B d\theta = \int_A^B \frac{M}{EI}\, dx$$

and is represented by the total area under the M/EI diagram between the specified ordinates, such as ordinates erected at A' and B'. Therefore, the following theorem may be stated:

Theorem I. When a straight beam is subjected to bending, the difference in the slopes of the elastic curve at any two points is represented in magnitude by the area of the M/EI diagram between ordinates at the corresponding points.

A second theorem stating the procedure for determining deflections may be obtained as follows. In Fig. 212c, let t_{AB} denote the distance of any point A on the elastic curve, measured in a direction perpendicular to the original position of the beam, from a tangent drawn at any other point B on the elastic curve. The distance t_{AB} will be called the *tangential deviation* of the point. Its value is found as the summation of the distances dt_{AB} corresponding to the changes in slope over the differential distances dx between A and B. These dt_{AB} deviations are caused by the bending moments in the various dx lengths of the beam. But dt_{AB} may be considered to be equal to $x\, d\theta$, since an arc is equal to the product of the radius and the angle. Hence,

$$t_{AB} = \int dt_{AB} = \int x\, d\theta \tag{114}$$

But, as previously shown, $d\theta = (M/EI)\, dx$, and, hence,

$$t_{AB} = \int_A^B \frac{Mx}{EI}\, dx \tag{115}$$

It is very important to note that, in the preceding equations, x is the distance of any point on the elastic curve (or of any ordinate in the M/EI diagram) from the point whose tangential deviation is to be found; it is not the distance from the origin.

But, as is evident from Fig. 212b, $(Mx/EI)\, dx$ is the moment of the differential area $M\, dx/EI$ of the M/EI diagram about the ordinate through point A whose tangential deviation is t_{AB}, and hence $\int \frac{Mx}{EI}\, dx$ is the moment of that part of the M/EI diagram that lies between the two ordinates considered, the moment being taken about the ordinate through the point whose tangential deviation is desired. The following theorem therefore may be stated:

Theorem II. When a straight beam is subjected to bending, the distance t_{AB} of any point A on the elastic curve, measured normal to the original position of the beam, from a tangent drawn to the elastic curve at any other point B, is represented in magnitude by the moment of the area of the M/EI diagram between the ordinates at the two points about an ordinate through A.

Sign Convention. In many problems the sign or direction of the tangential deviation can be determined by inspection. It is helpful to note, however, that, if moments of positive areas are considered as positive, point A lies above the tangent drawn at point B for positive

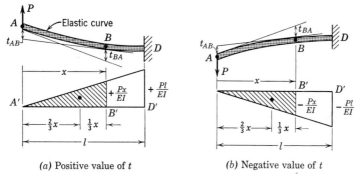

(a) Positive value of t (b) Negative value of t

Fig. 213. Method for determining sign of tangential deviation.

moments (Fig. 213a) and lies below the tangent for negative moments (Fig. 213b). For example, in Fig. 213a,

$$t_{AB} = \left(\frac{2}{3}x\right)\left(\frac{1}{2}\frac{Px^2}{EI}\right) = \frac{1}{3}\frac{Px^3}{EI}$$

and

$$t_{BA} = \left(\frac{1}{3}x\right)\left(\frac{1}{2}\frac{Px^2}{EI}\right) = \frac{1}{6}\frac{Px^3}{EI}$$

Note that t_{AB} is not equal to t_{BA}. In Fig. 213b,

$$t_{AB} = \left(\frac{2}{3}x\right)\left(-\frac{1}{2}\frac{Px^2}{EI}\right) = -\frac{1}{3}\frac{Px^3}{EI}$$

and

$$t_{BA} = \left(\frac{1}{3}x\right)\left(-\frac{1}{2}\frac{Px^2}{EI}\right) = -\frac{1}{6}\frac{Px^3}{EI}$$

Furthermore, in solving Eq. 115 mathematically for t_{AB}, if it is assumed that the y axis is positive upward, t_{AB} will be positive when point A is above the tangent at B and negative when A is below the tangent at B. If the y axis is chosen positive downward, Eq. 115 should be written

$$t_{AB} = -\int_A^B \frac{Mx}{EI}\,dx$$

Applications of Moment-area Method

66. Cantilever beam; concentrated load at free end. In Fig. 214, AB represents the elastic curve of the beam, and $A'B'H$ represents the M/EI diagram. The beam is assumed to have a constant cross section, and the weight of the beam is neglected.

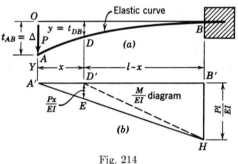

Fig. 214

Maximum Deflection. The maximum deflection of the beam may be found as follows. The tangential deviation t_{AB} of A from a tangent drawn at B is equal to the maximum deflection Δ of the cantilever beam (it will be seen later that the tangential deviation is not always equal to the deflection). Thus, from Theorem II, the magnitude of Δ is

$$\Delta = t_{AB} = \text{moment of area } A'B'H \text{ about ordinate through } A'$$

$$= \text{area } A'B'H \text{ times distance to centroid}$$

$$= \frac{1}{2}\frac{Pl^2}{EI} \cdot \frac{2}{3}l = \frac{1}{3}\frac{Pl^3}{EI} \tag{116}$$

Deflection of Any Point. The deflection y of a point D at the distance x from the free end may be found as follows: The tangential deviation t_{DB} of D from a tangent at B is equal to y; thus, if we use Theorem II,

$$y = t_{DB} = \text{moment of area } B'D'EH \text{ about } D'E$$

Let the area $B'D'EH$ (Fig. 214b) be divided into two triangular areas as indicated by the dotted line. Then,

$$y = t_{DB} = \frac{Px}{2EI} \cdot \frac{(l-x)^2}{3} + \frac{Pl}{2EI} \cdot \frac{2}{3}(l-x)^2$$

Hence,

$$6EIy = P(x^3 - 3l^2x + 2l^3) \qquad (117)$$

which is the elastic-curve equation for the beam.

Illustrative Problem

Problem 204. A 10-in., 40-lb-per-ft steel I beam is used as a horizontal canti-lever beam (Fig. 215). The beam supports a uniformly distributed load of 200

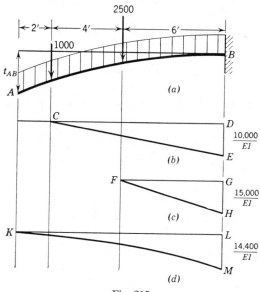

Fig. 215

lb per ft, including the beam weight, and two concentrated loads; one load of 1000 lb acts 2 ft from the free end and the other of 2500 lb acts at the midpoint. Compute the maximum bending stress and the maximum deflection of the beam.

Solution. From Table A in Appendix II, we find $I = 158$ in.[4] The maximum bending moment, including the weight of the beam, is 39,400 lb-in. Hence, the maximum bending stress is

$$\sigma_{max} = \frac{39,400 \times 12 \times 5}{158} = 15,000 \text{ lb/in.}^2$$

The M/EI diagram for the beam is given in three parts (see Chap. III) as shown in Fig. 215b, c, and d, where part b is for the 1000-lb load, part c is for the 2500-lb load, and part d is for the distributed load. Figure 215d is a parabola that is tangent to the line KL at K. Its area and centroidal distances are discussed in Appendix I. By using Theorem II, the magnitude of the maximum deflection Δ is found to be

$\Delta = t_{AB}$ = sum of moments of areas CDE, FGH, and KLM about ordinate through A

$$= \frac{1}{2} 10 \left(\frac{10,000}{EI}\right)\left(2 + \frac{20}{3}\right) + \frac{1}{2} 6 \left(\frac{15,000}{EI}\right)(6 + 4) + \frac{1}{3} 12 \left(\frac{14,400}{EI}\right)\left(\frac{3}{4}\right) 12$$

$$= \frac{1,398,000}{EI}$$

$E = 30 \times 10^6$ lb/in.^{2}, and $I = 158$ in.^{4}, in which the length units are inches. In obtaining the foregoing result for the deflection, the length units were feet. Hence the numerator quantity 1,390,000 is in lb-ft^3. To keep the units consistent, we must therefore multiply the numerator by the quantity $12^3 = 1728$ to convert the units to lb-in.^{3} Hence,

$$\Delta = \frac{1,398,000 \times 12^3}{30 \times 10^6 \times 158} = 0.51 \text{ in.}$$

Problems

205. A horizontal cantilever beam of constant cross section supports a uniformly distributed load of w lb per ft over its entire length l (Fig. 216a). The

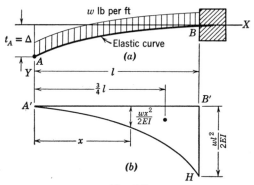

Fig. 216

M/EI diagram is shown in Fig. 216b. Determine the maximum deflection of the beam in terms of w, l, E, and I.   *Ans.* $\Delta = \frac{1}{8}wl^4/EI = \frac{1}{8}Wl^3/EI$.

206. A horizontal cantilever beam of constant cross section supports a uni-

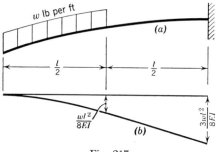

Fig. 217

formly distributed load over one-half its length, as shown in Fig. 217a. The M/EI diagram is shown in Fig. 217b. Determine the maximum deflection of the beam in terms of w, l, E, and I.

207. A vertical cantilever beam is subjected to a bending couple M_0 at its free end, as shown in Fig. 218. Determine the deflection Δ at the free end in terms of M_0, l, E, and I.

$Ans.$ $M_0 l^2/2EI.$

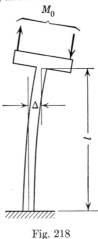

Fig. 218

208. A yellow-pine timber member is used as a horizontal cantilever beam with a span of 10 ft and loaded as shown in Fig. 219. The depth of the rectangular section is 12 in., and its width is 6 in. Determine the maximum value of P if the

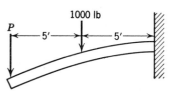

Fig. 219

deflection of the beam at the free end must not exceed 0.4 in. Do these loads cause the maximum bending stress to exceed the elastic limit of the material? Neglect the weight of the beam.

$Ans.$ $P = 770$ lb.

209. Determine the deflection at the left end of the beam shown in Fig. 220a, which is a fix-ended beam subjected to a bending couple and a concentrated load at each end, as shown in Fig. 220b. The known quantities are P, M_0, E, and I.

$Ans.$ $\Delta = \frac{1}{2}M_0 l^2/EI - \frac{1}{3}Pl^3/EI.$

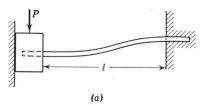

(a)

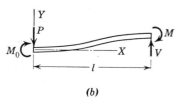

(b)

Fig. 220. Deflection of a beam subjected to a concentrated load and a bending couple at each end.

210. Find the slope of the midpoint B of the beam shown in Fig. 221, and the deflection of the free end A in terms of w, l, E, and I.

$Ans.$ $\theta_B = wl^3/48EI$; $\Delta = -0.0182wl^4/EI.$

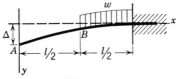

Fig. 221

211. A light pointer AB (Fig. 222) is attached at A to a cantilever beam that supports a concentrated load P at A. Determine the vertical and horizontal deflections Δ_v and Δ_H of the end B of the pointer.

$$Ans. \quad \Delta_v = \tfrac{1}{3}Pl^3/EI; \; \Delta_H = Pl^3/4EI.$$

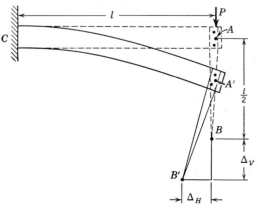

Fig. 222

212. A cantilever beam has a rectangular cross section of constant width b and of varying depth as shown by the taper in Fig. 223. Show that the value of M/EI at any distance x from the load is $3P/2Ebx^2 \tan^3 \theta$ and that the deflection of the point A (a short distance a from the load P) is $\Delta_A = \dfrac{3P \log (l/a)}{2Eb \tan^3 \theta}$.

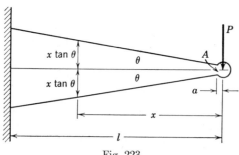

Fig. 223

67. Simple beam; concentrated load at midspan. The beam is shown in Fig. 224a; the weight of the beam is assumed to be negligible. Figure 224b shows the M/EI diagram; the dangerous section is at the midspan; the maximum bending moment is $Pl/4$, and the bending moment at a section the distance x from the left support is $(P/2)x$. Since the beam is assumed to be homogeneous and to have a constant cross section, the M/EI diagram has the same form as the moment diagram. In Fig. 224c, ACB represents the elastic curve of the beam.

Slope at End of Beam. The slopes of the elastic curve at certain points are frequently of importance. In Fig. 224 let it be required to find the slope at the left-hand end of the beam (at A). The difference or change in slopes at the end and midspan (at A and C) in Fig. 224

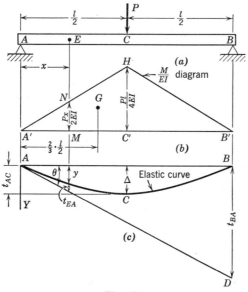

Fig. 224

is equal to the slope at A since the slope at C is zero. Thus, in accordance with Theorem I, we obtain, by use of Fig. 224,

$$\text{Slope at } A = \text{area of } A'C'H = \frac{1}{2} \cdot \frac{Pl}{4EI} \cdot \frac{l}{2} = \frac{1}{16} \frac{Pl^2}{EI}$$

This result could also be obtained directly by the integration of Eq. 109 for values of x between 0 and $l/2$. Thus, noting that $M = \frac{1}{2}Px$ and that EI is a constant for the conditions specified, we find

$$\text{Slope at } A = \Delta\theta_{AC} = \theta_C - \theta_A = \int_A^C \frac{M}{EI} \, dx$$

$$= \int_0^{l/2} \frac{Px}{2EI} \, dx = \frac{1}{4} \frac{P(l/2)^2}{EI} = \frac{1}{16} \frac{Pl^2}{EI}$$

Maximum Deflection. Let it be required to find the maximum deflection Δ, which occurs at the center of the span. The tangential deviation of the point A from a tangent at C is t_{AC} (Fig. 224c), which is equal in magnitude to Δ, and which may be found from Theorem II.

Thus, the magnitude of Δ is

$\Delta = t_{AC}$ = moment of area $A'C'H$ about ordinate through A'

= area $A'C'H$ times distance to centroid G of area $A'C'H$ from ordinate through A'

$$= \frac{1}{2}\frac{Pl}{4EI}\frac{l}{2} \cdot \frac{2}{3}\frac{l}{2} = \frac{Pl^3}{48EI}$$

The value of Δ also could be found directly by the integration of Eq. 115: namely, $t_{AC} = \int_A^C \frac{Mx}{EI}\, dx$, in which x is measured from the point A, whose tangential deviation t_{AC} is desired. Thus,

$$\Delta = t_{AC} = \int_0^{l/2} \frac{Mx}{EI}\, dx = \frac{1}{EI}\int_0^{l/2} \frac{P}{2}x^2\, dx = \frac{1}{48}\frac{Pl^3}{EI} \qquad (118)$$

Deflection at Any Section. Next let it be required to find the equation of the elastic curve of the beam in Fig. 224; in other words, let it be required to find the deflection y of a point E (Fig. 224a) at any distance x from the left support when x is not greater than $l/2$. If a tangent AD is drawn to the elastic curve at A, t_{BA} is the tangential deviation of B, and t_{EA} is the tangential deviation of the point E. From the geometry of the figure,

$$\frac{y + t_{EA}}{t_{BA}} = \frac{x}{l} \quad \text{or} \quad y = t_{BA}\frac{x}{l} - t_{EA}$$

and, since the slopes of the elastic curve are small, $\theta = t_{BA}/l$. Therefore,

$$y = \theta x - t_{EA}$$

in which θ as found in the foregoing paragraph is $\theta = \frac{1}{16}Pl^2/EI$. Hence, according to Theorem II, we obtain

$$t_{EA} = \text{moment of area } A'MN \text{ about } MN$$

$$= \frac{1}{2}\frac{Px}{EI}\cdot\frac{x}{2}\cdot\frac{x}{3} = \frac{Px^3}{12EI}$$

Therefore.

$$y = \frac{Pl^2x}{16EI} - \frac{Px^3}{12EI}$$

or

$$48EIy = Px(3l^2 - 4x^2) \qquad (119)$$

which is the elastic-curve equation for the left half of the beam.

68. Simple beam; cross section not constant. Let a concentrated load P act at the center of a simply supported beam as indicated in Fig. 225a, and let the moment of inertia of each cross section in the central half of the beam be I and for each section in the outer quarters $I/2$. The M/EI diagram is shown in Fig. 225b. Let it be required to determine Δ, the maximum deflection of the beam.

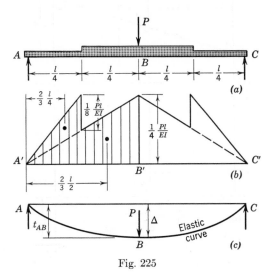

Fig. 225

By using Theorem II in connection with Fig. 225, the magnitude of the maximum deflection shown in Fig. 225c may be found as follows:

$\Delta = t_{AB}$ = moment about A' of shaded area of M/EI diagram

$$= \frac{1}{2}\frac{1}{4}\frac{Pl}{EI}\frac{l}{2}\cdot\frac{2}{3}\frac{l}{2} + \frac{1}{2}\frac{Pl}{8EI}\frac{l}{4}\cdot\frac{2}{3}\frac{l}{4}$$

$$= \frac{Pl^3}{48EI} + \frac{Pl^3}{384EI} = \frac{9}{384}\frac{Pl^3}{EI} = \frac{3}{128}\frac{Pl^3}{EI} \tag{120}$$

69. Simple beam; concentrated load not at midspan. In Fig. 226a is shown such a beam with the load P at a distance kl from the right support; k will be assumed to be less than $\frac{1}{2}$. The maximum moment is at the load point; its value is $M_{\max} = Pkl(1 - k)$. At any point E to the left of the load at the distance x from the left support, the moment is $M = kPx$. Let it be required to find the deflection at the point E. If a tangent AD is drawn (Fig. 226d) to the elastic curve

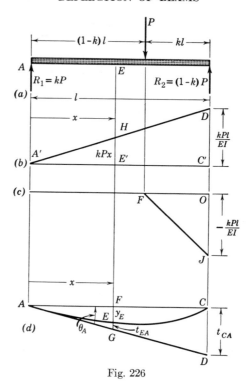

Fig. 226

at A, t_{CA} is the tangential deviation of C, and t_{EA} is the tangential deviation of the point E. From the geometry of the figure,

$$y_E = FG - EG = \theta_A x - t_{EA} = \frac{t_{CA}}{l}\, x - t_{EA}$$

But t_{EA} and t_{CA} are found from Theorem II as follows (see Fig. 226b and c which represent the M/EI diagram by the method of parts):

t_{EA} = moment of area $A'E'H$ about HE'

$$= \frac{1}{2}\frac{k}{EI}\frac{Px^2}{EI}\left(\frac{x}{3}\right)$$

t_{CA} = moment of area $A'DC'$ about $C'D$ − moment of area FOJ about OJ

$$= \frac{kPl^2}{2EI}\frac{l}{3} - \frac{Pk^2l^2}{2EI}\frac{1}{3}(kl) = \frac{Pkl^3}{6EI}(1 - k^2)$$

Therefore, by substituting these values of t_{EA} and t_{CA} into the equation for y_E, we get

$$y_E = \frac{Pkl^2(1-k^2)}{6EI}\,x - \frac{Pk}{6EI}\,x^3 \tag{121}$$

Maximum Deflection. We obtain the maximum deflection by equating the first derivative of y_E with respect to x to zero and solving this equation for the value of x. Let x_1 represent this value of x which makes $dy_E/dx = 0$, and hence is the value that gives the maximum value for y_E. It is found to be

$$x_1 = l\sqrt{(1-k^2)/3}$$

By substituting this value of x_1 into Eq. 121, we find

$$y_{E\max} = \frac{Pkl^3}{3EI}\left(\frac{1-k^2}{3}\right)^{3/2} \tag{122}$$

Approximate Location of Maximum Deflection. It is not always as easy to locate the section of the beam at which the maximum deflection occurs as it was for the beam in Fig. 226, especially for more complex loading. A close approximation to the maximum deflection can be obtained, however, from inspection of the sketch of the elastic curve and making an estimate of the distance to the section where the maximum deflection occurs. For example, let us assume (guess) that the maximum deflection of the beam in Fig. 226 occurs at the midpoint, no matter where the concentrated load is located. The maximum error in the deflection obtained by the foregoing assumption is only 2.6 per cent. In most of the problems that follow, the location of the section of maximum deflection may be estimated without introducing serious errors.   *do not assume the Tangent to be Horizontal at the assumed point*

Illustrative Problem

Problem 213. A simply supported horizontal beam is loaded as shown in Fig. 227a. The beam is a 9-in. 10.68-lb aluminum alloy I beam. The value of $E = 10^7$ lb/in.^{2}, and $I = 102.3$ in.^{4} Compute the maximum elastic deflection of the beam by assuming that it occurs at the point B which is 9 ft from the left end.

Solution. As shown in Fig. 227b, the deflection y_B at B is

$$y_B = DE - t_{BA} = 9\theta_A - t_{BA}$$

The value of θ_A is found from triangle ACF by making use of the fact that $\theta_A = t_{CA}/l = t_{CA}/20$. Thus $y_B = (9t_{CA}/20) - t_{BA}$.

By using Theorem II, we compute the values of t_{CA} and t_{BA} and then substitute these values in the foregoing equation. The M/EI diagram for the beam is con-

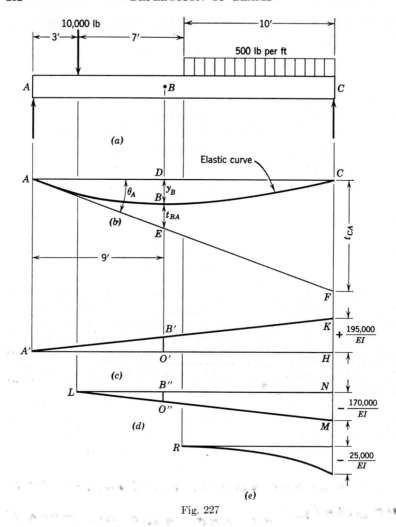

Fig. 227

structed in separate parts as shown in Fig. 227c, d, and e, where part c is for the left reaction, part d is for the concentrated load, and part e is for the distributed load.

t_{CA} = sum of moments about ordinate through C of areas $A'HK$, LMN, and in Fig. 227e

$$= \frac{20}{2}\left(\frac{195,000}{EI}\right)\frac{20}{3} - \frac{17}{2}\left(\frac{170,000}{EI}\right)\frac{17}{3} - \frac{10}{3}\left(\frac{25,000}{EI}\right)\frac{10}{4}$$

$$= +\frac{4,590,000}{EI}$$

t_{BA} = sum of moments about ordinate through B of areas $A'B'O'$ and $LB''O''$, if B is between 3 and 10 ft from the left end.

$$= \frac{9}{2}\left(\frac{9750 \times 9}{EI}\right)\frac{9}{3} - \frac{(9-3)}{2}\left[\frac{10{,}000(9-3)}{EI}\right]\frac{(9-3)}{3} = \frac{723{,}000}{EI}$$

$$y_B = \left(\frac{9}{20}\right)\left(\frac{4{,}590{,}000}{EI}\right) - \frac{723{,}000}{EI} = \frac{1{,}240{,}000}{EI}$$

When the values of E and I are substituted in this equation, and the factor 12^3 is multiplied into the numerator (see solution of Prob. 204), the result is

$$\Delta = \max y_B = \frac{1{,}240{,}000 \times 12^3}{10^7 \times 102.3} = 2.09 \text{ in.}$$

The maximum bending moment is 29,500 lb-ft. Therefore, the maximum bending stress is

$$\sigma_{\max} = \frac{29{,}500 \times 12 \times 4.5}{102.3} = 15{,}600 \text{ lb/in.}^2$$

This stress is less than the elastic limit of the aluminum alloy. (See Table 1.)

Problems

214. By making use of Fig. 228, show that the maximum elastic deflection of the beam of constant cross section is $\Delta = \dfrac{5}{384}\dfrac{wl^4}{EI}$.

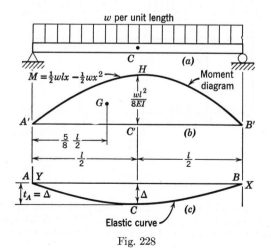

Fig. 228

215. Determine the elastic deflection of the point B of the beam of constant cross section shown in Fig. 229, in terms of P, l, a, E, and I.

$$Ans. \quad \Delta = \frac{Pa^2}{6EIl}(l - 2a)^2.$$

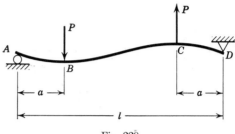

Fig. 229

216. A beam is 20 ft long and is simply supported at one end and at the middle. It carries a uniformly distributed load of 400 lb per ft between the supports. What will be the elastic deflection of the free end of the beam if the beam is made of steel and has a circular cross section 4 in. in diameter?

217. A 10-in. 40-lb steel I beam is used as a simple beam on a span l of 16 ft. A concentrated load P of 14,000 lb is applied at a point $l/4$ from the right support. If the beam acts elastically, determine the maximum deflection of the beam, assuming that it occurs at the middle of the beam.   *Ans.*   0.30 in.

218. Draw the moment diagram for the beam shown in Fig. 230, and determine the value of the elastic deflection Δ at the center of the beam. Also find the value of the slope of the elastic curve over the left support.

$$Ans. \quad \Delta = -\frac{5}{384}\frac{wl^4}{EI} + \frac{1}{16}\frac{wl^2a^2}{EI}.$$

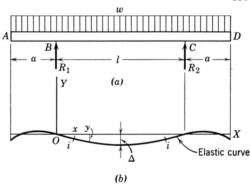

Fig. 230

219. A timber beam having a rectangular cross section 6 in. wide by 8 in. deep is used as a simple beam on a span of 15 ft. A load P of 600 lb is applied at a section 5 ft from the left support, and a uniformly distributed load of 80 lb per ft, including the weight of the beam, is applied over the entire length. Calculate the elastic deflection at the section beneath the concentrated load. Assume $E = 10^6$ lb/in.^{2} *Ans.* $y = 0.53$ in.

220. Calculate the maximum elastic deflection of a steel shaft 4 in. in diameter used as a simple beam on a span of 10 ft, to support a uniformly distributed load (including the weight of the beam) that causes a maximum bending stress of 16,000 lb per sq in.   *Ans.*   0.4 in.

221. A beam (Fig. 231) is simply supported at its quarter points and is subjected to a concentrated load P at its center and to bending couples each equal to $Pl/32$

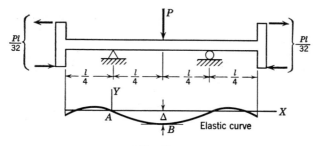

Fig. 231

at the free ends as shown. Find the slope to the elastic curve at point A, and the deflection Δ at the center in terms of P, l, E, and I.

222. A light pointer AB (Fig. 232) is attached at A, by two nails a short distance apart, to a simple beam that supports concentrated loads P at the quarter points.

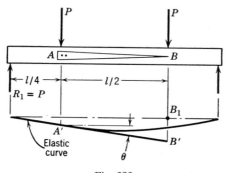

Fig. 232

If the beam acts elastically, determine the slope (tan θ) of the pointer $A'B'$ and the deflection B_1B' of the end B of the pointer in terms of P, l, E, and I.

$$Ans. \quad \tan \theta = \frac{1}{16} \frac{Pl^2}{EI} \; ; \; B_1B' = \frac{5}{96} \frac{Pl^3}{EI}.$$

223. A light pointer AB (Fig. 233) is attached at A to a simple beam by two nails a short distance apart. Determine the total deflection B_1B' of the end of the pointer in terms of P, l, E, and I. Assume that the beam acts elastically.

Ans. $Pl^3/32EI$.

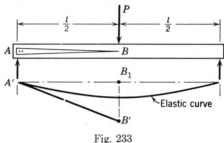

Fig. 233

224. Find the slope to the elastic curve at the left end of the beam shown in Fig. 234. The known quantities are P, w, l, E, and I.

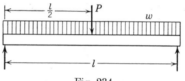

Fig. 234

225. Calculate the maximum elastic deflection of the beam shown in Fig. 234, assuming that the beam is made of steel and that the cross section is rectangular, 2 in. wide, and 6 in. deep. Assume also that $P = 3000$ lb, $w = 100$ lb/ft, and $l = 10$ ft.

226. A beam (Fig. 235) is fixed at one end and is subjected to a bending couple M_0 at the free end. Find the deflection of the free end in terms of M_0, l, E, and I. Neglect the weight of the beam and assume that the beam acts elastically.

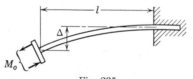

Fig. 235

227. The horizontal beam of length $3l/2$ shown in Fig. 236 overhangs its right support. The beam is subjected to a vertical load P at its right end. Determine the elastic deflection Δ at the load P. *Ans.* $\Delta = Pl^3/8EI$.

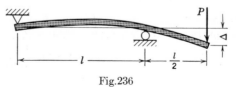

Fig.236

228. A flat plate in the shape of an isosceles triangle ABC (see Fig. 237a) is used as a cantilever beam with side AB fixed and vertex C the free end. A concentrated load P is applied at C perpendicular to the plane ABC. Show that the M/EI diagram for the beam is a rectangle as indicated in Fig. 237b and that the deflection at the load is $\Delta = 3Pl^2/(Ed^3 \tan \theta)$.

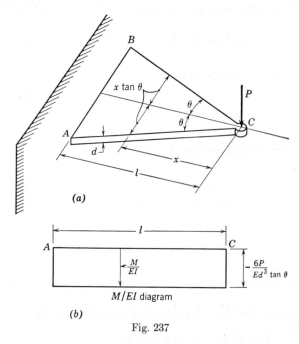

(a)

(b)

M/EI diagram

Fig. 237

70. Relationship between maximum deflection and maximum stress.

It will be well at this point to summarize some of the results obtained in this and the preceding chapter and to call attention to the relationship between the maximum bending moment (and hence the maximum elastic stress) and the maximum elastic deflection for a beam. Such a summary may be convenient for use in the design of a beam to resist elastic deflection.

In Table 5, W is the total load on the beam having a span l, E is the modulus of elasticity of the material, and I is the moment of inertia of the cross section of the beam about the centroidal axis, the cross section being assumed constant.

Tables similar to Table 5 for additional types of beam and of loading may be found in various handbooks dealing with load resisting members, such as Steel Construction, American Institute of Steel Construction, and the Aluminum Company of America Structural Handbook.

TABLE 5

Type of Beam and of Loading	Maximum Bending Moment, M	Maximum Deflection
Cantilever, load at end	$1Wl$	$\dfrac{1}{3}\dfrac{Wl^3}{EI}$
Cantilever, uniform load	$\dfrac{1}{2}Wl$	$\dfrac{1}{8}\dfrac{Wl^3}{EI}$
Simple beam, load at center	$\dfrac{1}{4}Wl$	$\dfrac{1}{48}\dfrac{Wl^3}{EI}$
Simple beam, uniform load	$\dfrac{1}{8}Wl$	$\dfrac{5}{384}\dfrac{Wl^3}{EI}$

It is seen from this table that, for a cantilever or simple beam subjected to any type of static loading, general expressions for M and Δ may be written as follows:

$$M = \alpha W l, \qquad \Delta = \beta \frac{Wl^3}{EI}$$

in which α and β are constants depending on the type of beam and of loading.

If W is eliminated from the preceding general expressions, the result is $\Delta = \dfrac{\beta}{\alpha}\dfrac{Ml^2}{EI}$. But $M = \dfrac{\sigma I}{c}$, and, hence,

$$\Delta = \frac{\beta}{\alpha}\frac{\sigma}{E} \times \frac{l^2}{c} \tag{123}$$

One way of interpreting this equation is as follows: If several beams, each having a constant cross section, are of the same type, are made of the same material, and are subjected to the same type of loading (in other words, if $\beta/\alpha E$ = a constant), then the deflections of the beams will vary directly with the maximum stress, with the square of the spans, and inversely with the distances from the neutral axis to the most remote fibers.

Design of a Beam. Thus if a beam is to be designed to resist a specified maximum elastic deflection, it is possible to limit the maximum deflection of a beam by the choice of a maximum value of the bending stress. For example, let a simply supported 10″, 30-lb steel I beam of 15-ft span length be subjected to a uniformly distributed load. For this beam Eq. 123 becomes, when values of α, β, E, l, and c are substituted,

$$\Delta_{max} = \frac{225}{10^7}\, \sigma_{max} \tag{124}$$

Illustrative Problem

Problem 229. A beam is simply supported at its ends and is subjected to a uniformly distributed load. The beam is made of steel and is 12 in. deep. It is specified that the maximum elastic deflection of the beam must not exceed 1/360 of the length l and that the maximum elastic tensile or compressive bending stress must not exceed 20,000 lb per sq in.; determine the maximum length l that the beam may have and still satisfy both the foregoing conditions.

Solution. From Eq. 123, we have

$$\frac{l}{360} = \left(\frac{\frac{5}{384}}{\frac{1}{8}}\right) \frac{20,000}{30 \times 10^6} \frac{l^2}{6}$$

Therefore, $l = 240$ in. $= 20$ ft.

Problems

230. If the beam in Prob. 229 must be 24 ft in length and 12 in. in depth, determine the maximum elastic tensile or compressive bending stress if it is assumed that the deflection must not exceed 1/360 of its length. *Ans.* 16,660 lb/in.[2]

231. A cantilever beam to be subjected to a concentrated load at its free end must be made so that the following conditions are fulfilled: The length must be 2 ft, the depth must be 3 in., the elastic deflection must not exceed 0.3 in., and the maximum tensile or compressive bending stress must not exceed 20,000 lb per sq in. Can the beam be made of a magnesium alloy? aluminum alloy? (See Table 1.)

232. If the length and depth of a beam made of steel are given, can the maximum elastic deflection be controlled (limited to a specified amount) by choosing a limiting value of the maximum tensile or compressive bending stress? *Hint.* Use Eq. 123.

71. Deflection of beam due to shear. The deflection of a beam due to the shearing stresses in the beam was assumed, in the preceding discussions, to be negligible. In relatively short deep beams, however, the deflection due to shear may require consideration. An approximate value for the deflection due to the shearing stresses may be found as follows:

The shearing deformation dy_τ of a small block, of length dx in the beam (Fig. 238) is

$$dy_\tau = \gamma\, dx = \frac{\tau}{G}\, dx$$

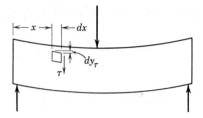

Fig. 238. Deflection of beam resulting from shearing deformation.

in which τ is the shearing stress on the face of the block; the deflection
of a fiber of length x (Fig. 238) is

$$y_\tau = \frac{1}{G} \int_0^x \tau \, dx \qquad (125)$$

If τ is constant throughout the length of all the fibers (as in Fig. 238),
the deflection of the beam at a section x distance from the end is

$$y_\tau = \frac{\tau x}{G} \qquad (126)$$

In general, however, τ varies over the section, but, if an average
value of τ (see Art. 49) is used in Eq. 125, an approximate value of the
deflection due to shear may be found which may be helpful in estimat-
ing to what extent the shearing stresses contribute to the deflection of
a beam.

A more exact analysis may be made by substituting for τ in Eq. 124
the value given by the equations in Art. 48.

Since the average shearing stress $\tau = V/a$, Eq. 125 may be
written

$$y_\tau = \frac{Vx}{aG} = \frac{M}{aG} \qquad (127)$$

where M is the bending moment at the distance x of any section between the end and the center of the beam in Fig. 238.

Chapter V

COMBINED AXIAL TENSILE
AND BENDING LOADS

72. Introduction. In the preceding chapters, stresses caused by static axial, torsional, and bending loads were found when a member was subjected to each one of these types of loads acting alone. Members of many structures and machines, however, are subjected to loads of two or more of these types. If the behavior or response of the member is wholly elastic, the stress developed at any point on a cross section of the member frequently may be found by assuming that the loads act independently—hence, each load is assumed to produce the same stress that it would produce if it were the only load acting on the member. For the loads treated in this chapter these stresses then may be added algebraically to obtain the actual stress. This principle, called the principle of superposition, is applicable if the member acts elastically, and it will be used here in determining the normal stress at a point on a cross section of the member when the member is subjected to combined axial tensile and bending loads.

It should be observed that an axial *compression* load combined with bending loads is not considered in this chapter; this combination of loads presents a problem quite different from the one involving combined *tension* and bending. In the next chapter (Chap. VI), the load-carrying capacity of a member subjected to a *compressive* axial load *alone* will be found, and the combined effect of an axial compressive load and a bending load will be treated. The failure under compressive loading usually is by buckling (involving unstable equilibrium).

Mode of Failure. A member subjected to combined tension and bending loads may fail in any one of the several ways that a beam subjected to bending alone may fail, as discussed in Art. 54. It is essential, therefore, that a relation between loads and stresses in the member be found (1) for elastic behavior of the member, (2) for inelastic behavior, and (3) for fracture (especially for brittle material). After the foregoing stress analyses are made, they may be used as a basis for design, as has been done in the first three chapters. The so-called elastic stresses will be found first.

§ 1   Elastic Behavior

73. A beam subjected to an axial tensile load. In Fig. 239a is represented a simple beam of length l ft subjected to transverse bend-

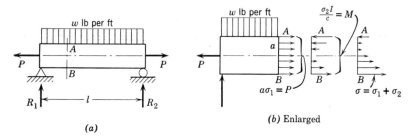

(a)

(b) Enlarged

Fig. 239.   Stresses in beam subjected to combined axial tension and bending.

ing loads consisting of a uniformly distributed load wl and the reactions R_1 and R_2; in addition axial tensile loads P, P are applied at its ends. It is assumed that all the conditions that are required to make the flexure formula applicable are satisfied. (See Art. 38.) Let it be required to find the maximum normal stress on a transverse cross section of the beam.

The maximum normal stress will occur at the midsection, since the stress due to the transverse bending loads is a maximum at the midsection, and the direct stress caused by P is the same for all sections except near the ends where the concentrated loads are applied. The deflection of the beam is neglected in the following analysis; for, the elastic deflections of beams of ordinary proportions are small, and the axial *tensile* load decreases the deflection caused by the transverse bending loads. As indicated in Fig 239b, if P were the only force acting, the stress would be uniformly distributed on the cross-sectional area a, the stress at any point in the area being σ_1. The (internal) force acting on the area a would be $a\sigma_1$ and would be equal and opposite to P since it would hold P in equilibrium. Hence,

$$P = a\sigma_1 \quad \text{or} \quad \sigma_1 = \frac{P}{a}$$

If, on the other hand, the bending loads were the only forces acting, the bending moment M at the midsection would develop the resisting moment $\sigma_2 I/c$, as shown in Fig. 239b, the fiber stress σ_2 varying directly as the distance of the fiber from the neutral axis, provided that its value does not exceed the proportional limit of the material. And, since the resisting moment holds the bending moment in equilibrium, the two moments are numerically equal. Hence,

$$M = \frac{\sigma_2 I}{c} \quad \text{or} \quad \sigma_2 = \frac{Mc}{I}$$

The normal elastic stress at any point of the midsection then, according to the principle of superposition, is the algebraic sum of the stresses caused by the loads acting separately; the maximum stress is a tensile stress and occurs on the bottom fiber; its value is

$$\sigma = \sigma_1 + \sigma_2 = \frac{P}{a} + \frac{Mc}{I} \tag{128}$$

The stress on the top fiber may be either tensile or compressive depending on whether σ_2 is larger or smaller than σ_1. As shown in Fig. 239b, σ_2 is larger than σ_1; therefore the stress on the top fiber is a compressive stress, and the surface of zero fiber stress (neutral surface) is located between the centroidal plane and the top fiber. *Note.* The solution of the following problem illustrates the use of the foregoing equations; all the problems given after the next article may be solved at this point by using directly the equations developed in this article, without employing the interaction curve developed in the next article, although the interaction curve is a convenient tool.

Illustrative Problem

Problem 233. The machine member shown in Fig. 240a is acted on by a force P of 3000 lb. Find the maximum normal stress on the rectangular area at section AB. The dimensions of the cross section of the bar at section AB are $b = \frac{3}{4}$ in. and $2c = 3$ in.

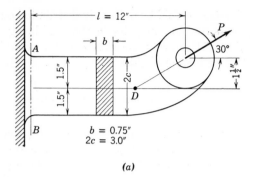

(a)

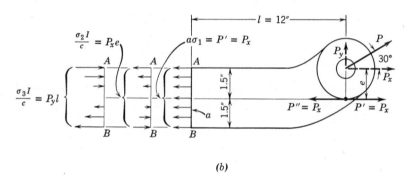

(b)

Fig. 240. Stress in beam subjected to combined axial tension and bending.

Solution. The load P may be resolved in two components: a cross-bending load P_y and a longitudinal eccentric load P_x (Fig. 240b); and P_x may be resolved further into a central or axial load P' and a couple having a moment $P_x e$, by the introduction of the two equal opposite and collinear forces P' and P'', each equal to P_x, as indicated in Fig. 240b.

Since P' is an axial load, it would, if acting alone, cause and be held in equilibrium by an internal force $a\sigma_1$, the stress σ_1 being constant over the area a of the section as indicated in Fig. 240b. The couple $P_x e$, if acting alone, would develop a resisting moment $\sigma_2 I/c$ equal to the moment $P_x e$ of the couple, as shown in Fig. 240b. Likewise, the cross-bending load P_y would develop a resisting moment $\sigma_3 I/c$ equal to the moment $P_y l$. The shearing stress on the area is of minor importance and is neglected in this discussion. Also, the stress concentration at A and B is neglected.

The normal stress, on the top fiber at A, then, is

$$\sigma_A = +\sigma_1 + \sigma_2 - \sigma_3$$

$$= +\frac{P\cos 30°}{2.25} + \frac{P\cos 30° \cdot 1.5 \cdot 1.5}{\frac{1}{12}\frac{3}{4}(3)^3} - \frac{P\sin 30° \cdot 12 \cdot 1.5}{\frac{1}{12}\frac{3}{4}(3)^3}$$

$$= \frac{2600}{2.25} + \frac{2600 \cdot 2.25}{1.69} - \frac{1500 \cdot 18}{1.69}$$

$$= +1150 + 3460 - 16{,}000$$

$$= -11{,}390 \text{ lb per sq in. compressive stress}$$

And at B the stress is

$$\sigma_B = +\sigma_1 - \sigma_2 + \sigma_3 = +1150 - 3460 + 16{,}000$$

$$= +13{,}690 \text{ lb per sq in. tensile stress}$$

74. Interaction curve for beginning of inelastic behavior. Let it be required to find the combination of axial load P and bending loads wl (and R_1 and R_2) for the member in Fig. 239a corresponding to the end of elastic behavior (or the beginning of inelastic behavior). In other words, let one of the loads (P or wl) be given, and let it be required to find the value of the other load, so that the combination of P and wl will cause a stress σ in the most stressed fibers equal to the tensile elastic limit σ_e of the material.

As previously noted, such a combination of loads would cause impending failure of the member if inelastic behavior of the member must be avoided. It should be recalled also that, if the material has a so-called flat-top stress-strain diagram (see Fig. 65c), the elastic limit is also the yield point σ_y ($\sigma_e = \sigma_y$).

Thus, if the stress in the most stressed fiber is σ_y, we obtain, from Eq. 128,

$$\sigma_y = \frac{P}{a} + \frac{Mc}{I} = \sigma_1 + \sigma_2 \qquad (129)$$

By dividing both sides of this equation by σ_y, we obtain

$$\frac{\sigma_1}{\sigma_y} + \frac{\sigma_2}{\sigma_y} = 1 \qquad (130)$$

Equation 130 is called the *interaction equation* for a combination of axial tensile load and bending loads that produces a condition of impending inelastic strain in the member. In this equation $\sigma_1 = P/a$ is the stress caused by the axial tensile load P, $\sigma_2 = Mc/I$ is the stress caused by the transverse bending loads, and σ_y is the elastic limit or yield point of the material.

Equation 130 can be represented graphically by the line AB in Fig. 241 where the abscissas represent values of the ratio σ_1/σ_y and the ordinates represent values of the ratio σ_2/σ_y. Point A represents the condition in which the member is subjected to bending only, corresponding to the stress ratio $\sigma_2/\sigma_y = 1$, which means that $\sigma_2 = Mc/I$ $= \sigma_y$. Point B represents the condition in which the member is subjected to an axial load P only, corresponding to a stress ratio σ_1/σ_y $= 1$, which means that $\sigma_1 = P/a = \sigma_y$. All points on the line between A and B represent stress ratios σ_1/σ_y and σ_2/σ_y for combinations of axial and bending loads that will cause a maximum stress equal to σ_y,

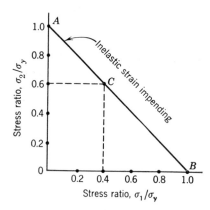

Fig. 241.   Elastic interaction curve for combined axial tension and bending.

and hence this line is often called the *interaction curve* for impending inelastic strain in the member.

As an example of the use that can be made of the interaction curve, let the bending load wl in Fig. 239 be such that the maximum bending stress is $\sigma_2 = Mc/I = 0.6\sigma_y$, which gives a ratio $\sigma_2/\sigma_y = 0.6$. In Fig. 241, C represents the point on the interaction curve whose ordinate is 0.6. We note that the point C has an abscissa of $\sigma_1/\sigma_y = 0.4$, which means that the stress $\sigma_1 = P/a$ cannot exceed $0.4\sigma_y$ if the member must not be allowed to have any inelastic strain. The following illustrative problem also shows the convenience of the interaction curve of Fig. 241. However, as noted at the end of Art. 73, the interaction curve of Fig. 241 is not a necessary tool for solving the following problems. But, in addition to its convenience, it is needed in the treatment of the topic in the next article.

Illustrative Problem

Problem 234.   The member in Fig. 242a and b has a rectangular cross section $b \times 2c$ and is made of steel having a yield point σ_y. Let $b = 1$ in., $c = 1.5$ in. and $\sigma_y = 45,000$ lb/in.² If the force $P = 30,000$ lb, determine the maximum value of the distance e of the force P from the center line of section AB if inelastic behavior of the member is not to be permitted.

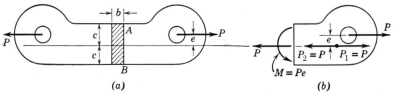

Fig. 242. Eccentrically loaded tension member.

Solution. We make use of the interaction curve of Fig. 241 as follows: the stress $\sigma_1 = 30,000/3 = 10,000$ lb/in.^{2} and $\sigma_1/\sigma_y = 10,000/45,000 = 0.22$. From the line AB in Fig. 241 the value of $\sigma_2/\sigma_y = 0.78$ corresponds to $\sigma_1/\sigma_y = 0.22$. Therefore,

$$\sigma_2 = 0.78\sigma_y = 0.78 \times 45,000 = 35,100 \text{ lb/in.}^2$$

But

$$\sigma_2 = \frac{Mc}{I} = \frac{Pec}{I} = 35,100 \text{ lb/in.}^{\prime\prime}$$

Therefore,

$$e = \frac{35,100 I}{Pc} = \frac{35,100 \times \frac{1}{12} \times 1(3)^3}{30,000 \times 1.5} = 1.75 \text{ in.}$$

Problems for Arts. 73 and 74

In each of the following problems the load lies in a plane of symmetry of the cross section of the area on which the stress acts:

235. In Prob. 233 let the force P in Fig. 240a be applied at the point D where the action line of P intersects the longitudinal central axis of the member. Should the solution give the same result for the stresses on section AB as was found in Prob. 233?

236. In Fig. 243a is shown a machine member having a rectangular cross section 1.5 in. by 4 in. It is acted on by a force $P_2 = 90,000$ lb and two equal forces P_1, the action lines of which are shown in the figure. Find the value of P_1 if the maximum elastic tensile stress in the member (at section AB) is 20,000 lb per sq in.

Ans. $P_1 = 3330$ lb.

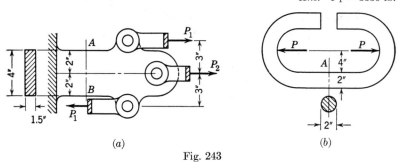

(a)

(b)

Fig. 243

237. The open-chain link shown in Fig. 243b is made of a steel bar having a diameter of 2 in. The yield point of the material is $\sigma_y = 40,000$ lb/in.^{2} If the value of P is 2390 lb, calculate the stress ratios, and, by use of the interaction curve (Fig. 241), determine whether or not the link will behave elastically.

238. The frame shown in Fig. 244 is used for small riveting, punching, and stamping machines. Find the elastic stress developed at A and at B when the load P is 2000 lb.

Ans. $\sigma_A = 1430$ lb/in.^{2} tension; $\sigma_B = 1810$ lb/in.^{2} compression.

1967 1873

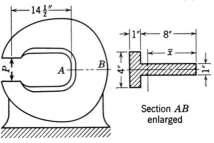

Section AB
enlarged

Fig. 244

239. Determine the value of P in Fig. 245 that will cause the maximum tensile stress to be equal to the yield point of the material. The tensile yield point of the material is $\sigma_y = 36,000$ lb/in.^{2} *Ans.*   8650 lb.

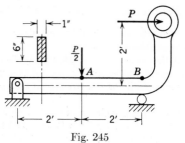

Fig. 245

240. The cross bar AB in the pin-connected frame shown in Fig. 246 is subjected at its midpoint to a load $Q = 4000$ lb. The cross bar is a 7-in. 15.3-lb I

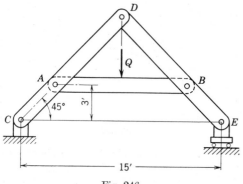

Fig. 246

beam. (See Table B in Appendix II.) The yield point of the material is σ_y = 40,000 lb/in.[2] Find the stress ratios σ_1/σ_y and σ_2/σ_y, and, from the interaction curve (Fig. 241), determine whether or not the behavior of the bar will be elastic.

241. What value should e, in Fig. 247, have in order that the stress at the top fiber within the middle third of the beam caused by the load P shall be equal (and opposite) to the stress caused by the cross-bending loads? Assume that $P = 8Q$, $l = 3$ ft, and that the member behaves elastically.

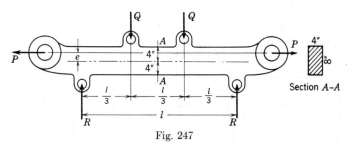

Fig. 247

242. A cast-iron machine frame shown in Fig. 248 is subjected to a load P of 8000 lb. The area of the cross section at AB is 40 sq in., and the centroidal axis YY is 6 in. from the outer edge of the section. The moment of inertia of the area with respect to the centroidal axis is 400 in.[4] Find the maximum elastic tensile and compressive stresses on the section AB.

Ans. σ_A = 1960 lb per sq in. tension; σ_B = 2440 lb per sq in. compression.

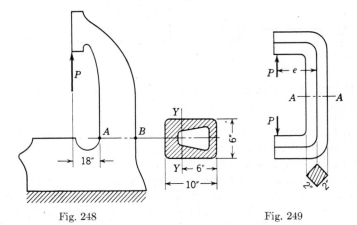

Fig. 248   Fig. 249

243. In Fig. 249 let P = 4000 lb, and let the member be made of steel for which the yield point σ_y = 35,000 lb/in.[2] Calculate the stress ratio σ_1/σ_y, and, by use of the interaction curve (Fig. 241), determine the bending moment $M = Pe$ which combined with P will produce a maximum stress equal to σ_y. Finally, calculate the corresponding value for e.

to HERE

§ 2   Inelastic Behavior

75. Interaction curve for fully plastic combination of loads. In the foregoing article, the combination of bending and axial loads that would start inelastic behavior in the most stressed fiber was found. However, these loads that *start* the inelastic behavior may be considered as lower limits, for in many members failure is not considered to have occurred until a rather large amount of inelastic deformation has taken place.

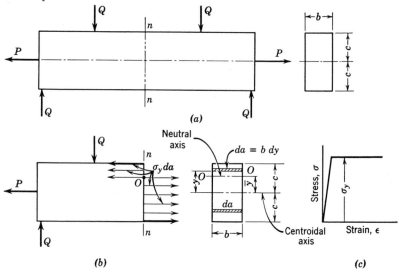

Fig. 250.   Inelastic behavior of beam subjected to combined axial tension and bending.

For such members we now wish to obtain the upper limit of the combination of loads that may be applied to the member. For this purpose failure is assumed to have occurred when the inelastic strains at the section of maximum stress have penetrated to the full depth of the member (designated as the fully plastic condition), thereby forming a so-called plastic hinge and permitting failure by general yielding to occur if the loads are increased above this upper boundary value (see Art. 53).

In Fig. 250a each section, such as *nn*, between the loads *Q* is in the fully plastic condition, and the problem is to determine the combination of loads *P* and *Q* that will cause this condition on section *nn* to occur. The stress distribution accompanying this *fully plastic* condition on section *nn* is as shown in Fig. 250b provided that the stress-strain curve for the material is as shown in Fig. 250c. It is required that an interaction curve be derived so that, if the stress σ_y is given, we can determine the combinations of loads P and Q that will cause the beam of *rectangular cross section* to be in the so-called fully plastic condition. For other cross sections see our book, *Advanced Mechanics of Materials*.

We start by making use of the equations of equilibrium for the free-body diagram of a portion of the beam shown in Fig. 250b. Let $\bar{y}$ be the distance from the centroid of the rectangular section to the neutral axis at O, and let y be the distance from the centroid to any element of area $b\,dy$. The equations of equilibrium for the forces acting on the body of Fig. 250b are as follows:

$$\sigma_y \int_{-c}^{+\bar{y}} b\,dy - \sigma_y \int_{+\bar{y}}^{+c} b\,dy = P \tag{131}$$

$$-\sigma_y \int_{-c}^{+\bar{y}} yb\,dy + \sigma_y \int_{+\bar{y}}^{+c} yb\,dy = M \tag{132}$$

where M is the bending moment at the section.

The integrals in Eqs. 131 and 132 are the areas and moments of the areas, respectively, of the parts of the section below and above the neutral axis. Equation 131 reduces to

$$\sigma_y b(\bar{y} + c) - \sigma_y b(c - \bar{y}) = P \tag{133}$$

From Eq. 133, we find

$$\bar{y} = \frac{P}{2\sigma_y b} \tag{134}$$

Equation 132 reduces to

$$M = (c^2 - \bar{y}^2)\sigma_y b \tag{135}$$

The substitution of $\bar{y}$ from Eq. 134 into Eq. 135 gives

$$M = \sigma_y b c^2 - \frac{P^2}{4\sigma_y b} \tag{136}$$

If both sides of Eq. 136 are divided by $\sigma_y b c^2$, the resulting equation is

$$\frac{M}{\sigma_y b c^2} + \frac{P^2}{4\sigma_y{}^2 b^2 c^2} = 1 \tag{137}$$

Equation 137 is the desired interaction equation or relationship among the loads P, M, the stress σ_y, and the dimensions b and c of the rectangular cross section.

Interaction Curve in Terms of Stresses. Since engineers usually prefer to deal with stresses rather than directly with loads, Eq. 137 will be transformed or expressed in terms of stresses as follows: Let

$$\sigma_1 = \frac{P}{a} = \frac{P}{2bc} \tag{138}$$

$$\sigma_2 = \frac{Mc}{I} = \frac{Mc}{\frac{1}{12}b(2c)^3} = \frac{3}{2}\frac{M}{bc^2} \tag{139}$$

where σ_1 and σ_2 are fictitious stresses (especially σ_2 since the flexure formula $\sigma_2 = Mc/I$ is not applicable when inelastic strains occur.

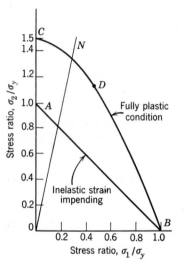

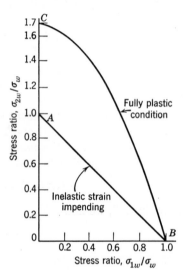

Fig. 251. Interaction curves for elastic and inelastic behavior of beam with rectangular cross section for combined tension and bending.

Fig. 252. Interaction curves (similar to Fig. 251) for beam having a circular cross section.

Nevertheless it is convenient to think of the value of σ_2 as a stress in the use of the foregoing equations and in Eq. 140). By substituting the values of P and M from Eqs. 138 and 139 in terms of σ_1 and σ_2 into Eq. 137, we obtain the following interaction equation, provided that the cross section is rectangular:

$$\frac{2}{3}\frac{\sigma_2}{\sigma_y} + \left(\frac{\sigma_1}{\sigma_y}\right)^2 = 1 \tag{140}$$

Equation 140 is represented in Fig. 251 by the curve *CDB* marked fully plastic condition. Note that in Fig. 251 the part OAB of the diagram is exactly the same as Fig. 241. The point C corresponds to the condition that the load $P = 0$; that is, $\sigma_2/\sigma_y = 1.5$ or $\sigma_2 = 1.5\sigma_y$. But, from Eq. 139, $\sigma_2 = Mc/I$. Therefore, at the point C, $Mc/I = 1.5\sigma_y$ or $M = 1.5\sigma_y I/c$, which is the value of the pure bending moment corresponding to the fully plastic condition for a rectangular cross section (see Table 4). The point B represents the condition of pure axial tension. The point D represents any point between B and C. With the coordinates of D given, we may quickly find the corresponding loads P and M by using Eqs. 138 and 139.

Two Limiting Cases. Figure 251 gives a graphical interpretation of the difference between the beginning of inelastic strain (line AB) and the fully plastic condition (curve CDB). The spread between the line AB and the curve CDB indicates that relatively large increases in load are necessary to cause the member to pass from the condition of inelastic strains impending to the fully plastic condition. The illustrative problem that follows will show this fact quantitatively.

Working or Allowable Values of Stress. Figure 251 can be used for determining working values of σ_1 and σ_2 if the working stress σ_w is substituted for σ_y. In other words, if we let σ_{1w} and σ_{2w} be the working values of σ_1 and σ_2, it follows that

$$\frac{\sigma_1}{\sigma_y} = \frac{\sigma_{1w}}{\sigma_w} \quad \text{and} \quad \frac{\sigma_2}{\sigma_y} = \frac{\sigma_{2w}}{\sigma_w}$$

Hence the abscissas and ordinates of Fig. 251 (see Fig. 252 for example) may be used for determining working values of stresses.

Illustrative Problems

Problem 244. In Prob. 234 let the value of $e = 1.75$ in., and compute the value of the load P that will correspond to the fully plastic condition of section AB.

Solution. From Eqs. 138 and 139 we find $\sigma_1 = P/2bc = \frac{1}{3}P$ and $\sigma_2 = Mc/I = \frac{3}{2}M/bc^2 = 1.16P$. Since σ_1 and σ_2 are each expressed in terms of P, we find that $\sigma_2 = 3.50\sigma_1$. We now seek from the interaction curve of Fig. 251 the point whose ordinate is 3.50 times its abscissa. This is accomplished by drawing a straight line through the origin, whose slope is 3.50 as shown in Fig. 251 by the line ON that intersects the curve CDB at an abscissa of 0.37. Therefore,

$$\frac{\sigma_1}{\sigma_y} = 0.37 \quad \text{or} \quad \sigma_1 = 0.37 \times 45,000 = 16,650 \text{ lb/in.}^2$$

and, hence, $P = \sigma_1 a = 16,650 \times 3 = 49,900$ lb.

Thus, from Prob. 234 we see that a load of $P = 30,000$ lb will cause yielding of the bar to start at the most stressed fiber in section AB, but, from the foregoing result in this problem, the load must be increased to $P = 49,900$ lb in order to cause the yielding of all the fibers at section AB. These two loads are thought of as lower and upper limiting values of the loads that correspond to the minimum and maximum amounts of inelastic strain that may be considered to cause failure and hence to limit the load-carrying capacity of the member.

Problem 245. A circular cylindrical bar of steel having a diameter d and a yield point $\sigma_y = 40,000$ lb per sq in. is used to resist static loads consisting of a combination of an axial tensile load $P = 20,000$ lb and a bending moment $M = 30,000$ lb-in. Determine the diameter d of the bar, using a factor of safety of 2, based on the assumption that failure of the bar will occur when it is in the fully plastic condition.

Solution. From Eqs. 138 and 139 we find that

$$\sigma_{1w} = \frac{P}{a} = \frac{20,000}{\pi d^2/4} = \frac{80,000}{\pi d^2}$$

$$\sigma_{2w} = \frac{Mc}{I} = \frac{30,000 \times d/2}{\pi d^4/64} = \frac{960,000}{\pi d^3}$$

where σ_{1w} and σ_{2w} are the working or allowable values of σ_1 and σ_2. The value of the working stress σ_w is obtained by dividing the yield point stress by 2 and is $\sigma_w = 20,000$ lb per sq in. Therefore,

$$\frac{\sigma_{1w}}{\sigma_w} = \frac{4}{\pi d^2} \quad \text{and} \quad \frac{\sigma_{2w}}{\sigma_w} = \frac{48}{\pi d^3}$$

In Fig. 252 is shown the interaction curve for a circular cross section (see our *Advanced Mechanics of Materials*, p. 559, for construction of this curve). By trial and error, we find that $d = 2.13$ in. gives the values $\sigma_{1w}/\sigma_w = 0.28$ and $\sigma_{2w}/\sigma_w = 1.58$ which is the set of coordinates that lie on the interaction curve in Fig. 252 representing the fully plastic condition. It should be noted that, if we substitute this value of d into the foregoing equations for σ_{1w} and σ_{2w}, we get

$$\sigma_{1w} = \frac{80,000}{\pi (2.13)^2} = 5620 \text{ lb/in.}^2$$

$$\sigma_{2w} = \frac{960,000}{\pi (2.13)^3} = 32,000 \text{ lb/in.}^2$$

Thus, the working or allowable loads (the given loads) will cause a maximum stress in the most stressed fiber of 37,620 lb/in.^{2}, and therefore the working or allowable loads do not cause any inelastic strain in the bar.

Problems

246. Determine the value of P in Fig. 245 that will cause the fully plastic condition to develop if the yield point of the material is 36,000 lb/in.^{2}

Ans. 13,500 lb.

247. Find the value of P in Prob. 244 (Fig. 242) that will cause the fully plastic condition in the member, if the yield point of the material is 35,000 lb/in.^{2}, and if $e = 0.5$ in.

248. Determine the load P_1 in Prob. 236, Fig. 243a, that will cause the fully plastic condition in the member if the yield point of the material is 36,000 lb/in.^{2}

Chapter VI

BUCKLING LOAD.

INSTABILITY. COLUMNS

§ 1   Elastic Buckling

76. Introduction. As previously emphasized, the primary objective in the subject of mechanics of materials or resistance of materials is to determine the load-carrying capacity of a member made of a given material and subjected to a given system of loads.

The engineer's usual method of doing this is to determine the relation between the loads and the stresses caused by the loads and then to assign values for the maximum (or allowable) stress and thus to determine the maximum (or allowable) load-carrying capacity. This method was used in the foregoing chapters. It is deeply embedded in the engineer's thinking. It is applicable and satisfactory for a great many problems, but it is not applicable, for example, to a so-called slender member subjected to an axial *compressive* load. Such a member is called a column. It fails by *buckling*, and the maximum load that can be applied to it cannot be determined from the stress in the slender compression member since the stress in the column is indefinite; the stress at failure bears no definite relationship to the load.

The lack of appreciation of this fact was responsible for the earlier unsuccessful attempts of investigators during the nineteenth century to obtain a satisfactory method for predicting the load-carrying capacity of columns.   They tried in vain to determine the load-carrying capacity of a column in terms of the bending stresses in the column under a condition of stable equilibrium, whereas buckling, as will be discussed later, grows out of a condition of unstable equilibrium.   The student, therefore, should be aware that a different approach to the problem treated in this chapter is needed.

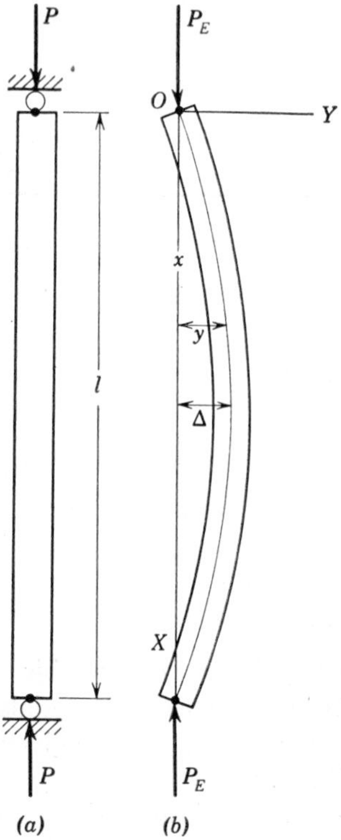

Elastic-buckling Behavior.   Elastic buckling can occur in compression members that have certain relative proportions. Such compression members are frequently called slender or thin-walled or light-weight members.   The simplest form of member that fails by buckling is a straight slender bar under an axial compressive load; this member is usually called a *slender column* but, as discussed in Art. 79, less slender similar compression members (so-called medium-slender or stocky members) that fail by *inelastic* buckling are also called columns, and hence the term column must be used with discretion.   A very stocky member is frequently called a compression block.

Members other than slender columns that may fail by elastic buckling include thin-walled cylinders under either axial compression or external radial (lateral) uniform pressure, compression flanges of lightweight wide-flanged beams, thin plates under edge compression or shear, primarily in aircraft construction.   To prevent elastic buckling or at least to increase the buckling load for such members, stiffeners are frequently attached to the members, especially in airplane construction.

The significant fact or dominant characteristic of elastic buckling, however, is the same in all instances: namely, that the elastic deflections and stresses in the member are *not* proportional to the loads as buckling takes place, even though the material acts elastically (stress is proportional to strain).

Meaning of Instability.   Elastic buckling arises out of a condition of neutral equilibrium that develops when the applied load on the member reached a so-called critical value, here indicated as P_{cr} or P_E.   This

Fig. 253.   Elastic behavior of slender column.

means that, at the critical load, the member is in neutral equilibrium; that is, it is in equilibrium in any position throughout a considerable range of small elastic deflections. This condition is called instability, and it is of great importance that the reader understands the physical meaning of instability. A brief explanation may be made as follows: If the *critical* axial load P_E is acting on the straight, slender (ideal) column (Fig. 253), and a lateral force is applied, causing a small (elastic) but indefinite deflection, the column will remain in the deflected position when the lateral force is removed. If now the axial load is decreased slightly below the value P_E, the column will spring back to its original position. If, however, the axial load is increased a very small amount above the critical load P_E, a large increase in the deflection will occur (not in proportion to the load), giving rise to an increased bending moment, which in turn causes a further increase in deflection, etc., finally resulting in total collapse of the column, as indicated by the line AB in Fig. 254.

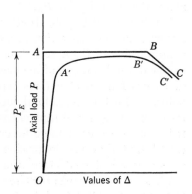

Fig. 254. Elastic buckling load of slender column.

Ultimate Load. The value P_E then is the maximum or ultimate axial compressive load that the straight slender member can resist; it is called the buckling load, and is shown in the next article to be given by the expression:

$$P_E = \frac{\pi^2 EI}{l^2} \quad \text{or} \quad \frac{P_E}{a} = \frac{\pi^2 E}{(l/r)^2}$$

in which I is the moment of inertia of the cross section a about the neutral axis. But $I = ar^2$, in which r is the radius of gyration of the area a about the neutral axis. The ratio l/r is called the slenderness ratio, in which l is the length of the column.

Thus the value of the buckling or critical load per unit area P_E/a for the column when it buckles is equal to $(\pi^2 E)/(l/r)^2$, and hence depends on the stiffness E of the material and the slenderness ratio l/r of the member. It is highly important to understand that, when *elastic* buckling starts, the stress P_E/a in the column is never greater than the elastic limit of the material, and it may be a great deal less than the elastic limit if E is small and l/r is large. Such a failure, therefore, is called *elastic* buckling.

The Problem Defined. It should be evident, therefore, that, in determining a safe or allowable load for a slender column (that would fail by elastic buckling), the problem is not one of preventing a specified or allowable stress from being exceeded, as was the case of a slender bar subjected to an axial tensile load (Chap. I), but one of avoiding the occurrence of a peculiar condition of unstable equilibrium, which leads to buckling of the column and which is characterized by large but indefinite deflections that result from a very slight increase in the load above the critical value P_E.

It is important to note also that the condition of elastic instability is a very dangerous condition to allow to develop in the member; there is no warning of the approach of buckling, and the failure is likely to be one of total collapse of the member or structure. Some of the most disastrous failures of various types of structures have been buckling failures. Furthermore, local inelastic deformation in a *compression* member caused by abrupt changes in cross section, etc., cannot be relied on to create a more favorable stress distribution to the same extent that they can in tension members and beams; in fact, local compressive inelastic deformation tends to lead to buckling.

77. Euler's formula for the elastic-buckling load. The formula giving the buckling load P_E for a straight axially loaded bar (ideal slender column) was first derived by Euler in 1757. Let the axial load P_E on the bar in Fig. 253b be the load that will just maintain the bar in the elastically bent condition as shown (exaggerated) if a lateral force is applied to deflect the column slightly and is then removed. The formula giving the value of the load P_E is derived as follows:

In Fig. 253a is represented a straight slender compressive member (a pivot-ended column) of constant cross section. Let the axial load P gradually increase to the value P_E which will hold the column in the elastically deflected position as shown in Fig. 253b. The elastic-curve equation for the deflected column is the same as that of a beam: namely (see Art. 63),

$$EI(d^2y/dx^2) = M \tag{141}$$

If the origin of the axes is chosen at the upper end of the column, and the positive direction of the x axis is downward and the positive direction of the y axis is the direction of the deflection, as shown in Fig. 253b, then d^2y/dx^2 is negative, and the preceding equation becomes

$$EI(d^2y/dx^2) = -P_Ey \tag{142}$$

in which P_Ey is the bending moment at the section whose distance is x

from the origin O. This equation may be written

$$EI \frac{d(dy/dx)}{dx} = -P_E y \tag{143}$$

and, if each side of the equation is multiplied by dy, each side becomes an exact differential of the form $u\,du$: namely, ·

$$EI(dy/dx)\,d(dy/dx) = -P_E y\,dy \tag{144}$$

The integration of this equation gives

$$EI(dy/dx)^2 = -P_E y^2 + C_1 \tag{145}$$

in which C_1 is a constant of integration. Since no set of simultaneous values of dy/dx and y are known, C_1 cannot be expressed in terms of the known quantities E, I, and l, but it may be expressed in terms of the maximum deflection Δ. Thus, since $dy/dx = 0$ when $y = \Delta$, Eq. 145 gives

$$0 = -P_E \Delta^2 + C_1 \quad \text{hence,} \quad C_1 = P_E \Delta^2$$

Thus Eq. 145 becomes

$$EI(dy/dx)^2 = P_E(\Delta^2 - y^2) \tag{146}$$

This equation may be integrated after the variables are separated; the equation may be written

$$\frac{dy}{\sqrt{\Delta^2 - y^2}} = \sqrt{\frac{P_E}{EI}}\,dx$$

the integration of which gives

$$\sin^{-1} \frac{y}{\Delta} = \sqrt{\frac{P_E}{EI}}\,x + C_2 \tag{147}$$

or

$$\frac{y}{\Delta} = \sin\left(\sqrt{\frac{P_E}{EI}}\,x + C_2\right)$$

But $y = 0$ when $x = 0$, and hence $C_2 = 0$. Therefore,

$$\frac{y}{\Delta} = \sin\sqrt{\frac{P_E}{EI}}\,x \quad \text{or} \quad y = \Delta \sin\sqrt{\frac{P_E}{EI}}\,x \tag{148}$$

At the other end of the member, $y = 0$ and $x = l$, if the deflection Δ is small.

The substitution of these latter values in Eq. 148 gives the following equation for determining the value of the buckling load P_E:

$$\sin\left(\sqrt{\frac{P_E}{EI}}\, l\right) = 0 \tag{149}$$

In Eq. 149 the angle $\left(\sqrt{\dfrac{P_E}{EI}}\, l\right)$ must be equal to π or some integral multiple of π. For the pivot-end conditions in Fig. 253, this angle must be π, and, hence, $\sqrt{\dfrac{P_E}{EI}}\, l = \pi$. Therefore,

$$P_E = \frac{\pi^2 EI}{l^2} \tag{150}$$

This equation is called Euler's formula. It gives the value P_E of an axial compressive load on a pivot-ended, straight column that will hold the column in a slightly deflected position if a small lateral force is applied and then removed, and, if P_E is increased by an extremely small amount, the column will deflect rapidly and thus fail by buckling.

The fact that an excessive elastic deflection occurs when the axial load P has a value equal to (or slightly larger) than P_E, as given by Eq. 150, is clearly shown when a slender steel column is tested and the deflections are measured. The load-deflection curve thus obtained under ideal conditions is shown as $OABC$ in Fig. 254. If the member is slightly crooked or if the load is not exactly axial, the test values of load and deflection will be represented by a curve such as $OA'B'C'$. Note that the curve $OA'B'C'$ approaches * the curve $OABC$; this means that the buckling load P_E for the ideal column is only slightly larger than the buckling load under conditions that deviate somewhat from ideal conditions. This fact indicates that Eq. 150 is reliable and useful for determining the buckling load for actual slender columns subjected to so-called axial compressive loads.

As previously noted, I in Eq. 150 is equal to ar^2, where a is the area of cross section and r is the radius of gyration of the cross section about

---

* This fact is not evident from the analysis of the column action here presented; it is shown by the true equation of the elastic curve; that is, the equation obtained when the assumption that the length along the axis is the same as the length along the curve ($dx = dl$) is not made. The truth of the statement, however, is clearly shown by experiments as indicated by the results represented in Fig. 254.

its neutral axis.   Thus, Euler's equation may be written

$$\frac{P_E}{a} = \frac{\pi^2 E}{(l/r)^2} \tag{151}$$

in which l/r is called the slenderness ratio of the slender column.   The term P_E/a is the uniformly distributed compressive stress caused by the axial load P_E just before the ideal column is bent slightly by applying the small lateral force; in an actual column the bending to start the buckling would be caused by slight eccentricity of loading and crookedness of the column, etc.   The expression P_E/a is frequently called the critical stress.

The Importance of Stiffness.   Attention was previously called to the fact that Eq. 151 shows that the only property of the material on which P_E depends is the stiffness of the material E.   Therefore, a slender column made of a high-strength steel such as high-carbon or special-alloy and heat-treated steels would buckle and hence fail, at the same load as would one made of low-strength steel such as low-carbon steel, provided that the values of l/r of the two columns were equal and were relatively large, so that the columns would fail by elastic buckling as assumed in the derivation of the equation.

Problems

249. A structural-steel cylindrical column has a diameter of 2 in. and has pivot ends.   What maximum length may it have without failing by elastic buckling under an axial load of 30,000 lb?   *Ans.*   88 in.

250. By using Euler's formula, determine the dimensions of the square cross section of a pivot-ended oak-timber column 24 ft long to resist a safe axial load of 18,000 lb.   Use a factor of safety of 8, which means that the buckling load is to be 8 times the given load.   Assume $E = 1,500,000$ lb per sq in.   Justify the use of Euler's formula by showing that P_E/a is less than the proportional limit of oak (see Table 1).   *Ans.* $b = 9.92$ in.

251. A 3-in.-by-3-in.-by-$\frac{1}{2}$-in. wrought-iron angle (see Appendix II) 15 ft long was tested as a column; spherical seated bearings at the ends were used.   The column failed by buckling when subjected to an axial load per unit area (critical stress) of 2650 lb per sq in.   What was the l/r for the column?   Calculate the maximum critical stress that the column would be expected to resist.   Let $E = 25,000,-000$ lb per sq in.   *Ans.* $l/r = 310$; $P_E/a = 2570$ lb per sq in.

252. What is the ratio of the strength of an ideal slender solid cast-iron column 6 in. in diameter to the strength of a slender hollow cast-iron column having a wall thickness of 1 in., the areas of cross section and the lengths of the two columns being equal?   *Ans.*   9 to 41.

253. A spruce airplane compression member is 66 in. long and has an elliptical cross section with major and minor diameters of 4 in. and $1\frac{1}{2}$ in., respectively, Calculate the slenderness ratio of the column, and, if Euler's formula is applicable calculate the safe axial load that this column will stand as a pivot-ended column, using a factor of safety of 3. Assume that $E = 1,600,000$ lb/in.[2], I about the major diameter b is $\pi bd^3/64 = 0.663$ in.[4], and $a = \pi bd/4 = 4.71$ in.[2]

Ans. $l/r = 176$; $P_w = 800$ lb.

254. Select a structural-steel I section (see Appendix II) to serve as a column 20 ft long to resist an axial load of 60,000 lb. Use a factor of safety of 4, and assume the column to have pivot ends. Justify the use of Euler's formula by showing that P_E/a is less than the proportional limit of the material.

78. Effect of end conditions on elastic buckling of slender columns. The more important ideal end conditions that are ap-

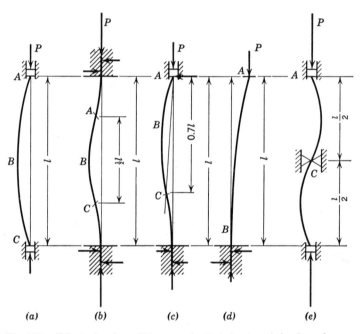

Fig. 255. Effect of end conditions on elastic behavior of slender columns.

proached more or less closely by the end conditions of slender columns in structures and machines are illustrated in Fig. 255.

(*a*) Figure 255*a* represents a pivot-ended (or pin-ended) slender column to which Eq. 151 applies.

(*b*) Figure 255*b* represents a fixed-ended slender column with ends restrained so that the tangents to the elastic curve at the ends are parallel to the original axis of the column. The points of inflection, A and C, are at a distance of $\frac{1}{4}l$ from the ends, and hence the middle half, ABC, is a column of the same type as that in Fig. 255*a*. Thus the maximum load P for a fixed-ended slender column is

$$P_E = \frac{\pi^2 EI}{(l/2)^2} = \frac{4\pi^2 EI}{l^2} \tag{152}$$

Therefore a fixed-ended slender column of length l will carry as large a load as a pivot-ended slender column of length $l/2$; that is, a fixed-ended slender column of a given length is four times as strong as it would be with pivot ends, if it is assumed that both columns would fail by elastic buckling. Equation 152 also applies to the pivot-ended column of Fig. 255e that has a lateral support at its midpoint which lets the column rotate but does not permit it to deflect laterally at the support.

(c) Figure 255c represents a slender column with one end fixed and one end free to turn but not free to move laterally. The inflection point C is at a distance of approximately 0.7l from A, and the part of the column ABC is of the same type as that of Fig. 255a. Hence,

$$P_E = \frac{\pi^2 EI}{(0.7l)^2} = \frac{2\pi^2 EI}{l^2} \quad \text{(approx.)} \tag{153}$$

Therefore a slender column with one end fixed and the other end pivoted is approximately twice as strong in resisting elastic buckling as it would be if both ends were pivoted.

(d) Figure 255d represents a column with one end fixed and the other end free from all restraints. The curve AB assumed by the column corresponds to the portion AB of the column in Fig. 255a, and hence Euler's equation for the column in Fig. 255d is

$$P_E = \frac{\pi^2 EI}{(2l)^2} = \frac{1}{4} \frac{\pi^2 EI}{l^2} \tag{154}$$

Therefore, a slender column fixed at one end and free from all restraint at the other end is only one fourth as strong in resisting buckling as is a pivot-ended column of the same length.

The buckling load of a column that has restraints at the ends that prevent rotation or a support between the ends that prevents deflection can be represented by the following equation:

$$P = \frac{\pi^2 EI}{(kl)^2}$$

in which k is a constant whose value depends on the type of restraints. The term kl is frequently called the effective length of the column.

Problems

255. Solve Prob. 249, assuming that the column is an ideal fixed-ended column.

256. What maximum load would the column described in Prob. 251 resist if we assume that it has fixed ends and that it would fail by elastic buckling ?

Ans. 28,300 lb.

257. Solve Prob. 250, assuming that the column is an ideal column having one end fixed and the other end is pivoted.   *Ans.* $b = 8.35$ in.

258. Two very slender columns having the same lengths and cross sections are subjected to axial loads. One column is made of steel and has round ends, and the other is made of aluminum and has fixed ends. What is the ratio of the maximum loads the two columns can carry? Consult Table 1, Chapter I.

Ans. $P_s = 0.75 P_a$.

§ 2   Inelastic Buckling

79. Graphical representation of formulas for buckling loads. Euler's equation (Eq. 151) is represented graphically by the curve

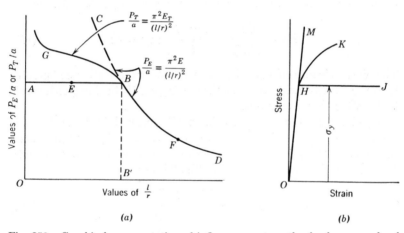

Fig. 256.   Graphical representation of influence on strength of columns made of material having different types of stress-strain diagrams.

$DFBC$ in Fig. 256, in which the ordinate to any point on the curve is the value of P_E/a, and the abscissa is the corresponding value of l/r. In the derivation of Eq. 151, it was assumed that the stress-strain curve for the material was a straight line, and, hence, that the stiffness E (modulus of elasticity) of the material remained constant as the load P increased to the value P_E. This condition limits the applicability of Euler's equation to *elastic* buckling, and hence to a column having a slenderness ratio l/r above a certain limiting value, depending on the properties of the materials.

For example, in Fig. 256 the lower portion of the curve, say from F to D, for which the values of l/r are relatively large, represent (slender) columns in which the stress P_E/a is much less than the elastic limit of the material. But, when l/r has a value (represented by the abscissa of the point B) such that the stress P_E/a is equal to the elastic limit, any increase in P_E will cause a rapid decrease in the stiffness from the value E to E_T (which is the slope to the stress-strain diagram at the inelastic stress caused by increasing P_E slightly). This decrease in stiffness permits the column to bend and quickly to acquire a large deflection with a small increase in load. This failure is called *inelastic* buckling; the derivation of the buckling load for such buckling is given in the next article. The buckling load, denoted by P_T, is found to be

$$P_T = \frac{\pi^2 E_T I}{l^2} \quad \text{or} \quad \frac{P_T}{a} = \frac{\pi^2 E_T}{(l/r)^2} \tag{155}$$

This equation is called the tangent-modulus formula for inelastic buckling of a straight column under a so-called axial load.

It is sometimes stated in the technical literature that, if the values of E and l/r for the column are such that the column does not fail by elastic buckling, the stress P/a in the column will reach the yield-strength value for the material of which the column is made, and the column will fail by direct inelastic deformation (yielding) under the approximately constant yield-strength load. This, however, is a misleading statement of the mode of failure, except for a very stocky column, usually designated as a compression block. Inelastic buckling, as explained in the foregoing paragraph, is more nearly the correct mode of failure for members that would be designated as columns. In fact, inelastic buckling is usually more sudden and dramatic than elastic buckling.

The tangent-modulus formula is represented by a line such as BG in Fig. 256 provided that the stress-strain diagram for the material above the elastic limit is represented by the line HK in Fig. 256b. The tangent-modulus line in Fig. 256a will always lie between the limiting positions BA or BC, which correspond, respectively, in Fig. 256b to the limiting stress-strain curves HJ for fully inelastic behavior and HM for fully elastic behavior. The curve, then, that represents buckling loads for all values of l/r is $GBFD$ in Fig. 256a. These curves are discussed in greater detail in Art. 81.

80. Tangent-modulus (Engesser's) formula. A satisfactory theoretical or rational treatment of inelastic buckling has developed slowly. In 1889, F. Engesser presented his tangent-modulus (single-modulus) theory, and a few years later (1895), after the contributions of A. Considère to column theory, Engesser presented the double-modulus formula,* in which the assumption is made that there is a reversal of strain on the convex side of the column when the column starts to buckle. The double-modulus theory, with the support of the results of careful tests by T. v. Kármán (1908) was widely regarded as a correct theory. But, as late as 1947, F. R. Shanley pointed out a basic inadequacy in the theory, and, as a result, the original Enges-

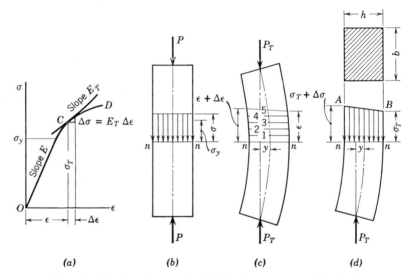

Fig. 257. Strain and stress distribution for tangent-modulus load.

ser single-modulus (tangent-modulus) formula is now generally accepted as the more significant formula in predicting the inelastic-buckling load. The tangent-modulus formula may be derived as follows:

Let Fig. 257b represent a column made of material whose stress-strain diagram is shown in Fig. 257a. It is subjected to an axial load P that increases gradually (or by small increments). Let it be assumed also that the slenderness ratio l/r is sufficiently small to prevent *elastic* buckling from occurring; that is, the stress P/a in the column reaches the elastic limit σ_y before elastic buckling takes place. The load P may therefore attain a value which causes a uniform stress σ on the cross section of the column that is greater than the elastic limit σ_y of the material, as shown in Fig. 257b. The uniform stress σ is accompanied by a uniformly distributed strain ϵ. It is assumed that the value of the ·

* See our *Advanced Mechanics of Materials* for a discussion of the meaning and significance of these two formulas.

inelastic-buckling load P_T (or buckling stress $\sigma_T = P_T/a$) and the corresponding inelastic strain are represented by a point such as C on the stress-strain curve, and hence impending inelastic buckling involves only small inelastic strains.

As increments of the axial force P are applied to the ideal, straight column, the longitudinal strains across section nn (Fig. 257b) increase but remain uniformly distributed, as shown by the lines marked 1, 2, 3, and 4 in Fig. 257c. As P approaches the value P_T, which we wish to determine, let a small lateral force be applied simultaneously with the last increment of load as P attains the value P_T, so that there is no reversal of strain (that is, the compressive strain on the convex side continues to increase) as P increases. The resulting distribution of strain is as shown by the line marked 5 in Fig. 257c, in which the lateral deflection is greatly exaggerated. The problem is to determine the smallest load $P_T = a\sigma_T$ that will cause the ideal columns to remain in a slightly deflected position when the lateral force is removed.

The resulting stress distribution on section nn is shown in Fig. 257d by the sloping line AB and is obtained from Fig. 257a by obtaining from the stress-strain diagram the stresses corresponding to the strains. The assumption that the line AB is straight is equivalent to the assumption that the slope of tangent lines to stress-strain curve, such as that shown at C in Fig. 257a, is constant during the change in strain from ϵ to $\epsilon + \Delta\epsilon$. This assumption is justified because the increment $\Delta\epsilon$ is small for the small lateral bending moment imposed on the column. The increment of stress corresponding to $\Delta\epsilon$ is therefore $\Delta\sigma = E_T \, \Delta\epsilon$. The value of P_T is now found in the same manner that the Euler buckling load P_E was found in Art. 77.

Let Fig. 257d be a free-body diagram showing the forces acting on the lower half of the column, whose cross section is here assumed to be rectangular for convenience only. Under this minimum value P_T, the column is in equilibrium, which requires that the external bending moment $P_T y$ for any cross section shall be equal and opposite to the resisting moment about the centroidal axis of the cross section of the internal forces on the section. This fact is expressed by the equation

$$P_T y = \frac{(\Delta\sigma/2)I}{h/2} \tag{156}$$

In Eq. 156 let $\Delta\sigma$ be replaced by $E_T \, \Delta\epsilon$, and in turn let $\Delta\epsilon$ be replaced by the expression h/R, which is obtained by relating the strain in the extreme fiber to the radius of curvature R of the column (see Art. 62). Furthermore, for small deflections the curvature $1/R$ is given by the expression $1/R = -d^2y/dx^2$. With these substitutions Eq. 156 becomes

$$E_T I (d^2y/dx^2) = -P_T y \qquad (157)$$

The solution of Eq. 157 is the same as that for Eq. 142 and is

$$P_T = \frac{\pi^2 E_T I}{l^2} \quad \text{or} \quad \frac{P_T}{a} = \frac{\pi^2 E_T}{(l/r)^2} \qquad (158)$$

which is the same as Eq. 155. This formula is called the tangent-modulus formula or Engesser's formula; it is also sometimes called the

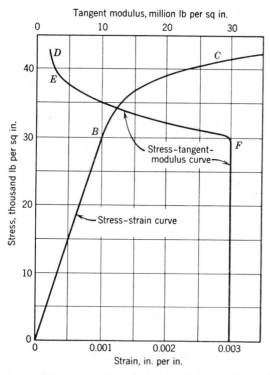

Fig. 258. Values of tangent modulus for a material not having a yield point.

generalized Euler formula. It is generally considered to give the maximum (buckling) load for an ideal column, but it has been found also that it gives the maximum load that a real column having slight imperfections can be expected to resist.

Trial-and-Error Procedure. The solution of the tangent-modulus equation for a column of given material and dimensions involves a trial-and-error process, for the reason that the value of E_T is not constant. Therefore values of the tangent modulus E_T must be known for every value of the stress above the elastic limit. Corresponding values of σ and E_T are found from an ordinary stress-strain curve and are usually given in the form of a curve. Figure 258 is a typical example of a curve from which corresponding values of σ and E_T may be found. The method of solution is illustrated in the following problems.

Illustrative Problem

Problem 259. A straight column having a square cross section 1 in. on a side and a length of 10 in. is loaded axially through special bearing blocks that allow free rotation when bending of the column starts. The member is made of material for which the compressive stress-strain curve and stress-tangent-modulus curve are shown in Fig. 258. Compute the load P_T.

Solution. The load P_T and the stress $\sigma = P_T/a$ have the same value since $a = 1$ in.^{2} By trial and error we must select from the curves of Fig. 258 a set of values of σ (or P_T) and tangent modulus E_T which will satisfy Eq. 158. After one or two trials we find that $E_T = 4,600,000$ lb per sq in. and $\sigma = 38,000$ lb per sq in. are a satisfactory set, because the substitution of these values in Eq. 158 gives the following:

$$\frac{\pi^2 4,600,000 \times \frac{1}{12} \times 1 \times (1)^3}{(10)^2} = 37,800 \text{ lb}$$

The value 37,800 lb is sufficiently close to the assumed value of 38,000 lb. Hence, $P_T = 37,800$ lb; it is the maximum axial load that can be applied to the member without causing it to fail by inelastic buckling.

Problems

260. A straight pivot-ended column whose cross section is an angle section $2'' \times 2'' \times \frac{7}{16}''$ (see Table C, Appendix II, for properties of the area) is made of the material whose stress-strain diagram and stress-tangent-modulus curve are given in Fig. 258. The length of the column is 30 in. Determine the value of the load P_T.   *Ans.* 50,000 lb.

261. A straight pivot-ended column whose cross section is circular is made of the material whose stress-strain diagram and stress-tangent-modulus curve are given in Fig. 258. If it is desired that the column shall not fail by buckling until it reaches a stress of 37,000 lb per sq in. or above, what maximum value of the ratio l/r should the column have?

81. Significance of Euler and tangent-modulus formulas. In the foregoing articles of this chapter the central idea was to find the maximum axial *compressive* load (buckling load) on a straight member. This was accomplished for members having slenderness ratios ranging from relatively large values (slender members) that fail by elastic buckling to those having relatively small values (stocky members) that fail by inelastic buckling. It is convenient to represent graphically the buckling loads for these two methods of computing these loads and to compare the computed values with experimental results. For this purpose an aluminum-alloy 2017-T4, which has a stress-strain diagram similar to OHK in Fig. 256b or similar to OBC in Fig. 258 has been chosen.

In Fig. 259 the curves show the results of computations of the buckling loads for columns made of this material, as obtained from Eqs. 151 and 158, and the small circles indicate the results found from tests.

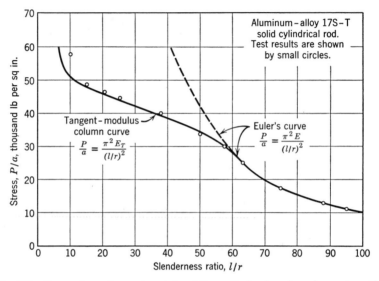

Fig. 259. Comparison of experimental and theoretical values for column strengths of an aluminum alloy 17S-T. (Test data taken from R. L. Templin, R. G. Sturm, E. C. Hartman, and M. Holt, *Aluminum Research Laboratory Technical Paper 1*, 1938.)

It will be noted that, when the value of l/r is greater than about 60 for this material, the Euler formula gives values of the buckling loads that agree well with experimental results. If l/r is less than about 60, the tangent-modulus formula gives values of the buckling load that agree well with the experimental results. It should be observed also that the curve representing the tangent-modulus values becomes tangent to the Euler curve at the point where the two curves merge. Thus, the continuous heavy-lined curve gives values for the buckling (maximum or ultimate) loads for all values of l/r. The dashed-line part of the Euler curve where it arises above the tangent-modulus curve has no physical significance.

Experimental results, therefore, indicate that columns made of this material and having slenderness ratios greater than about 60 fail by *elastic* buckling in accordance with Euler's equation, and those having values of l/r less than about 60 fail by *inelastic* buckling in accordance with the tangent-modulus formula.

82. Influence of shape of stress-strain diagram on the tangent-modulus column curves.   In Figs. 260*b*, 261*b*, and 262*b* are

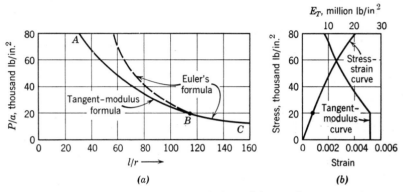

Fig. 260. Column loads for stainless steel.

given the stress-strain diagrams and also the stress-tangent-modulus curves for three typical materials frequently used as compression members.   These materials are stainless steel, aluminum-alloy 6061-T6 and mild steel.   In Figs. 260*a*, 261*a*, and 262*a* are given the column curves

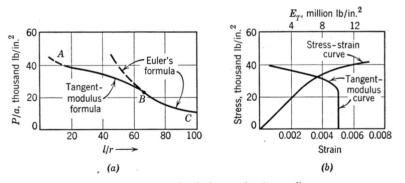

Fig. 261. Column loads for an aluminum alloy.

(Euler's curves and the tangent-modulus curves) relating the buckling (or critical) load per unit area (P/a) and the slenderness ratio l/r of columns made of each of the three materials; the column curves were constructed by using the data obtained from Figs. 260*b*, 261*b*, 262*b* for computing corresponding values of P/a and l/r from Eqs. 151 and 155, respectively, in the same way that the curves in Fig. 259 were obtained.

These curves (ABC in each figure) show the rather large influence that the shape (change in slope) of the stress-strain curve for a short distance above the proportional limit has on the computed value of the buckling load. In Fig. 260a, the curve AB, representing the tangent-modulus formula (for stainless steel) departs from the Euler curve at a relatively low stress (the proportional limit) but stays relatively

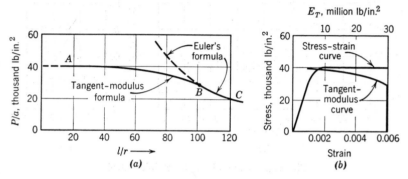

Fig. 262. Column loads for a structural steel.

close to it until much higher stresses are reached. This is caused by the very slow rate of change of slope of the stress-strain curve just above the proportional limit (Fig. 260b).

On the other hand, the curve AB in Fig. 262a departs from the Euler curve and quickly becomes almost horizontal, rising no higher than the yield point of the mild steel, and the curve for the aluminum alloy (in Fig. 261a) lies between the other two curves. These three curves illustrate the variety of shapes of the column curves, indicating the buckling strength of columns; they should give the reader a hint as to the reason for the existence of such a large number of different simplified column formulas as presented in the next section.

§ 3 Simplified, Approximate Column Formulas

83. Three main forms of approximate column formulas. The inconvenient form of the tangent-modulus formula requiring a solution by trial and error has lead to simplified but reliable column formulas that approximate the tangent-modulus formula for a column of given material subjected to an axial load. There are three main mathematical equations that may be used to approximate the relationship between the buckling load per unit area P/a (or average buckling stress) and the slenderness ratio l/r for a column, such as those given by the curves ABC in Figs. 260a, 261a, and 262a. The curves representing

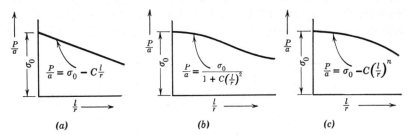

Fig. 263. Three types of equations (and curves) used to approximate the tangent-modulus column curve.

the approximate relationships are shown in Fig. 263a, b, and c, and the equations for these curves are as follows:

$$\frac{P}{a} = \sigma_0 - C\frac{l}{r} \qquad \text{(straight line)} \qquad (159)$$

$$\frac{P}{a} = \frac{\sigma_0}{1 + C\left(\dfrac{l}{r}\right)^2} \qquad \text{(Gordon-Rankine)} \qquad (160)$$

$$\frac{P}{a} = \sigma_0 - C\left(\frac{l}{r}\right)^n \qquad \text{(parabolic)} \qquad (161)$$

These equations are known by the names shown in parentheses after each equation. In each of these equations σ_0 and C are constants for any given material. For a given material the value of σ_0 (and of C) will usually be a different constant in each of these three equations. The intercept of each curve on the P/a axis is σ_0; thus σ_0 represents the approximate value of the ultimate compressive strength of a very short bar (compression block) of the given material. The values of the constant C in each of the equations, and of the exponent n in Eq. 161, are determined for the given material so that the best fit is obtained of the curve to the ABC curve for the material, such as those shown in Figs. 260a, 261a, and 262a.

Determination of Constants σ_0 and C. To illustrate the determination of the constants σ_0 and C, let us find these values for Eq. 159 so that it represents approximately the curve ABC in Fig. 261a for aluminum-alloy 6061-T6. This is done in Fig. 264 where the straight line BE is constructed so that it intersects the Euler curve at B and intercepts the P/a axis at E so that BE is intended as an approximation of the curve BA. BE is drawn below BA purposely to represent a somewhat conservative approximation. When drawn in this manner, CBE represents approximately the combined tangent-modulus and Euler

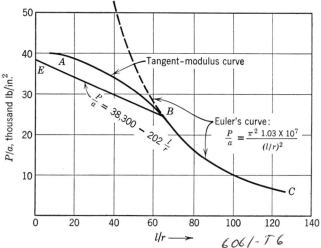

Fig. 264. Column curves for aluminum alloy 61S-T6 extrusion.

curves for all values of l/r. From Fig. 264 we observe that $\sigma_0 = 38,300$ lb per sq in. and that $P/a = 25,700$ lb per sq in. when $l/r = 63$. Therefore Eq. 159 is

$$\frac{P}{a} = 38,300 - 202\,\frac{l}{r} \qquad (162)$$

Equation 162 is the equation given in the Aluminum Company of America structural handbook (1955) for the buckling load per unit area P/a (for the average stress at the buckling load) of a pivot-ended column of aluminum-alloy 6061-T6 for values of l/r from 0 to 63. If l/r is greater than 63, the value of P/a for the buckling load is given by the Euler equation, and, since for this alloy $E = 1.03 \times 10^7$ lb/in.^{2}, the equation is

$$\frac{P}{a} = \frac{\pi^2 1.03 \times 10^7}{(l/r)^2} \qquad (163)$$

Effect of End Conditions. If there are restraints (moments) at the ends of the column that prevent rotation at the ends when the buckling load is reached and the column starts to buckle, or if there is lateral support to prevent deflection of the column at some point between the supports, Eqs. 160, 161, and 162 are written as follows:

$$\frac{P}{a} = \sigma_0 - C\frac{kl}{r} \tag{164}$$

$$\frac{P}{a} = \frac{\sigma_0}{1 + C\left(\dfrac{kl}{r}\right)^2} \tag{165}$$

$$\frac{P}{a} = \sigma_0 - C\left(\frac{kl}{r}\right)^n \tag{166}$$

In these equations the value of kl is called the effective length of a pivot-ended column, and the effective length is obtained in the same manner as in Art. 78. That is, kl is the distance between points of inflection, such as A and C in Fig. 255b, or between C and A in Fig. 255c and e, respectively.

84. Application of factor of safety. In the formulas for the approximate values of the buckling loads (Eqs. 159, 160, and 161), the value of P/a represents the average stress on the cross section of the column just before the buckling load P is reached. Thus, a reduction of the value of P/a to a working or allowable value is accomplished by dividing the right side of each equation by a factor N which is always greater than unity. The value of N will depend largely on the service conditions under which the column is used. For example, the value of N usually is about 2 to 2.2 for structural-grade steel columns used in buildings or bridges, and it is usually about 1.5 for aluminum-alloy columns used in the structure of some types of aircraft.

The deviations from the assumed conditions of straightness and of axiality of loading in a column have much more influence on the resistance of a column to loads than do similar eccentricities and crookedness and lack of symmetry of loading of a beam or a tension member. As a rule, such deviations in a column are fortuitous and unpredictable, and are usually provided for, along with other uncertainties, by the factor of safety. However, the trend, especially in airplane design, is to reduce somewhat the factor of safety as the uncertainties and inaccuracies are reduced, by giving greater attention to careful design and construction methods.

The value of N to be used is often controlled by certain legal requirements, and in many cases its value is specified in codes that are formulated by organizations such as the American Institute for Steel Construction for steel buildings and bridges; by governmental organizations such as the United States Air Force, the Bureau of Aeronautics of the United States Navy, and the Civil Aeronautics Administration for the design of airplane structures.

85. Some commonly used column formulas. The formulas given in this article have been rather widely used in design of columns and have proved reliable.

Formulas for Structural-steel Columns. The American Institute of Steel Construction specifications (AISC 1955) give the following formulas for *working* loads:

$$\frac{l}{r} \leqq 120, \qquad \frac{P_w}{a} = 17{,}000 - 0.485 \left(\frac{l}{r}\right)^2 \tag{167}$$

for both main and secondary members (such as bracing). This is, of course, a parabolic formula.

$$\frac{l}{r} > 120, \qquad \frac{P_w}{a} = \frac{18{,}000}{1 + (1/18{,}000)(l/r)^2} \tag{168}$$

for secondary members only (such as bracing). This is a Gordon-Rankine formula.

$$\frac{l}{r} > 120, \qquad \frac{P_w}{a} = \frac{18{,}000}{1 + (1/18{,}000)(l/r)^2} \left[1.6 - \frac{(l/r)}{200}\right] \tag{169}$$

for main members only.

The New York City Building Code specifications (1945) for structural-steel columns give the following formulas for *working* loads:

$$\frac{l}{r} < 60, \qquad \frac{P_w}{a} = 15{,}000 \tag{170}$$

$$\frac{l}{r} > 60, \qquad \frac{P_w}{a} = \frac{18{,}000}{1 + (1/18{,}000)(l/r)^2} \tag{171}$$

l/r must not exceed 120 for main columns or 200 for secondary columns (bracing).

Formulas for Structural-aluminum-alloy Columns. The Aluminum Company of America handbook (1955) gives the following formulas for the *ultimate* or *buckling* load of pin-ended aluminum-alloy columns:

Alloy 2014-T6: No safety factor

$$\frac{l}{r} < 54, \qquad \frac{P}{a} = 64{,}700 - 543\,\frac{l}{r} \qquad (172)$$

$$\frac{l}{r} > 54, \qquad \frac{P}{a} = \frac{\pi^2 E}{(l/r)^2} \qquad (173)$$

Alloy 6061-T6:

$$\frac{l}{r} < 63, \qquad \frac{P}{a} = 38{,}300 - 202\,\frac{l}{r} \qquad (174)$$

$$\frac{l}{r} > 63, \qquad \frac{P}{a} = \frac{\pi^2 E}{(l/r)^2} \qquad (175)$$

It should be noted that for small and intermediate values of l/r a straight-line formula is recommended, but for higher values of l/r the Euler formula is recommended in which $E = 10{,}300{,}000$ lb/in.^{2} is used. All values of P/a computed by these formulas (Eqs. 172 through 175) should be reduced by a factor of safety N to obtain the working load for the aluminum-alloy columns.

Timber Columns. Based on an extensive series of tests of timber, the Forest Products Laboratory recommended a fourth-power parabola for *working axial* loads for timber columns having intermediate values of l/r. The formula is

$$\frac{P_w}{a} = \sigma_0 \left[1 - \frac{1}{3}\left(\frac{l}{Cd}\right)^4 \right] \qquad (176)$$

in which σ_0 is the allowable compressive stress for short blocks tested parallel to the grain, C is a constant for a given grade and species of timber, and d is the least lateral dimension of the cross section. The value of C is equal to the value of l/d at the point where the parabola is tangent to Euler's curve and is given by the expression

$$C = \frac{\pi}{2}\sqrt{\frac{E}{6\sigma_0}}$$

For example, in the case of an oak column having a rectangular cross section and used under dry conditions, as in most buildings, Eq. 176 becomes ($E = 1{,}500{,}000$ lb per sq in.)

$$\frac{P_w}{a} = 1000 \left[1 - \frac{1}{164{,}000{,}000}\left(\frac{l}{r}\right)^4 \right] \qquad (177)$$

in which $r = d/\sqrt{12}$ is the least radius of gyration.   This equation is valid for values of l/d up to 25, l/r up to 86.

The Forest Products Laboratory formulas for various grades of timber have been adopted by the Building Code committee of the United States Department of Commerce and by the National Lumber Manufacturer's Association.

Illustrative Problems

Problem 262.   The parallel rod AB (Fig. 265) of a locomotive has a rectangular cross section 1 in. by 3 in. and is 6 ft long.   It is made of structural steel.   When the locomotive is starting, the rod acts mainly as an axially loaded column, the

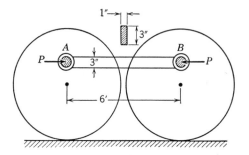

Fig. 265.   Locomotive parallel rod in compression.

cross bending due to the weight and to the inertia forces being negligible.   The rod may be considered to be a pin-ended column as regards bending in the vertical plane and a fixed-ended column as regards bending in a horizontal plane; owing to the shape of cross section, the bar tends to bend in the horizontal plane, but the restraint of the pins tends to cause it to bend in a vertical plane as a pin-ended column.   Find the working load to which the rod should be subjected, assuming that the effective length is the full length of the column ($k = 1$) if it acts as a pin-ended column and that $k = \frac{1}{2}$ if it acts as a fixed-ended column.

Solution.   (a) If we treat the rod as a pin-ended column:

$$r^2 = \frac{I_x}{a} = \frac{\frac{1}{12}bd^3}{bd} = \frac{1}{12}d^2 = \frac{1}{12}(3)^2 = 0.75 \text{ in.}^2$$

$$\left(\frac{l}{r}\right)^2 = \frac{(72)^2}{0.75} = 6910 \quad \text{and} \quad \frac{l}{r} = 83.2$$

If the Gordon-Rankine formula is used, we have

$$\frac{P_w}{a} = \frac{18,000}{1 + (1/18,000)(83.2)^2} = 13,000 \text{ lb/in.}^2$$

$$P_w = 3 \times 13,000 = 39,000 \text{ lb}$$

(b) If we treat the rod as a fixed-ended column:

$$r^2 = \frac{I_y}{a} = \frac{\frac{1}{12}db^3}{db} = \frac{1}{12} \text{ in.}^2, \qquad \left(\frac{l}{r}\right)^2 = \frac{(72)^2}{\frac{1}{12}} = 62,300 \quad \text{and} \quad \frac{l}{r} = 249$$

$$\frac{P_w}{a} = \frac{18,000}{1 + (1/18,000)(0.5 \times 249)^2} = 9670 \text{ lb/in.}^2$$

$$P_w = 3 \times 9670 = 29,000 \text{ lb}$$

Hence, for the problem as stated, the maximum working load would be 29,000 lb. If, however, the ends cannot be regarded as "fixed" with respect to bending in the horizontal plane, because of loose bearings, the value of k should be chosen larger than $\frac{1}{2}$. If k were chosen equal to $\frac{3}{4}$, the working load would be 18,300 lb, which would be the maximum working load for the bar.

Problem 263. An aluminum-alloy 6061-T6 column consists of a thin sheet 2 in. by 0.05 in., stiffened by riveting to the sheet a T section whose dimensions are as shown in Fig. 266. The column is 20 in. in length and is subjected to an

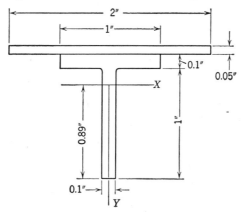

Fig. 266. Aluminum-column cross section.

axial load P. It is assumed that the column is pivot-ended. Compute the maximum value of the working or allowable load P based on a factor of safety $N = 1.5$.

Solution. By making use of the methods of Appendix I, we find the location of the centroidal axes x and y; we also find that $I_x = 0.0318$ in.^{4} and $I_y = 0.0408$ in.^{4} Hence the column will bend with respect to the x axis when it buckles. The least radius of gyration is

$$r_x = r = \sqrt{I_{x/a}} = \sqrt{0.0318/0.3} = 0.325 \text{ in.}$$

and

$$l/r = 20/0.325 = 61.5$$

The ultimate (buckling) load for a column made of this alloy is given by the equation

$$P/a = 38,300 - 202 l/r = 38,300 - 202 \times 61.5 = 25,900 \text{ lb/in.}^2$$

or

$$P = 25,900 \times 0.3 = 7770 \text{ lb}$$

The working or allowable load $P_w = P/N = 7770/1.5 = 5170$ lb.

Problem 264. Select a structural-steel I section for a column 7 ft long to resist an axial compressive working load of 90,000 lb, assuming that the column has round ends. Use AISC formulas.

Solution. The solution requires a method of trial and error. An approximate value of the area of the section needed may be found by considering the member to be a very short compression block for which $P/a = 17,000$ lb/in.^{2}, and, hence, $a = 90,000/17,000 = 5.3$ in.^{2}

From Table B, Appendix II, it is found that the minimum radius of gyration for I sections having areas from 5 to 6 in.^{2} is approximately 0.7, and hence l/r is approximately 120, which means that the area a in the formula $P_w/a = 17,000 - 0.485(l/r)^2$ must be considerably larger than 5.3 in.^{2} if P_w is to equal 90,000 lb when l/r is 120.

As a second trial select a 9-in. 21.8-lb I section for which $a = 6.32$ in.^{2} and $r_{min} = 0.90$ in. Then $l/r = 84/0.9 = 93.3$. Hence,

$$\frac{90,000}{a} = 17,000 - 0.485(93.3)^2 \quad \text{or} \quad a = 7.0 \text{ in.}^2 \quad \text{(approx.)}$$

Therefore a section having an area larger than 6.32 in.^{2} is needed. As a further trial select a 10-in. 22.4-lb I section for which $a = 6.54$ in.^{2}, $r_{min} = 1.17$ in., and hence $l/r = 72$. Then

$$a = \frac{90,000}{17,000 - 0.485(72)^2} = 6.2 \text{ in.}^2$$

Therefore, a 10-in. 22.4-lb I section having an area of 6.54 in.^{2} would be adequate

Problems

265. An aluminum-alloy 2014-T6 I section 8 in. deep weighing 8.81 lb per ft is used as a column having a length of 4 ft. The column has pivot ends. The structural aluminum handbook gives the following data for the I section: area of cross section: 7.49 in.^{2}, principal moments of inertia: 68.73 in.^{4} and 4.66 in.^{4}, corresponding radii of gyration: 3.03 in. and 0.79 in. Calculate the allowable load, using a factor of safety of 2.   *Ans.* $P_w = 103,700$ lb.

266. A standard 12-in. 27.9-lb structural-steel I beam 9 ft long is used as an axially loaded column with pivot ends. What is the allowable load for the column? (See Table B, Appendix II.)

267. An aluminum-alloy 6061-T6 round tube 6 in. outside diameter and $\frac{1}{4}$ in. thick weighing 5.311 lb per ft is used as a column having a length of 12 ft. Let it be assumed that the ends of the column are partly fixed so that the value of $k = 0.75$. The structural aluminum handbook gives the following data for the tube: area of cross section: 4.516 in.^{2}, moment of inertia: 18.7 in.^{4}, radius of gyration: 2.035 in. Determine the allowable load for the column using a factor of safety of 1.5.   *Ans.* $P_w = 83,000$ lb.

268. A structural-steel column assumed to have pin ends has a length of 20 ft and is made up of a 12-in.-by-$\frac{1}{2}$-in. plate, to which are riveted four 5-in.-by-3$\frac{1}{2}$-in.-by-$\frac{1}{2}$-in. angles, as shown in Fig. 267. Find the allowable axial load.

269. The member BC of the truss shown in Fig. 268 consists of an angle section having equal legs. Select the proper size of angle (use Table C, Appendix II), assuming the column to have pivot ends and to be axially loaded.

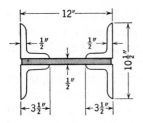

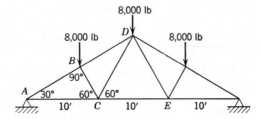

Fig. 267. Structural-steel-column cross section.

Fig. 268. Truss in which some members act as columns.

270. A cross section of a column is shown in Fig. 269. The column consists of four equal legs, 4-in.-by-4-in.-by-$\frac{1}{4}$-in. 6.6-lb-per-ft structural-steel angles (see Table C, Appendix II). *Hint.* $I_{1-1} = I_{2-2} = 21.2$ in.^{4} is the least moment of inertia (also $I_x = I_y = 21.2$ in.^{4} where x and y are horizontal and vertical axes).

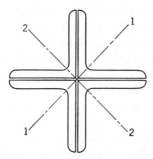

Fig. 269. Cross section of a steel column.

The column is used as a pin-ended column whose length is 18 ft. Compute the working or allowable axial load for the column if it is to be used in a structure as a secondary member.   *Ans.* $P_w = 72,000$ lb.

271. A 4-in.-by-4-in. oak timber is used as a pin-ended axially loaded column of length 6 ft. Compute the allowable or working load for the column.

    Ans. $P_w = 14,500$ lb.

272. A 4-in.-by-10-in. oak timber 16 ft long is used as an axially loaded column. The column has a lateral support at its midpoint that prevents lateral deflection in the direction of the 4-in. dimension but does not prevent lateral deflection in the direction of the 10-in. dimension. Compute the allowable or working load if the ends are considered as pivoted.   *Ans.* $P_w = 28,000$ lb.

§ 4   Columns under Combined Axial Compressive and Bending Loads. Beam Column

86. Two limiting cases. Two modes of failure. Let a straight bar be subjected to combined axial compressive and bending loads as indicated by Fig. 270. A member that is subjected to this combination of loads is sometimes called a beam column. Let it be required that a method be found for determining the maximum values of the combined loads P and M that the bar of Fig. 270 can resist. We consider first two special (limiting) cases of the combination of loads.

Axial Load Zero. Let it be assumed that the axial load is zero, which means that the remaining (bending) loads are resisted by the bar act-

ing as a beam (Chap. III), and hence the maximum value of M (the fully plastic value) for a ductile metal is $M_{fp} = K(\sigma_y I/C)$, as explained in Art. 53. It should be noted that, under the assumed conditions and for $P = 0$, the member fails by yielding, and the maximum value of M depends on the strength of the material as indicated by a stress (the yield point or yield strength of the material).

Bending Load Zero. If, however, the bending load M is zero, the remaining load P is an axial compressive load that is resisted by the bar acting as a column. If the axial load is increased, the bar (column) will fail by buckling, as described in this chapter, when the load per unit area P/a (or average stress σ) reaches a certain critical value P_{cr}/a (or σ_{cr}), as given by Eqs. 151 and

Fig. 270. Combined column and beam be-havior. A beam column.

158. For such a failure, the maximum load will not ordinarily be dependent on the strength of the material but on the stiffness of the material.

Thus, the maximum values of P and M must be such as to satisfy the condition that neither type of failure shall occur. This condition is difficult to satisfy exactly, but an inter-action curve, as discussed briefly in the next article, is a useful ap-proach to the problem.

87. Interaction curve for beam column. Let P/P_{cr} be the ratio of the axial load P in Fig. 270 to the load P_{cr} that would cause the col-umn to buckle if there were no bending load M, and let M/M_{fp} be the ratio of the bending moment M in Fig. 270 to the bending moment M_{fp} that would cause the bar to fail in bending if there were no axial load P. There is no satisfactory theoretical interaction equation for a *compressive* axial load combined with bending, but the following equa-tion is frequently used for approximate results:

$$P/P_{cr} + M/M_{fp} = 1 \qquad (178)$$

which is represented graphically in Fig. 271a by a straight line, AB. The ends A and B of this line have special significance. The point A represents the condition in which $M = 0$, and hence $P/P_{cr} = 1$ or

$P = P_{cr}$. The point B represents the condition in which $P = 0$, and hence $M/M_{fp} = 1$ or $M = M_{fp}$. The coordinates of any other point on the straight line between A and B, such as C, represent a combination of loads P and M that will, according to the assumed interaction relationship in Eq. 178, bring the beam column to the condition of impending failure, either by yielding in bending as a beam or by buckling as a column. The straight line AB is the simplest interaction relationship that can be written. A substantial number of tests of columns that were subjected to load P and M (as shown in Fig. 270) have been made in which the ultimate values of P and M have been determined. From

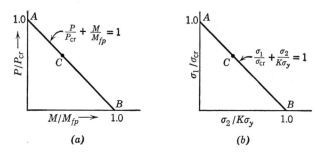

Fig. 271. Interaction curve for beam column.

the data obtained in these tests, the ratios P/P_{cr} and M/M_{fp} have been computed. When corresponding pairs of these values of P/P_{cr} and M/M_{fp} are plotted to represent points in Fig. 271a, the points in many instances lie above the line AB, and in some cases, though less frequently, the points lie below AB. However, the straight line AB has been used as a basis for the analysis of beam columns. It is given, for example, in the 1955 AISC specifications for the design of eccentrically loaded steel columns.

The reason that the interaction curve in Fig. 271a does not lie considerably above a straight line from A to B, as it did for combined *tension* and bending (Fig. 251), is that the deflection caused by M gives a moment to P which has the same sense as that of M, whereas, if P is a tensile load, the moment of P is opposite in sense to that of M.

For other forms of the interaction curve drawn between the points A and B, see, for example, that proposed for aluminum alloys by H. N. Hill, E. C. Hartman, and J. W. Clark in "Designing Aluminum Alloy Members for Combined End Load and Bending," *Proceedings American Society of Civil Engineering*, vol. 79, Separate no. 300.

Interaction Equation in Terms of Stresses. As previously noted, engineers usually prefer to deal with stresses in determining the load-carrying capacity of members. Therefore, Eq. 178 is frequently transformed so that it is stated in terms of stresses. In Eq. 178 we let $P = \sigma_1 a$, $P_{cr} = \sigma_{cr} a$, $M = \sigma_2 I/c$, $M_{fp} = K\sigma_y I/c$, where K is a factor that depends on the shape of the cross section (see Art. 53). When these values are substituted in Eq. 178, the following equation is the result:

$$\frac{\sigma_1}{\sigma_{cr}} + \frac{\sigma_2}{K\sigma_y} = 1 \tag{179}$$

Equation 179 is represented graphically in Fig. 271b. The coordinates of any point such as C on the line AB have similar meaning to those in Fig. 271a.

Working or Allowable Stresses. Let N_1 be the factor of safety for determining the working stress in an axially loaded column, and let N_2 be the factor of safety for determining the working stress in pure bending of a beam. These factors of safety are applied to the stresses in Eq. 179 as follows:

$$\frac{\sigma_1/N_1}{\sigma_{cr}/N_1} + \frac{\sigma_2/N_2}{K\sigma_y/N_2} = 1 \tag{180}$$

By letting $\sigma_a = \sigma_1/N_1$, $\sigma_A = \sigma_{cr}/N_1$, $\sigma_b = \sigma_2/N_2$ and $K\sigma_B = K\sigma_y/N_2$, we may rewrite Eq. 180 as follows:

$$\frac{\sigma_a}{\sigma_A} + \frac{\sigma_b}{K\sigma_B} = 1 \tag{181}$$

In Eq. 181, σ_A is the working stress in the member if it is subjected to an axial load only; $K\sigma_B$ is the working value of the maximum bending stress in the member if it is subjected to a bending load only (see Art. 53 for values of K). We let P_w be the working or allowable values of the axial load (see Fig. 270), and let M_w be the working or allowable value of the maximum bending moment. Then $\sigma_a = P_w/a$, and $\sigma_b = M_w c/I$, where σ_a and σ_b are the stresses as given by Eq. 181.

The use of Eqs. 178 through 181 is illustrated in the following problems.

Illustrative Problem

Problem 273. Calculate the working load for the eccentrically loaded aluminum-alloy 2014-T6 compression member shown in Fig. 272. Assume that the pins have slight "play" in their bearings and that the end conditions are intermediate between fixed ends and pivot ends, and hence the effective length of the column is between $\frac{1}{2}l$ and l. Assume the effective length to be $\frac{3}{4}l$. The value of the yield strength $\sigma_y = 63{,}000$ lb/in.^{2} Let $N_1 = N_2 = 2$.

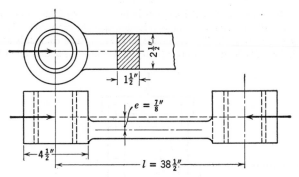

Fig. 272. Eccentrically loaded compression member (beam column).

Solution. $r_{\min} = \dfrac{d}{\sqrt{12}} = \dfrac{1.5}{3.46} = 0.433; \dfrac{kl}{r} = \dfrac{0.75 \times 38.5}{0.433} = 66.6.$

We use Eq. 181. The value of the stress σ_A in Eq. 181 is found as follows:

$$\sigma_A = \frac{\sigma_{\mathrm{cr}}}{N_1} = \frac{P}{2a} = \frac{1}{2}\frac{\pi^2 \times 10^7}{(66.6)^2} = 11,100 \text{ lb/in.}^2$$

The value of $K\sigma_B$ in Eq. 181 is found as follows: $K = 1.5$ since the cross section is a rectangle, and $K\sigma_B = K\sigma_y/N_2 = 1.5 \times 63,000/2 = 47,250$ lb/in.^{2} The value of σ_a in Eq. 181 is $\sigma_a = P_w/a = P_w/3.75$. The value of σ_b is $\sigma_b = \dfrac{Mc}{I} = \dfrac{0.875P_w(0.75)}{\frac{1}{12} \times 2.5(1.5)^3}$ $= 0.935P_w$. These values are substituted in Eq. 181, which gives

$$\frac{P_w/3.75}{11,100} + \frac{0.935P_w}{47,250} = 1 \quad \text{or} \quad P_w = 22,800 \text{ lb}$$

Problems

274. A pin-ended structural-steel column 20 ft long has the cross section shown in Fig. 273. It is subjected to a load applied at A having an eccentricity of 2 in. Calculate the allowable load for the column by using Eq. 181. Let $K = 1$, and let $\sigma_B = 20,000$ lb/in.^{2} in Eq. 181.

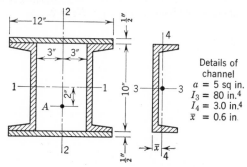

Fig. 273. Cross section of eccentrically loaded steel compression member.

275. A latticed pin-ended steel column is made of two 10-in. 15.3-lb channels (Fig. 274). The distance h between backs is such that the moments of inertia about the x and y axes are equal. The column is 20 ft long. The column is subjected to an eccentric load P_w having an eccentricity of 1.5 in., the action line of the load

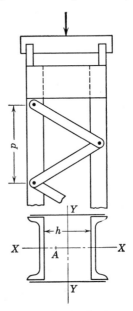

Fig. 274. Latticed column.

passing through the point A. Calculate the slenderness ratio and the working load for the column. Assume that the effective length of the column is $\frac{7}{8}l$. Use Eq. 181 and let $K = 1$, and let $\sigma_B = 20{,}000$ lb/in.[2]

276. An aluminum-alloy 2014-T6 bar, 6 ft long and 3 in. in diameter, is subjected to an eccentric load whose action line is parallel to the longitudinal axis of the bar and is 1 in. from the axis. Compute the working load for the bar by using Eq. 181. For a circular section $K = 1.7$. (See Art. 53.) Assume $\sigma_y = 63{,}000$ lb/in.[2] The ends are assumed to be pivoted. Let $N_1 = N_2 = 2$.

Chapter VII

STATICALLY INDETERMINATE

MEMBERS

§ 1 Elastic Behavior

88. Introduction. In determining the stresses in, and deformation or deflection of, a member as treated in the preceding chapters, it was assumed that all the forces (loads and reactions) acting on the member were known or could be found from the equation of equilibrium. Even though a member is known to be in equilibrium under the action of an external-force system, it may not be possible to determine all the unknown forces and couples acting on the member from the equations of equilibrium alone. The reason for this situation is that the number of unknowns in the force system may be greater than the number of equations of equilibrium for the force system involved. Such a force system, and also the member on which it acts, is said to be statically indeterminate.

A force system in which the number of unknowns is greater by one than the number of equations of equilibrium for the force system is said to be statically indeterminate to the first degree. Similarly, if the number of unknowns exceeds by two the number of equations of equilibrium, the force system is said to be statically indeterminate to the second degree, etc.

The equations of equilibrium are always applicable to a statically indeterminate force system, but additional equations involving the forces must be found, to be used in conjunction with the equations of equilibrium, in order to determine all of the unknown forces and couples acting on the statically indeterminate member. These additional equations are obtained from the relationships developed in the preceding chapters as explained later in this article and in Art. 89.

Redundant Member. The physical meaning of statical indeterminateness is seen in the condition that there are more supports or more mem-

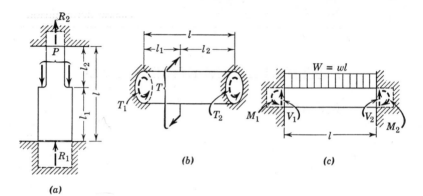

Fig. 275. Members with one redundant element.

bers present in the member or structure than are necessary to maintain stability or equilibrium of the structure. Supports or members that may be removed without the equilibrium of the structure being destroyed are said to be redundant elements, or, more specifically, redundant supports or redundant members. Thus a statically indeterminate structure is transformed to a stable statically determinate structure by the removal of the redundant elements.

For example, in Fig. 275a and b, the members have one redundant element, and either one of the unknown reactions (indicated by dashed lines) may be considered to be the redundant element and may be removed without the equilibrium of the member being destroyed; in other words, the remaining structure is a statically determinate structure. Likewise, in Fig. 275c, two of the four unknown reactions (shown by dashed lines) are redundant elements and may be removed without the equilibrium of the remaining structure being destroyed.

Importance of Deformations of the Members. The additional equations needed to supplement the equations of equilibrium in determining the reactions on a statically indeterminate member are obtained by expressing the fact that the unknown reactions must be such that the total force system acting on the member, will be consistent with the geometry of the deformations of the member. For example, in Fig. 275c the ends of the beam are fixed, which means that the slope and deflection of the elastic curve of the beam at each end must be equal to zero. By use of these conditions, two equations involving unknown reactions may be found, which may be used in conjunction with the two equations of equilibrium for the force system, in order to evaluate the four unknown reactions.

In the foregoing chapters the relationships of the forces acting on certain types of members and the corresponding elastic deformations were found. These relationships will be used in this chapter as indicated in the next article. Furthermore, several relatively simple types of problems involving statically indeterminate members were treated in the preceding chapters, although they were not classified as such (see Probs. 209 and 221). It is desirable, however, to have available a general method or procedure for determining the forces acting on statically indeterminate members as developed in Art. 89.

Two Uses of Relationships between Loads and Elastic Deflections. It is important to observe that the relationships between loads and elastic deflections, as developed for beams in Chapter IV and for tensile and torsional members in parts of Chapters I and II, are used for two purposes: (1) to determine the desired deflections of the member in terms of the known forces (loads and reactions) acting on the member, and (2) to obtain equations to supplement the equations of equilibrium in determining the forces acting on a statically indeterminate member; after the second use has been made of the relationships and the forces acting on the statically indeterminate member are known, the first use may be made of the relationships for determining the deflection of the statically indeterminate member.

89. Method of solution. The procedure for determining the forces and couples exerted by redundant elements of statically indeterminate members varies somewhat according to the type of problem, but the main steps in the procedure may be stated as follows:

First, draw a free-body diagram of the member showing all loads and reactions and then remove the redundant elements (force or couple), thereby making the remaining loads and reactions on the member statically determinate; the reactions that act on *this* member may, of course, be found if needed from the equations of equilibrium. Next, by use of the principles discussed in the preceding chapters, write an expression, in terms of the forces acting on this statically determinate member, for the elastic deformations of the member at the point or sections where the redundant members or reactions were removed; these deformations (linear and angular) should be in the direction of the redundant force or couple that was removed.

Now draw a second free-body diagram of the member with the loads removed but with the redundant forces and couples that were removed in the first step *reapplied to the member*, and, by use of the same principles, write expressions for the elastic deformations that are produced at the points or sections where the redundant forces or couples are reapplied.   *HAVE A KNOWN RELATION SHIP*

Thus an expression is found for each of two deformations that ~~have the same magnitudes~~; one expression involves *known* forces acting on a statically determinate member, and the other involves unknown forces exerted by the redundant elements.   By equating these expressions, an additional equation or equations are obtained, and thus a solution is found.   After the forces exerted by the redundant elements are obtained, the original member then becomes statically determinate and can be analyzed for stresses and deflections as in the preceding chapters.

The foregoing procedure will be used in the following illustrative problems which deal with the three simple examples of statically indeterminate members shown in Fig. 275.

Illustrative Problems

Problem 277.   The member in Fig. 276a is held by two rigid supports A and B.   When the load P is applied, the supports exert the reactions R_1 and R_2 on

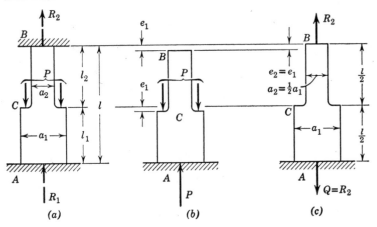

Fig. 276.   Method of solution for determining redundant element in axially loaded member.

the member. Determine the magnitudes of R_1 and R_2 if $a_2 = \frac{1}{2}a_1$, where a_1 and a_2 are the cross-sectional areas of the two parts AC and CB, and $l_1 = l_2 = \frac{1}{2}l$. The known quantities are P, a_1, a_2, l, and E, the modulus of elasticity of the material. Assume that the elastic limit of the material is not exceeded.

Solution. From equilibrium: $P = R_1 + R_2$. The geometry of deformation of the member must be such that the deflection of B (also of A) shall be equal to zero. In Fig. 276a let the redundant element R_2 be removed; the remaining member as shown in Fig. 276b is statically determinate, and the deformation e_1 of part AC, and also the deflection of B is $e_1 = P(l/2)/a_1E$. Now let the load P be removed and the reaction R_2 be reapplied at B as shown in Fig. 276c; this will cause A to exert a reaction Q that is equal and opposite to R_2. The deformation or deflection e_2 at the section B may now be calculated. Thus,

$$e_2 = \frac{R_2l/2}{a_2E} + \frac{R_2l/2}{a_1E} = \frac{3}{2}\frac{R_2l}{a_1E}$$

But since B does not deflect, $e_1 = e_2$. Hence,

$$\frac{1}{2}\frac{Pl}{a_1E} = \frac{3}{2}\frac{R_2l}{a_1E}$$

Therefore, $R_2 = P/3$, and $R_1 = 2P/3$. The stresses and deformation of the member of Fig. 276a may now be found in accordance with the principles of Chapter I.

Problem 278. The cylindrical bar in Fig. 277a is prevented from twisting at its ends by rigid supports which exert the reactions T_1 and T_2 when a twisting

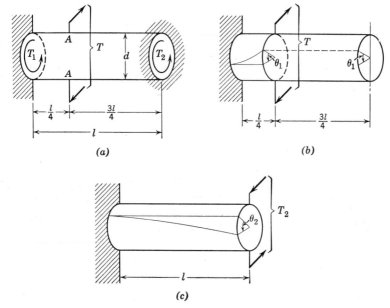

(a) (b)

(c)

Fig. 277. Method of solution for determining redundant element in torsion member.

moment T is applied at section AA. Determine the reactions T_1 and T_2 of the rigid supports if it is assumed that the elastic limit of the material is not exceeded. The known quantities are T, l, J, and G.

Solution. Equilibrium gives $T = T_1 + T_2$. The geometry of deformations of the member must be such that the angle of twist at each end shall be equal to zero. Let the redundant element T_2 be removed; the remaining member is shown in Fig. 277b. The angle of twist of section AA with respect to the left support is $\theta_1 = (Tl/4)/JG$ (see Art. 28), and the right-hand end has the same angle of twist.

Now let the twisting moment T be removed, and let the reaction T_2 be reapplied as shown in Fig. 277c. The resulting angle of twist θ_2 of the right-hand end is $\theta_2 = T_2l/JG$. But, since the end of the bar does not turn, we have

$$\theta_1 = \theta_2. \quad \text{Thus} \quad \frac{Tl/4}{JG} = \frac{T_2l}{JG} \quad \text{or} \quad T_2 = \frac{T}{4}$$

Therefore, $T_1 = 3T/4$.

Problem 279. The beam in Fig. 278a is rigidly held (fixed) at each end so that the ends cannot deflect vertically or rotate when the uniformly distributed total load W is applied. Determine the reacting shear and bending couple shown

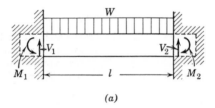

(a)

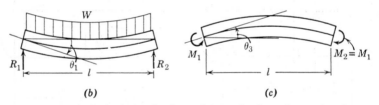

(b)   (c)

Fig. 278. Method of solution for determining redundant element in a beam.

at each end in Fig. 278a. The known quantities are W, l, I, and E. Assume that the elastic limit of the material is not exceeded.

Solution. By use of the two equations of equilibrium and the condition of symmetry, we find $V_1 = V_2 = W/2$, and $M_1 = M_2$. Therefore, by use of symmetry in addition to equilibrium, the two redundant elements are reduced to one. Let the redundant moment $M_1 = M_2$ at each end be removed; the remaining member is shown in Fig. 278b. The changes of slope θ_1 and θ_2 at the two ends are equal and are given by the expression $\theta_1 = \theta_2 = \frac{1}{24} Wl^2/EI$. (See Art. 61.) The redundant couple M_1 must produce a change of slope θ_3 equal and opposite to θ_1, but $\theta_3 = M_1l/2EI$. (See Art. 61.) Therefore,

$$\frac{1}{24} \frac{Wl^2}{EI} = \frac{M_1l}{2EI}. \quad \text{Hence,} \quad M_1 = \frac{1}{12} Wl$$

Problems

280. In Fig. 279, AB is a rigid bar that is supported at A by a frictionless pin and by wires CD and EF; each wire has a cross-sectional area of 0.10 sq in. and a length of l in. Wire CD is made of steel, and EF is made of an aluminum alloy.

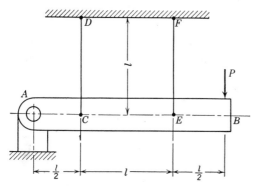

Fig. 279. Statically indeterminate tension members.

(See Table 1.) If the maximum allowable elastic stress in either wire is 20,000 lb/in.², determine the maximum allowable value of P. *Ans.* $P = 2000$ lb.

281. In Fig. 280 a cylindrical shaft of length l and diameter $2c$ is fixed at each end and is subjected to twisting moments T and $2T$ at the third points. Determine the resisting twisting moments at the fixed ends in terms of T; assume that the shaft is not stressed above the elastic limit of the material.

Ans. $T_A = 0$; $T_B = T$.

282. A horizontal cantilever beam rests at its free end on a spring so that, when there is no load applied, the beam and spring are just barely in contact (no force exerted on beam by the spring). The downward load P then is applied at the free end of the beam. The spring is now deflected the same amount δ as is the free end of the beam. If the reaction R of the spring on the beam is $R = K\delta$, where K is the spring constant, determine the deflection δ and the force R in terms of K, l, E, I, and P. Assume that the elastic limit of the material in the beam or spring is not exceeded.

Ans. $R = \dfrac{Pl^3}{(3EI/K) + l^3}$.

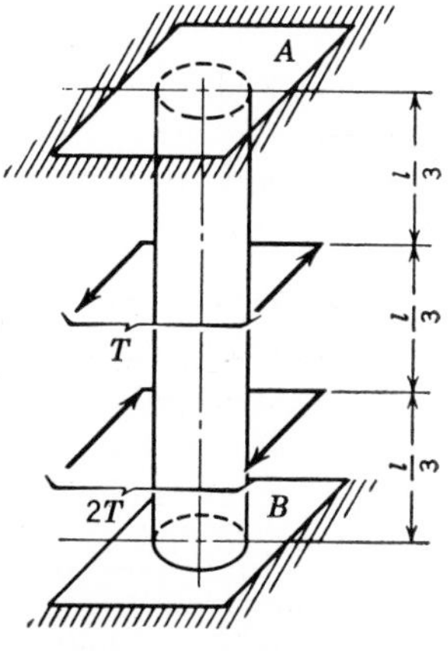

Fig. 280. Statically indeterminate torsion member.

283. Two cantilever beams of identical lengths, cross sections, and materials are arranged as shown in Fig. 281, with a roller that just fits snugly between them when there is no load on either beam. The load P then is applied on the upper beam directly above the roller. Assume that the elastic limit of the material is

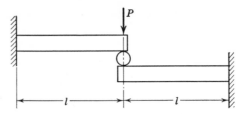

Fig. 281. Statically indeterminate beams.

not exceeded. Determine the vertical deflection at the roller and the reaction R of the roller on the beams.   *Ans.* $R = P/2$.

284. The tapered shaft with a circular cross section shown in Fig. 282 is fixed at each end. If the shaft is subjected to a twisting moment T at its midsection,

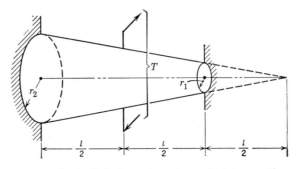

Fig. 282. Statically indeterminate tapered torsion member.

determine the values of the resisting twisting moment at each end. Assume that the elastic limit of the material is not exceeded. *Ans.* $T_1 = \frac{19}{208}T$; $T_2 = \frac{189}{208}T$.

90. Further study of statically indeterminate beams.

In a *statically determinate* beam, as shown in Chapter III, the elastic strength of the beam is determined by the stresses at only one section of the beam—the section at which the maximum moment occurs. The maximum loads are limited to the values that cause the elastic limit on the most stressed fiber at this one section. This means that all *other* sections are understressed, provided that the beam has a constant cross section, and hence much of the material in the beam is not used effectively.

On the other hand, in a *statically indeterminate* beam, such as a fixed-ended beam or one that is continuous over three or more supports, the bending moment is distributed along the length of the beam so that more effective use is made of the beam. Thus, in general, the elastic strength and stiffness of a statically indeterminate beam are greater than those of a statically determinate beam, other conditions being assumed to be the same.

These facts will be emphasized in the following articles of § 1. The method of analysis discussed in the foregoing articles of this chapter will be applied in detail, in the next article, to one type of fixed-ended beam. Other fixed-ended beams may be treated by the same method.

Continuous Beam. Statically indeterminate beams especially in the form of continuous beams are treated further in Chapter XV.

91. Beam fixed at one end, supported at other end; uniform load. Figure 283a represents such a beam, the tangent line to the elastic curve at the wall being horizontal; the length of span is l, and the load per unit of length is w. It is assumed that the elastic limit of the material in the beam is not exceeded. As shown in Fig. 283b, the beam is held in equilibrium by parallel forces of which all three reactions, R_1, R_2, and R_3, are unknown. Thus, it is necessary to use an equation obtained from the deformation of the member in addition to the two equations of equilibrium in order to determine the reactions. The equations for the deflection of beams are obtained from Chapter IV by the moment-area method, but they may just as well be obtained by the double-integration method (Chap. XIII) or by the conjugate-beam method (Chap. XIV).

The forces R_2 and R_3 are equivalent to an upward force and a bending couple, and, since the part of the beam outside the wall is of prime importance, it is convenient to assume that the beam is cut off flush with the face of the wall at the section AA (Fig. 283b) and that R_2 and R_3 are replaced by the forces which they cause on this section: namely, the upward shearing force V_0 and the bending couple M_0, as shown in Fig. 283c. It should be observed that V_0 and M_0 are the resisting shear and resisting moment, respectively, at the section for the beam shown in Fig. 283c, and are equal in magnitude but opposite in sense to the vertical (external) shear and bending (external) moment for the section of the beam.

The three reactions to be found, then, are R_1, V_0, and M_0. The value of R_1 may be found by the method of Art. 89, and V_0 and M_0 then may be found from the two equations of equilibrium:

Reaction R. If the left support were removed, the beam would become a cantilever beam, as shown in Fig. 283d, and the uniform load on the beam would cause the free end to deflect a distance $\delta_1 = wl^4/8EI$ (see Prob. 205). But, since the end does not deflect, the reaction R_1 must be a force which, if acting alone (Fig. 283e) on the end of the cantilever, would cause an upward deflection equal to δ_2. But the deflection due to the concentrated load R_1 on the free end of a cantilever is

$$\delta_2 = \frac{1}{3}\frac{R_1 l^3}{EI} \quad \text{(Art. 66)} \quad \text{and since} \quad \delta_1 = \delta_2$$

$$\frac{1}{3}\frac{R_1 l^3}{EI} = \frac{1}{8}\frac{wl^4}{EI}. \quad \text{Therefore,} \quad R_1 = \frac{3}{8}wl$$

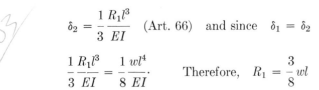

Reactions M_0 and V_0. From the two equations of equilibrium ($\Sigma F = 0$ and $\Sigma M = 0$), we obtain the values of V_0 and M_0. Thus,

$$\Sigma F = \tfrac{3}{8}wl + V_0 - wl = 0; \quad \text{hence} \quad V_0 = \tfrac{5}{8}wl$$

$$\Sigma M_A = \frac{3}{8}wl \cdot l - wl\frac{l}{2} + M_0 = 0; \quad \text{hence} \quad M_0 = \frac{1}{8}wl^2$$

As previously noted, the vertical shear and bending moment at the wall are equal *but opposite* to the reactions V_0 and M_0 and hence are negative, the vertical shear being downward and the bending moment causing tensile stress on the top side of the beam. Thus, if V_0 and M_0 denote the vertical shear and bending moment at the wall (as indicated in Fig. 283f),

$$V_0 = -\tfrac{5}{8}wl \quad \text{and} \quad M_0 = -\tfrac{1}{8}wl^2$$

Shear and Moment Diagrams. Maximum Positive Moment. The vertical shear for a section at distance x from the right support is

$$V_x = \tfrac{5}{8}wl - wx$$

and this equation shows that the shear is zero when $x = \tfrac{5}{8}l$; the shear diagram is shown in Fig. 283f.

The bending moment for a section at the distance x from the support is

$$M_x = \frac{5}{8}wlx - wx \cdot \frac{x}{2} - \frac{1}{8}wl^2 \tag{182}$$

The bending moment has its maximum value at the section for which the vertical shear is zero (Art. 41), and hence the maximum positive bending moment is

$$\text{Pos. } M_{\max} = \tfrac{5}{8}wl \cdot \tfrac{5}{8}l - w\tfrac{5}{8}l \cdot \tfrac{1}{2}\tfrac{5}{8}l - \tfrac{1}{8}wl^2 = \tfrac{9}{128}wl^2 \tag{183}$$

The inflection point is found by equating M_x to zero. Thus,

$$\frac{5}{8}wlx - \frac{wx^2}{2} - \frac{1}{8}wl^2 = 0; \quad \text{hence} \quad x = \frac{1}{4}l$$

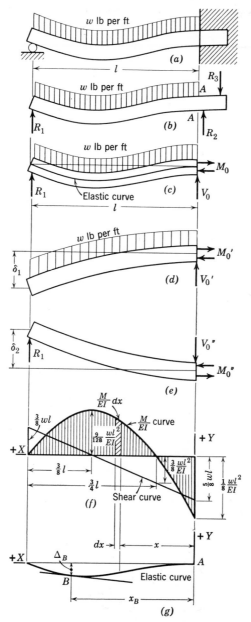

Fig. 283. Method of analysis of elastic stresses and deflections for one type of statically indeterminate beam.

The bending-moment diagram is shown in Fig. 283f. It should be observed that the M diagram and the M/EI diagram have the same shape if the cross section of the beam is constant.

The maximum negative bending moment $(-\frac{1}{8}wl^2)$, which occurs at the wall, is greater than the maximum positive moment. Thus the greatest elastic stress in this type of beam occurs at the wall and may be found from the flexure formula $\sigma = Mc/I$ by usiug $\frac{1}{8}wl^2$ for M.

Beam Deflection. The deflection Δ at any point B whose distance is x from the right-hand end (Fig. 283g) is obtained here by using the moment-area method, but the reader who has learned the double-integration method (Chap. XIII) or the conjugate-beam method (Chap. XIV) should find the deflection by one of these methods. Thus, in Fig. 283g the deflection Δ_B at any point B on the elastic curve at the distance x_B from the right end is equal to the tangential deviation t_{BA} of the point B from the horizontal tangent at A. From Fig. 283f, we have, by taking the sum of the moments of the areas $\dfrac{M \, dx}{EI}$ about an ordinate through B,

$$\Delta_B = t_{BA} = \int_0^{x_B} \frac{M(x_B - x)}{EI} \, dx \tag{184}$$

From Eq. 182 we substitute the value of M_x for M in the integral of Eq. 184 which gives

$$\Delta_B = t_{BA} = \frac{1}{EI} \int_0^{x_B} \left(\frac{5}{8} wlx - \frac{wx^2}{2} - \frac{1}{8} wl^2 \right) (x_B - x) \, dx$$

$$= \tfrac{5}{48} wlx_B{}^3 - \tfrac{1}{24} wx_B{}^4 - \tfrac{1}{16} wl^2 x_B{}^2$$

The maximum deflection is found from the equation $d\Delta_B/dx = 0$ to occur at the distance $x = 0.5785l$ from the right end, and its value is

$$\Delta_{\max} = -0.0054 \frac{wl^4}{EI} \tag{185}$$

Problems

285. In Fig. 284 a rigid (but weightless) member ABC is subjected to a load P which does not cause stresses above the elastic limit of the material. The steel wires AD and CF each have a cross section of $a = 0.05$ in.^{2} Which one of the wires carries the larger stress? Compute the value of P that will cause the greater stressed wire to be on the verge of yielding if the yield point of the steel is 100,000 lb/in.^{2} *Note.* The general procedure of Art. 89 may be shortened somewhat if

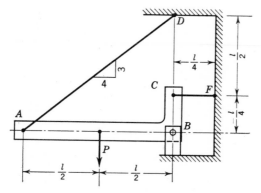

Fig. 284. Statically indeterminate beam.

advantage is taken of the fact that there is a direct relationship between the elongation of AD and CF when the rigid bar ABC rotates about the pin B; namely $e_{AD} = \frac{12}{5}e_{CF}$.

286. Show that, for the beam in Fig. 285a, the elastic bending moments at the wall sections of the beam are $M_1 = M_2 = -\frac{1}{12}wl^2$ as indicated in Fig. 285b and

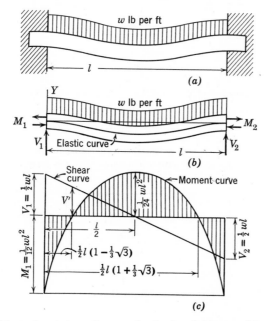

Fig. 285. Moment and shear diagrams for fixed-ended beam with uniform load.

$c.$ Also show that the maximum positive bending moment is $\frac{1}{24}wl^2$ and that the maximum elastic deflection Δ is $-\dfrac{1}{384}\dfrac{wl^4}{EI}$.

287. For the beam illustrated in Fig. 286a, show that the elastic moments at the wall sections are $M_1 = M_2 = -\frac{1}{8}Pl$. Also show that the shear and moment

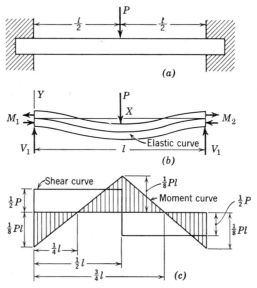

(a)

(b)

(c)

Fig. 286. Moment and shear diagrams for fixed-ended beam with concentrated load at center of span.

diagrams in Fig. 286c are correct and that the maximum elastic deflection is

$$\Delta = -\frac{1}{192}\frac{Pl^3}{EI}$$

288. For the elastic behavior of the beam indicated in Fig. 287 with one end fixed and the other end simply supported, show that the reaction at A and the

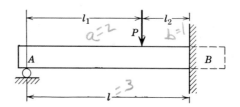

Fig. 287. Beam fixed at one end.

fixed-end moment at B are

$$R_A = \frac{Pl_2{}^2}{l^3}\left(\frac{3}{2}l_1 + l_2\right) \quad \text{and} \quad M_B = -\frac{Pl_1l_2(2l - l_2)}{2l^2}$$

289. Show that, for the elastic behavior of the fixed-end beam indicated in

Fig. 288, the moments at the ends A and B are

$$M_A = -\frac{wl_2^3}{3l}\left(1 - \frac{3}{4}\frac{l_2}{l}\right), \qquad M_B = -wl_2^2\left(\frac{1}{2} - \frac{2}{3}\frac{l_2}{l} + \frac{1}{4}\frac{l_2^2}{l^2}\right)$$

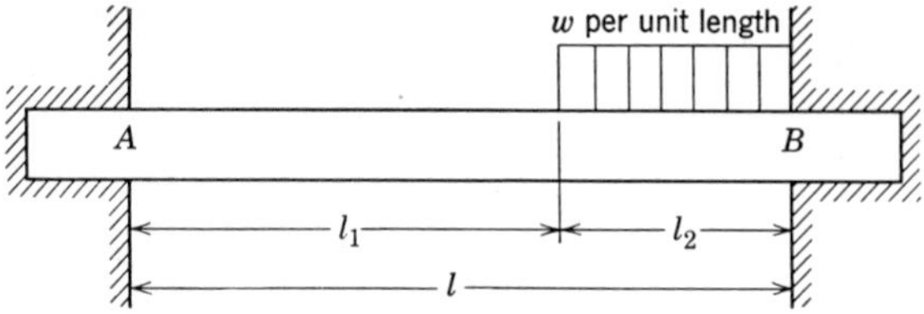

Fig. 288. Beam fixed at both ends.

92. Comparison of simply supported and fixed-ended beams.

For purely elastic action Table 6 gives a summary of some of the results that may be obtained for statically indeterminate (fixed-ended) beams by the procedure discussed in Art. 89. These results should be compared with those given in Table 5 in Art. 70 for simply supported

TABLE 6

Type of Beam and of Loads	Maximum Bending Moment		Maximum Deflection, Δ
	Positive	Negative	
Fixed at both ends:			
(a) Uniform load	$\frac{1}{24} Wl$	$\frac{1}{12} Wl$	$\frac{1}{384}\frac{Wl^3}{EI}$
(b) Concentrated load at center	$\frac{1}{8} Wl$	$\frac{1}{8} Wl$	$\frac{1}{192}\frac{Wl^3}{EI}$
Fixed at one end; supported at other end:			
(a) Uniform load	$\frac{9}{128} Wl$	$\frac{1}{8} Wl$	$0.0054\frac{Wl^3}{EI}$
(b) Concentrated load at center	$\frac{5}{32} Wl$	$\frac{3}{16} Wl$	$0.0093\frac{Wl^3}{EI}$

beams, and it should be observed that the conclusion reached in Art. 70 as expressed by Eq. 123 also applies to fixed-ended beams. In Table 6, W is the total load on the beam and l is the span.

Influence of Fixing Ends of Beam. In the preceding articles it has been shown that a fixed-ended beam is elastically stronger and stiffer than a similar beam that is simply supported at its ends. This is true because the positive bending moment in the central portion of a beam is decreased, owing to the negative moment at the ends, and thus more of the material of a fixed beam is effective in resisting the loads than in the simply supported beam.

The effect of applying negative moments at the ends of a simply supported beam is shown in Fig. 289. The curve CED, referred to CD as a base line, represents the bending-moment diagram for a simply supported beam subjected to a uniformly distributed load of w per unit length, the maximum elastic bending moment is at the midspan and is equal to $\frac{1}{8}wl^2$. If the beam were a fixed-ended beam, the nega-

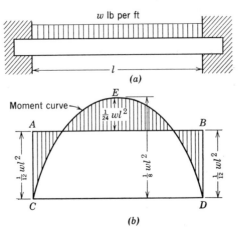

Fig. 289. Comparison of simply supported and fixed-ended beams.

tive moments at the ends would be $\frac{1}{12}wl^2$ (as given in Fig. 285), and the curve CED still would represent the moment diagram if AB (Fig. 289) instead of CD represents the axis or base line. Thus the moment at the center is decreased by the amount of the negative moment at the end.

Generalizing, in a beam fixed at both ends, and uniformly loaded, the sum of the maximum elastic negative and positive moments is equal to the maximum moment in a similarly loaded simple beam. The student should show that this statement is true also if the load is concentrated at the midspan.

93. Need for modifying results of elastic analysis. Frequently it is difficult to determine to what extent a beam is restrained at the ends, since yielding or inelastic behavior of the end-restraining bodies such as abutments and riveted end connections redistributes the bending moments over the length, so that the values of the maximum positive and maximum negative moments approach each other in magnitude. Likewise, unequal settlements of the ends and temperature changes influence the stresses in fixed-ended beams to a greater extent than in simply supported beams. For these reasons stresses and deflections of beams as found from an elastic analysis of statically indeterminate members frequently are modified, based on observations and results of experience and experimental investigations. This fact does not mean that the results of an elastic analysis are not important. In fact, frequently, it is the only analysis that can be made, and even though it is known to be only an approximation to the information desired for the real physical problem, it gives pertinent information that is conservative (on the safe side), and the results often may be modified to obtain a still more satisfactory solution.

The modifications of the elastic analysis consist mainly of the introduction of the influences of small amounts of inelastic deformations at sections of maximum stress in the member. This topic is discussed briefly in § 2 which follows.

§ 2   Inelastic Behavior

94. Introduction.   In § 1 it was assumed that a statically indeterminate member would be damaged (would fail to perform its load-resisting function) if the stress at any point in the member exceeded the elastic limit of the material. The load (or system of loads) acting on the member when the maximum stress reaches the elastic limit is called the elastic-limit load and is designated by P_y.

If now the loads are increased above P_y, inelastic strains will, in general, penetrate across the section or sections where the elastic-limit stress first occurred (see Art 52 and Fig. 187). And, since the material is assumed to be ductile or to have a stress-strain diagram like that shown in Fig. 63, the stress in the inelastically strained section (or sections) will remain constant and be equal to the yield point of the material as the applied loads increase until the fully plastic condition is reached (plastic hinges are formed) at a sufficient number of sections to cause the member or structure to collapse if the loads are increased.

The behavior of the member or structure as a whole is substantially elastic until the fully plastic loads for the whole member or structure are reached. For, as was pointed out in Arts. 17 and 52, the inelastic strains at any section where the fully plastic condition develops are of the same order of magnitude as the elastic-limit strains for the material, until the fully plastic condition for the whole member or structure is reached, after which the inelastic strains on all sections where the fully plastic condition has developed increase rapidly as the member becomes greatly distorted or collapses.

The fully plastic load is designated as P_p, and it, rather than P_y, often represents the maximum load that the member can resist without being damaged. It is seen, therefore, that both the elastic analysis and the inelastic analysis are important in determining the significant load-carrying capacity of a member. The value of P_y is one limiting value of the maximum load (the lower limit), and P_p is another limiting value (the upper limit) that may be applied to the member without damaging its load-carrying function. The specifications in various design codes are often determined by requiring that the maximum load that the member can be expected to resist shall lie between these two limits.

The method of determining the value of P_p is best described by examples which are provided in the remaining portion of this chapter.

95. Fully plastic load for simple axially loaded structure. The method of determining the fully plastic load will be demonstrated first for axially loaded statically indeterminate members, but the same method is used for members subjected to torsional or to bending loads.

Illustrative Problem

Problem 290. Let a rigid bar AB be supported by the three pin-connected members CD, EF, and GH as shown in Fig. 290. Let it be assumed that the three members are made of the same material, and hence have the same yield point σ_y. Let it be assumed also that the three members have the same cross-sectional area a. It is required to find, in terms of σ_y and a, the value of the load P_p that will cause all three members CD, EF, and GH to be in the fully plastic condition. This means that the stress in each member will have reached the yield point σ_y when the load reaches the value P_p. But first we shall solve the problem by assuming elastic behavior in all three members so that a value of the elastic-limit load P_y can be computed to be compared with P_p.

Elastic Solution. The method of § 1 of this chapter is used to express the load P in terms of the elastic forces T_1, T_2, and T_3 in the members CD, GH, and EF, respectively. Let Fig. 290*b* represent a free-body diagram of the rigid bar AB. From the two equilibrium conditions we have the following equations:

$$\Sigma F = 0, \qquad P = T_1 + T_2 + T_3$$

$$\Sigma M = 0, \qquad T_1 = T_3 \qquad\qquad (a)$$

To obtain one additional equation needed for the solution, we use the special method demonstrated in Illustrative Prob. 277; that is, a relationship among T_1, T_2, and T_3 is found from the fact that all three members elongate the same amount e. Hence,

$$e_1 = e_2 = e, \qquad \frac{T_1 l_1}{a_1 E_1} = \frac{T_2 l_2}{a_2 E_2} \qquad\qquad (b)$$

But $a_1 = a_2 = a$, and $E_1 = E_2 = E$, since the members have the same cross-sec-

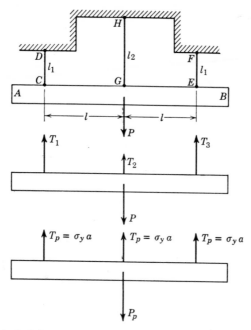

Fig. 290. Method of determining the fully plastic load in axially loaded members of a simple statically indeterminate structure.

tion area and are of the same material. Therefore,

$$T_2 = \frac{l_1}{l_2} T_1 \qquad (c)$$

By combining Eq. c with the equilibrium equations (Eqs. a), the following results are obtained:

$$T_1 = T_3 = \frac{P}{2 + l_1/l_2} \quad \text{and} \quad T_2 = \frac{l_1}{l_2}\left(\frac{P}{2 + l_1/l_2}\right) \qquad (d)$$

Elastic-limit Load P_y. The elastic-limit load P_y is obtained from Eqs. d by assuming that the tensile stress in members CD and EF, which are the highest-stressed members, have reached σ_y, the yield-point (also elastic-limit) stress. For this assumption, $T_1 = T_3 = \sigma_y a$, and this value is substituted in Eqs. d which gives the value of P_y. The result is:

$$P_y = \sigma_y a \left(2 + \frac{l_1}{l_2}\right) \qquad (e)$$

It should be noted that, when the load is P_y, the two members CD and EF are on the verge of behaving inelastically while the member GH is behaving elastically, since the stress in this member is still well below σ_y.

Method of Determining P_p. From the foregoing discussion it is seen that it is necessary to increase the load above the value P_y, in order to cause the third (and last) member GH to be stressed to the value σ_y, and hence to be on the verge of inelastic behavior. Let it be assumed that the load is increased to values greater than P_y. At some load $P_p > P_y$ the stress in the third member GH will reach σ_y. While this is occurring, the stress in members CD and EF remains at the value σ_y, since, at the yield-point stress, each of the members will continue to elongate (for small amounts) at that stress. The free-body diagram in Fig. 290c shows that, when the load reaches the value P_p, the forces in all three members CD, GH, and EF are equal to $\sigma_y a$. Hence, from the equilibrium equation $\Sigma F = 0$, we have

$$P_p = 3\sigma_y a \qquad (f)$$

Comparison of P_p and P_y. By dividing Eq. f by Eq. e, the following ratio of P_p to P_y is obtained:

$$\frac{P_p}{P_y} = \frac{3}{2 + l_1/l_2} \qquad (g)$$

For example, if $l_1 = l_2$, $P_p/P_y = 1$, and hence the fully plastic load becomes the same as the elastic-limit load. However, if l_1 is very small in comparison to l_2, the ratio of P_p/P_y approaches the value 1.5. It should be noted that the ratio P_p/P_y is usually considerably greater than 1 for most statically indeterminate members, and, since the behavior of the member is essentially elastic until the load P_p is reached, this fact makes the fully plastic load a significant value; as previously stated, it is usually regarded as the upper limiting load, and P_y is the lower limiting load.

96. Fully plastic twisting moment and bending moment.
Fully plastic moments for a statically indeterminate torsional cylindrical bar and for a bar subjected to bending are treated in the following illustrative problems.

Illustrative Problems

Problem 291. The cylindrical bar in Fig. 291a is prevented from twisting at its ends by rigid supports. A twisting moment T is applied at section AA. De-

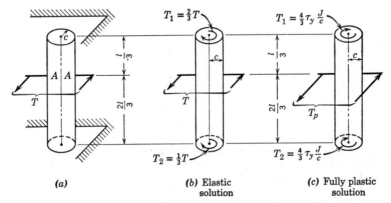

| (a) | (b) Elastic solution | (c) Fully plastic solution |

Fig. 291. Fully plastic twisting moment for statically indeterminate torsion member.

termine the values of the elastic-limit twisting moment T_y and the fully plastic twisting moment T_p if the material is assumed to have a shearing yield point τ_y.

Solution. (a) *Elastic-limit Load* T_y. The elastic solution of this problem is given in Prob. 278, the results of which are shown in Fig. 291b. The maximum resisting twisting moment is $T_1 = \frac{2}{3}T$. When $T = T_y$, the maximum twisting moment T_1 will be accompanied by a maximum shearing stress of τ_y at the extreme fiber of the shaft at the section where T_1 occurs. For this condition, if we neglect the stress concentration at the fixed-end grip, $\tau_y = T_1 c/J$ or $T_1 = \tau_y J/c$. Since $T_1 = \frac{2}{3}T_y$ we have $T_y = \frac{3}{2}\tau_y J/c$.

(b) *Fully Plastic Load* T_p. Figure 291c represents the free-body diagram of the shaft for the conditions that exist when the fully plastic load T_p is applied; that is, the fully plastic resisting moment is assumed to have been reached at each end of the shaft. This fully plastic resisting moment is $\frac{4}{3}\tau_y J/c$. (See Art. 31.) Hence, $T_1 = T_2 = \frac{4}{3}\tau_y J/c$. From the equilibrium equation $\Sigma T = 0$, we have

$$T_p = T_1 + T_2 = \frac{8}{3}\frac{\tau_y J}{c}$$

A comparison of T_p and T_y shows that the ratio of these two limiting values is $T_p/T_y = \frac{16}{9} = 1.78$.

Problem 292. A beam of length l is fixed at each end and is loaded at the quarter point by a concentrated force P (Fig. 292a). Let the beam be made of a ductile material whose yield point is σ_y. Determine the elastic-limit load P_y in terms of σ_y, c, l, and I, and the fully plastic load P_p for the beam in terms of σ_y, c, l, I, and K, where K is a factor from Table 4 (Chap. III) that depends on the shape of the cross section.

Solution. (a) *Elastic-limit Load.* Figure 292b shows the fixed-end moments and shears as determined by the methods of § 1 of this chapter. (See Prob. 279.) The maximum resisting moment in the beam is $M_{\max} = \frac{9}{64}Pl$, which occurs at the right end. When the maximum bending stress at the right end reaches the value σ_y, the following equation holds if we neglect the stress concentration caused by the grip at the fixed end:

$$M_{\max} = \frac{\sigma_y I}{c} = \frac{9}{64}P_y l, \qquad \therefore \quad P_y = \frac{64}{9}\frac{\sigma_y I}{cl}$$

(b) *Fully Plastic Load.* The fully plastic load P_p is the value of the load P when the fully plastic moment $K(\sigma_y I/c)$ (see Art. 53) occurs at the three sections A, B, and C, as shown by the free-body diagrams in Fig. 292c and d. The forces and moments in each of Fig. 292c and d must satisfy the equilibrium conditions, $\Sigma F = 0$ and $\Sigma M = 0$. From Fig. 292d the equation $\Sigma M_C = 0$ gives

$$\Sigma M_C = \frac{3}{4}V_1 l - 2K\frac{\sigma_y I}{c} = 0, \qquad V_1 = \frac{8}{3}K\frac{\sigma_y I}{cl}$$

From Fig. 292c, the equation $\Sigma M_B = 0$ gives

$$\Sigma M_B = V_1 l - \frac{P_p l}{4} = 0, \qquad P_p = 4V_1 = \frac{32}{3}K\frac{\sigma_y I}{cl}$$

Also, from Fig. 292c, the equation $\Sigma F = 0$ gives

$$V_1 + V_2 = P_p, \qquad V_2 = P_p - V_1 = \frac{32}{3}K\frac{\sigma_y I}{cl} - \frac{8}{3}K\frac{\sigma_y I}{cl} = 8K\frac{\sigma_y I}{cl}$$

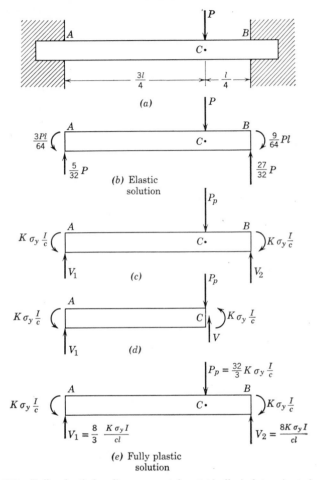

Fig. 292. Fully plastic bending moment for statically indeterminate beam.

In Fig. 292e are shown the moments and shears on the beam when the fully plastic load is applied. This load will cause the beam to be in a condition of impending collapse since the fully plastic hinges that occur at A, B, and C will allow the beam to fold if the load exceeds P_p.

(c) *Comparison of P_p and P_y.* The ratio of the value of P_p to the value of P_y is

$$\frac{P_p}{P_y} = \left(\frac{32}{3} K \frac{\sigma_y I}{cl}\right) \Big/ \frac{64}{9} \frac{\sigma_y I}{cl} = 1.5K$$

Problems

293. Determine the fully plastic load P_p for the structure in Prob. 285 (Fig. 284). *Ans.* 8500 lb.

294. A rigid bar EF is supported by a frictionless pin at E and by two steel wires AB and CD as shown in Fig. 293. If the yield point of the wire is 100,000 lb per sq in., determine the elastic-limit load P_y and the fully plastic load P_p.

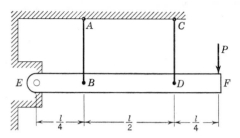

Fig. 293. A simple structure in which P may lie between the elastic-limit load and the fully plastic load.

The cross-section area of each wire is 0.1 in.², and $l = 10$ ft. Neglect the weight of the rigid bar.

295. In Prob. 288 (Fig. 287) let $l_1 = 5$ ft and $l_2 = 5$ ft. If the beam is a steel 10-in. 25.4-lb I beam, determine the value of the elastic-limit load P_y and the fully plastic load P_p for the beam. Assume that the yield point is $\sigma_y = 35,000$ lb per sq in. and that the value of $K = 1.1$ for this cross section (see Table 4, Chap. III).

296. A beam of span length $l = 24$ in. has each end fixed and is subjected to a concentrated load P at its midpoint. If the beam is a solid circular cylindrical steel bar whose yield point is $\sigma_y = 50,000$ lb per sq in., determine the value of the elastic-limit load P_y and of the fully plastic load P_p. The diameter is 2 in.

297. A beam of span length l is fixed at each end and is subjected to a uniformly distributed total load W. Let the beam have a solid circular cross section of radius r and be made of a steel whose yield point is σ_y. Determine the values of the elastic-limit load W_y and the fully plastic load W_p in terms of σ_y, r, and l.

298. Use the results of Prob. 290 to show the following facts:

(a) The movement downward e of the bar AB in Fig. 290 due to the load P is given by the equation $e = \dfrac{Pl_1}{aE(2 + l_1/l_2)}$ when the stress in all three members CD, GH, and EF is within the elastic limit.

(b) The movement downward e of AB after the stress in members CD and EF has reached σ_y and before the stress in GH reaches σ_y is given by the equation $e = (l_2/aE)(P - 2\sigma_y a)$. $\left(OVER \right)$

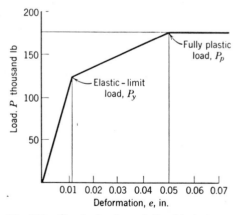

Fig. 294. Graph showing relationship between P and e for three stages in the loading on the member in Prob. 290.

(c) In parts a and b of this problem, let $l_1 = 10$ in., $l_2 = 50$ in., $a = 2$ in.^{2}, $E = 30 \times 10^6$ lb/in.^{2}, $\sigma_y = 30,000$ lb/in.^{2}, and show that, in the graph in Fig. 294, the line from zero to the elastic limit represents the relationship between e and P for part a of this problem, the line from the elastic limit to the fully plastic load represents the relationship between e and P for part b of this problem, and the horizontal line to the right from the fully plastic load represents the relationship between P_p and e for the fully plastic condition.

Chapter VIII

RELATIONS BETWEEN STRESSES AT A POINT ON DIFFERENT PLANES PASSING THROUGH THE POINT. COMBINED STATIC LOADS

97. Introduction. It will be observed that the static loading suggested in the title of this chapter consists of certain combinations of the loadings considered in the first three chapters. Furthermore, the general problem to be considered in this chapter is the same as that dealt with in the foregoing chapters. It may be desirable, however, to review the problem very briefly; it consists of two parts.

Elastic Behavior. The first part is to obtain relations between the static loads and the maximum *elastic* normal and shearing stresses in the member. For, under some service conditions, the member may fail to resist satisfactorily any further increase in the loads after the maximum stress reaches the elastic limit (or yield point) in tension or in shear. The tensile elastic limit is usually considered to limit the static loads that can be allowed to act on the member if the member is made of brittle material and fails by fracture when the tensile elastic limit (and also ultimate strength) is reached. Whereas the shearing elastic limit (or yield point) usually is considered to limit the loads if the material is ductile and fails when a slight amount of inelastic deformation (yielding) develops in the most stressed fibers of the member, although the essential behavior of the member as a whole is elastic.

291

Inelastic Behavior. The second part of the problem (arising only with ductile members) is to express the loads in terms of the yield point after this yield-point stress has spread over the whole area of the most stressed cross section of the member giving rise to the fully plastic condition (referred to as a plastic hinge), which leaves no elastic core at the section, and hence may lead to failure by unrestrained (general) yielding and collapse of the member if further increases of the loads occur, except as is noted in the next paragraph.

As already noted, the maximum loads that can be applied to a member frequently are assumed to be limited by the beginning of yielding in the most stressed fiber or by the fully plastic condition, as obtained from the solutions of the two parts of the foregoing problem. These loads are regarded as the lower and upper limits of the maximum loads that can be allowed to act on the member, *provided that the member is used under stress conditions in which the member as a whole is not restrained from yielding.* Certain restraints on yielding permit only localized yielding, which does not spread throughout the member, as the loads increase, and hence fracture of the member may occur with very little inelastic deformation of the member as a whole, even though it is made of *ductile material.* Such restraints usually consist of a very abrupt change in cross sections or a manner of loading that causes stresses essentially on one cross section, even though the member is free from abrupt changes in cross section, such as the shearing stresses in the rivets on one cross section.

The problem considered in this chapter is similar to that treated in Chapter V, in that the loads are a combination of those dealt with in the first three chapters. But the problem in Chapter V was simplified by the fact that the maximum normal stress caused by each part of the combined loading (axial and bending loads) occurred in the same cross section of the member, and hence could be added algebraically to obtain the final normal stress at the point. Whereas, in the problem considered in this chapter, the stresses at any point caused by the two parts of the loading (bending and torsional loads, for example) cannot be added to obtain the maximum stresses at the point. For example, the cylindrical bar shown in Fig. 295a is subjected on any section nn to a bending moment $M = P_1 b = Pb$ and a twisting moment $T = Pp$, which produce on the horizontal and vertical faces of a small (differential) block, at any point A on the section, the stresses σ and τ, as shown in Fig. 295a; the same state of stress is caused by a combination of axial and torsional loads as shown in Fig. 295b.

These stresses (σ and τ) are not the maximum normal and shearing stresses at the point, and the maximum values cannot be found by direct addition as was done in Chapter V.   It becomes necessary, therefore, to express the maximum stresses in terms of σ and τ, and hence finally in terms of the loads, since, in Fig. 295a, $\sigma = Mc/I$ and $\tau = Tc/J$ (or, in Fig. 295b, $\sigma = P/a$ and $\tau = Tc/J$).

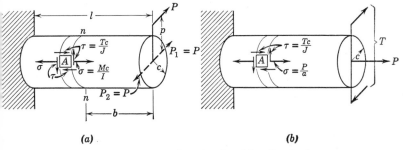

Fig. 295.   Combined torsional and bending loads.

The bending moment M and twisting moment T in Fig. 295a (or the axial load P and twisting moment T in Fig. 295b) may be applied in any order in reaching the values that cause the stresses σ and τ, provided that the member behaves elastically.   But, if the member deforms inelastically under the final values of M and T, the order in which they are applied (the history of loading) must be known, as is pointed out in Art. 104.

§ 1   Elastic Behavior

98. Method of determining relations of stresses at a point on different planes passing through the point.   It is well to recall that a stress or internal force should not be thought of apart from the area on which it acts, and hence the idea of an internal force per unit area (stress) *at a point*, to be definite, must involve a plane passing through the point.   The term "state of stress at a point" frequently is used when the stresses on several planes passing through the point are involved.

Two important relations between the stresses at a point on different planes passing through the point already have been found in Arts. 25 and 26.   But the method used may be stated in more general form as follows: The method consists first of considering that a small part or elementary block of the body (including the point) is severed from the body by planes, on which the stresses at the point are assumed to be given or known (as for example those indicated in Fig. 295).   This small block constitutes a new body that is acted on by forces which are external to the block (although they are internal forces with respect to the whole body); these external forces acting on the areas *da* of the faces of the elementary block, as shown in Fig. 296a, hold it in equilibrium. The force on each face of the block may be considered to be uniformly distributed since each face is very small, and hence the force acting on each face is equal to the stress on the face times the area of the face; furthermore, the weight of the block may be considered to be negligible.

The stress at the point on a plane having a specified direction such as *FC* or *OY'* now may be found (in terms of the stresses at the point

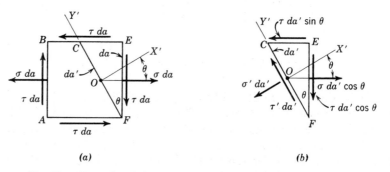

(a)   (b)

Fig. 296. Normal and shearing stresses at a point on various planes.

on the planes represented by the faces of the block) by passing a plane through the elementary block, parallel to the specified direction, and applying the equations of equilibrium to the forces acting on either of the two portions of the block thus formed, as indicated in Fig. 296b. This method is applied in subsequent articles. In applying the method, it is very important to note that the equations of equilibrium are applied to the *forces* acting on the elementary block and not directly to the stresses.

99. Maximum normal and shearing stresses at a point. The problem discussed in this article may be stated as follows: Given, at a point in a body, a shearing stress τ on each of two planes at right angles to each other, and a normal stress σ on one of the two planes, as illustrated in Figs. 295 and 296; required to find, in terms of the given stresses, the values of the normal and shearing stresses at the same point on any other plane that passes through the point and is perpendicular to the plane of the paper, and, in particular, to find the maximum values of these stresses at the point. The significance or use of the relationships between the stresses at a point will be discussed later in this chapter. We are here concerned primarily with obtaining the relationships.

In accordance with the procedure outlined in the preceding article, the differential block in Fig. 296a is shown with the forces that are exerted on its faces; this is a free-body diagram of the block. These forces are expressed in terms of the known stresses σ and τ.

Now let a plane CF making any angle θ with the plane EF be passed through the block in Fig. 296a and a free-body diagram be drawn of the portion to one side (right side) of the plane. This free-body diagram is shown in Fig. 296b. The area of the plane CF is denoted by da', and the stresses (to be found) that act on this area are designated by σ' and τ'. The forces acting on the wedge-shaped block in Fig. 296b hold the block in equilibrium. By applying the equations of equilibrium to these forces, we obtain expressions for σ' and τ' in terms of the known stresses σ and τ. Thus,

$$\Sigma F_{x'} = 0, \qquad \sigma'\, da' = \sigma\, da' \cos\theta \cos\theta - \tau\, da' \cos\theta \sin\theta$$

$$- \tau\, da' \sin\theta \cos\theta$$

$$\sigma' = \sigma \cos^2\theta - 2\tau \sin\theta \cos\theta \tag{186}$$

$$\sigma' = \sigma \left(\tfrac{1}{2} + \tfrac{1}{2} \cos 2\theta\right) - \tau \sin 2\theta$$

$$= \frac{\sigma}{2} + \frac{\sigma}{2} \cos 2\theta - \tau \sin 2\theta \tag{187}$$

Similarly, by applying the equilibrium equation $\Sigma F_{Y'} = 0$ to the forces in Fig. 296b, an expression for τ' in terms of σ and τ is found to be

$$\tau' = \frac{\sigma}{2} \sin 2\theta + \tau \cos 2\theta \tag{188}$$

Equations 187 and 188 give the magnitudes and directions of the normal stress σ' and shearing stress τ' at the point considered on any plane passing through the point, making an angle θ with the plane on which σ occurs.

Maximum Value of σ'. Principal Stresses. As previously noted, the maximum values of σ' and τ' usually are the desired stresses. The value of θ in Eq. 187 that will give σ' its maximum (or minimum) value is the value of θ (herein denoted by θ_1) that will make the first derivative of σ' with respect to θ equal to zero. Thus,

$$\frac{d\sigma'}{d\theta} = -\frac{\sigma}{2} 2 \sin 2\theta - 2\tau \cos 2\theta = 0 \tag{189}$$

Hence,

$$\tan 2\theta_1 = -2\tau/\sigma \tag{190}$$

If now the values of $\sin 2\theta_1$ and $\cos 2\theta_1$ are substituted in Eq. 187, the maximum (or minimum) value of σ' will be found. The values of $\sin 2\theta_1$ and $\cos 2\theta_1$ may be found by interpreting Eq. 189, as indicated

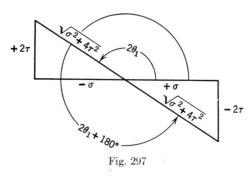

Fig. 297

in Fig. 297, from which the values of $\sin 2\theta_1$ and $\cos 2\theta_1$ are given by Eqs. 191 and 192:

$$\tan 2\theta_1 = \frac{2\tau}{-\sigma}$$

$$\sin 2\theta_1 = \frac{2\tau}{\sqrt{\sigma^2 + 4\tau^2}} \tag{191}$$

$$\cos 2\theta_1 = \frac{-\sigma}{\sqrt{\sigma^2 + 4\tau^2}} \tag{192}$$

Thus, by substituting these values of $\sin 2\theta_1$ and $\cos 2\theta_1$ in Eq. 187, we obtain

$$\sigma'_{\min} = \frac{\sigma}{2} + \frac{\sigma}{2}\frac{-\sigma}{\sqrt{\sigma^2 + 4\tau^2}} - \tau\frac{2\tau}{\sqrt{\sigma^2 + 4\tau^2}}$$

$$\sigma'_{\min} = \frac{\sigma}{2} - \frac{1}{2}\sqrt{\sigma^2 + 4\tau^2} \tag{193}$$

and, by substituting the values of $\sin (2\theta_1 + 180)$ and $\cos (2\theta_1 + 180)$, we obtain

$$\sigma'_{\max} = \frac{\sigma}{2} + \frac{1}{2}\sqrt{\sigma^2 + 4\tau^2} \tag{194}$$

The stresses $\sigma'_{\max}$ and $\sigma'_{\min}$ are called *principal stresses* at a point and are frequently designated by σ_1 and σ_2, respectively.

Planes on Which Principal Stresses Occur.   Referring to Eq. 189 and noting that there are always two angles between $\theta°$ and $360°$, for which the tangents are equal in magnitude and sign, the two angles differing by $180°$, we may state that there are two values of θ_1 that differ by $90°$. Therefore, the *principal stresses act on planes that are perpendicular to each other.*

Furthermore, *principal stresses occur on planes on which no shearing stresses act.* This fact may be verified by setting τ' in Eq. 188 equal to zero and solving for $\tan 2\theta_1$; the value for $\tan 2\theta_1$ thus found is the same as that in Eq. 190. Therefore, we may conclude that principal stresses occur on planes on which no shearing stresses act. These planes are called principal planes, and, as previously noted, the normal stresses on these planes are called principal stresses and are the maximum and minimum stresses at the point.

Plane State of Stress.   There are, in general, three principal stresses at a point in a stressed body on three mutually perpendicular planes; one of the principal stresses is the maximum normal stress at the point; one is the minimum normal stress; and the other is, of course, intermediate between the two. If one of the principal stresses is equal to zero, as was assumed in the foregoing analysis, the state of stress is said to be two-dimensional, or biaxial, or a plane state of stress; and, if two principal stresses are zero, the state of stress is one-dimensional or uniaxial. If all three principal stresses have values other than zero, the state of stress is said to be three-dimensional or triaxial. At a free surface of a body, the state of stress is, of course, always either uniaxial or biaxial (never triaxial), and the maximum value of the principal stress frequently occurs at a free surface.

Maximum Value of Shearing Stress.   By treating Eq. 188 in the same way that Eq. 187 was treated in obtaining the maximum value of σ', we may obtain the maximum value of τ'. Thus the value that θ in Eq. 188 must have (denoted by θ_2), in order that τ' in Eq. 188 will be its maximum value, is given by the expression

$$\tan 2\theta_2 = \sigma/2\tau \qquad (195)$$

and the maximum or minimum values of τ' are found to be

$$\tau'_{max} = \sqrt{\left(\frac{\sigma}{2}\right)^2 + \tau^2} \qquad (196)$$

$$\tau'_{min} = -\sqrt{\left(\frac{\sigma}{2}\right)^2 + \tau^2} \qquad (197)$$

It is evident that the maximum and minimum shearing stress are equal in magnitude, differing only in sign.

Planes on Which Maximum and Minimum Shearing Stresses Act. Equation 195 indicates that the planes on which such shearing stresses act are at right angles to each other. Moreover these planes bisect the angles between planes on which the principal normal stresses at the point act; this fact is obtained by comparing Eqs. 190 and 195, since the value of $\tan 2\theta_2$ in Eq. 195 is the negative reciprocal of the value of $\tan 2\theta_1$ in Eq. 190.

100. Maximum shearing stress expressed in terms of principal stresses. Frequently it is convenient to obtain the maximum shearing stress at a point from the principal stresses at the point. This may be

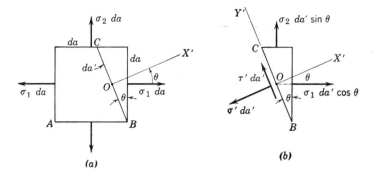

(a)   (b)

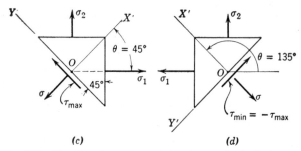

(c)   (d)

Fig. 298. Shearing stress at a point in terms of principal stresses.

done by use of the fact that the maximum shearing stress is equal to one half of the algebraic difference of the maximum and minimum principal stresses at the point. Thus,

$$\tau'_{max} = \tfrac{1}{2}(\sigma_{max} - \sigma_{min}) \tag{198}$$

and it acts on planes bisecting the angle between the planes on which $\sigma_{\max}$ or $\sigma_{\min}$ act.

This statement may be proved as follows: Let the differential block in Fig. 298a represent a small part of a body subjected to principal stress of σ_1 and σ_2 ($\sigma_1 > \sigma_2$) on faces of the block perpendicular to the plane of the paper and a third principal stress σ_3 (not shown) on faces parallel to the plane of the paper. The coplanar forces acting on the block are shown in Fig. 298a. A plane BC is passed through the block, and the portion ABC is removed. The forces acting on the remaining portion are shown in Fig. 298b. By applying an equation of equilibrium ($\Sigma F_{Y'} = 0$), we obtain

$$\tau' \, da' = -\sigma_2 \, da' \sin\theta \cos\theta + \sigma_1 \, da' \cos\theta \sin\theta$$

$$\tau' = (\sigma_1 - \sigma_2) \sin\theta \cos\theta$$

$$= \tfrac{1}{2}(\sigma_1 - \sigma_2) \sin 2\theta \tag{199}$$

Since $\sin 2\theta$ reaches its maximum value (unity) when $\theta = 45°$, the value of the maximum shearing stress at the point acts on the plane as shown in Fig. 298c and is

$$\tau'_{\max} = \tfrac{1}{2}(\sigma_1 - \sigma_2) \tag{200}$$

When $2\theta = 270°$ or $\theta = 135°$, the value of $\sin 2\theta = -1$, and, hence, $\tau_{\min} = -\tau_{\max}$ acts on the other $45°$ plane as shown in Fig. 298d. Hence, the maximum shearing stress acts on planes that bisect the angles between the planes on which σ_1 and σ_2 act; this fact is illustrated again in Fig. 299a by the diagonal planes of the cube.

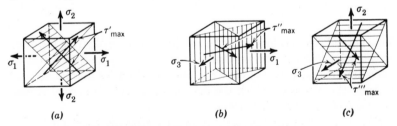

Fig. 299.   Planes of maximum shearing stresses.

Similarly, another maximum shearing stress occurs on a plane which bisects the angle between the planes on which σ_1 and σ_3 act (see Fig. 299b); and its value is $\tau''_{\max} = \tfrac{1}{2}(\sigma_1 - \sigma_3)$; likewise $\tau'''_{\max} = \tfrac{1}{2}(\sigma_2 - \sigma_3)$; see Fig. 299c. Thus the maximum shearing stress at the point is the largest of the preceding three values; it is given by the expression

$$\tau_{\max} = \tfrac{1}{2}(\sigma_{\max} - \sigma_{\min}) \tag{201}$$

and it acts on a plane, making an angle of 45° with each of the planes on which σ_{max} and σ_{min} act.

It is important to note that the parentheses in Eq. 201 constitute the *algebraic difference* of the maximum and minimum principal stresses. For example, if in Fig. 298a the maximum principal stress is $+\sigma_1$ (tension) and the minimum principal stress is zero ($\sigma_3 = 0$ and σ_2 is intermediate between 0 and σ_1), $\tau_{max} = \frac{1}{2}\sigma_1$, and it acts on a plane, making 45° with the plane of the paper. Likewise, if two of the principal stresses are zero ($\sigma_2 = \sigma_3 = 0$) as in a simple tension member, $\tau_{max} = \frac{1}{2}\sigma_1$, as shown also in Art. 10. If, however, σ_2 in Fig. 298 were a compressive stress, σ_{min} would be $-\sigma_2$; hence, Eq. 201 would become $\tau_{max} = \frac{1}{2}(\sigma_1 + \sigma_2)$, and τ_{max} would act on a plane perpendicular to the plane of the paper bisecting the angle between the planes on which σ_1 and σ_2 act.

Normal Stress on Plane of Maximum Shearing Stress. The normal stress σ' (Fig. 298b) on any plane making an angle θ with the plane on which σ_1 acts is found by applying one of the equations of equilibrium to the forces in Fig. 298b. Thus, $\Sigma F_{x'} = 0$ gives, after simplifying modifications,

$$\sigma' = \frac{\sigma_1 + \sigma_2}{2} + \frac{\sigma_1 - \sigma_2}{2} \cos 2\theta \tag{202}$$

The value of σ in Fig. 298c for the value of $\theta = 45°$ on which the maximum shearing stress acts is

$$\sigma = \frac{\sigma_1 + \sigma_2}{2} \tag{203}$$

This normal stress is less than the maximum principal stress (σ_1 or σ_2) at the point. But it is important to note that the planes on which the maximum shearing stresses act are also acted on by normal stresses, whereas the planes on which the maximum (principal) normal stresses act are free from shearing stress.

Sign Convention for Stresses. A normal stress is considered to be positive if it is tensile and negative if it is compressive. A shearing stress is considered to be positive if it produces a clockwise moment about the centroid of the block (or element) on which it acts and negative if it produces a counterclockwise moment about the centroid of the block. For example, in Fig. 296a the shearing stresses on planes AB and EF are positive, but on planes BE and AF the shearing stresses are negative. Also, in Fig. 296b the shear on plane CF is positive. In using the equations in this article, care must be exercised in following these sign conventions. The illustrative problems that follow will demonstrate the use of proper signs.

Illustrative Problems

Problem 299. The stresses on a set of perpendicular planes at a given point are as shown in Fig. 300a on an element cut from a body. Let $\sigma_3 = 0$. Determine the stresses σ' and τ' on the plane CE that makes the angle $\theta = 30°$ with BC.

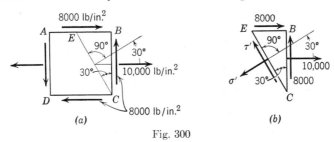

(a)   (b)

Fig. 300

Solution. It is noted that the shearing stress on plane BC in Fig. 300a is negative, and hence must be given a minus sign in the equation that follows. From Eq. 187, we find

$$\sigma' = \frac{10,000}{2} + \frac{10,000}{2} \cos 60° - (-8000) \sin 60° = +14,430 \text{ lb/in.}^2$$

and, from Eq. 188, we find

$$\tau' = + \frac{10,000}{2} \sin 60° + (-8000) \cos 60° = +330 \text{ lb/in.}^2$$

The positive sign of σ' indicates that it is a tensile stress, and the positive sign of τ' shows that it acts upward to the left in plane CE, as shown in Fig. 300b, since it must produce a clockwise moment with respect to the centroid of the block BCE.

Problem 300. In Prob. 299 determine the values of the maximum and minimum principal stresses and the value of the maximum shearing stress at the point.

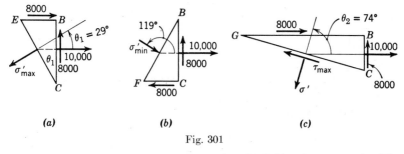

(a)   (b)   (c)

Fig. 301

Determine the location of the plane on which each of these stresses acts (see Fig. 301).

Solution. From Eq. 194, we find

$$\sigma'_{max} = \frac{\sigma}{2} + \frac{1}{2}\sqrt{\sigma^2 + 4\tau^2} = \frac{10{,}000}{2} + \frac{1}{2}\sqrt{(10{,}000)^2 + 4(-8000)^2}$$

$$= 14{,}440 \text{ lb/in.}^2$$

From Eq. 193,

$$\sigma'_{min} = \frac{10{,}000}{2} - \frac{1}{2}\sqrt{(10{,}000)^2 + 4(-8000)^2} = -4440 \text{ lb/in.}^2$$

And, from Eq. 196, we find that

$$\tau'_{max} = \sqrt{\left(\frac{\sigma}{2}\right)^2 + \tau^2} = \sqrt{\left(\frac{10{,}000}{2}\right)^2 + (-8000)^2} = 9440 \text{ lb/in.}^2$$

From Eq. 190,

$$\tan 2\theta_1 = \frac{-2(-8000)}{10{,}000} = 1.6$$

$$2\theta_1 = 58° \text{ or } 238° \quad \text{and} \quad \theta_1 = 29° \text{ or } 119°$$

One of these values of θ_1 corresponds to the location of σ'_{max} and the other value to σ'_{min}. The substitution of these values of θ_1 (and of the values of σ and τ with the proper sign) into Eq. 187 shows that $\theta_1 = 29°$ gives the plane on which σ'_{max} acts (Fig. 301a) and that $\theta_1 = 119°$ gives the plane on which σ'_{min} acts (Fig. 301b). The maximum shearing stress τ'_{max} acts on a plane given by $\theta_2 = 29° + 45° = 74°$, as shown in Fig. 301c.

Problems

301. The state of stress at a given point in a body is as described in Fig. 302. Determine the values of σ'_{max}, σ'_{min}, and τ'_{max}, and location of the plane on which each of these stresses acts. Draw a sketch showing the location of each plane.

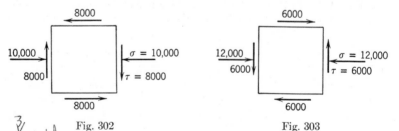

Fig. 302   Fig. 303

302. Determine the values of σ'_{max}, σ'_{min}, and τ'_{max}, and the location of the plane on which each of these stresses acts for the state of stress described by Fig. 303.

303. On the triangular block of Fig. 304, the state of stress is described by the given quantities, $\tau = 0$, θ, and σ'. Determine the values of τ' and σ'_{max} in terms of the given quantities. *Hint.* Let the area of face $AB = 1$, and hence the area of $AC = \sin \theta$, and area of $BC = \cos \theta$. Use equations of equilibrium.

$$Ans. \quad \sigma' \max = \frac{\sigma'}{\cos^2 \theta} \; ; \; \tau' = \sigma' \tan \theta.$$

304. Two principal stresses at a point consist of a tensile stress $\sigma_1 = 4000$ lb per sq in. and a compressive stress $\sigma_2 = 2000$ lb per sq in.; the third principal stress is zero. Determine the maximum shearing stress by using Eq. 198, and show the planes on which it acts. $\qquad$ *Ans.* $\tau_{\max} = 3000$ lb/in.²

305. Show by the use of Eq. 198 that, for a state of two-dimensional stress at a point at which the two principal stresses σ_1 and σ_2 are equal tensile stresses and the third principal stress is zero, the maximum shearing stress is equal to $\frac{1}{2}\sigma_1$ or $\frac{1}{2}\sigma_2$.

306. A cylindrical boiler 6 ft in diameter is made of plates $\frac{3}{4}$ in. thick and is subjected to an internal steam pressure of 200 lb per sq in. Find by the use of Eq. 198 the maximum shearing stress in the plate, and draw a sketch showing the planes on which it acts. $\qquad$ *Ans.* $\tau_{\max} = 4900$ lb/in.²

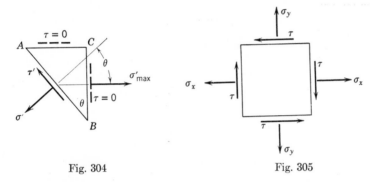

Fig. 304 $\qquad\qquad\qquad\qquad$ Fig. 305

307. Show that, for the general case of a plane state of stress as described by Fig. 305, the following equations give the values of $\sigma'_{\max}$, $\sigma'_{\min}$, $\tau'_{\max}$, and θ_1:

$$\sigma'_{\max} = \frac{\sigma_x + \sigma_y}{2} + \frac{1}{2} \sqrt{(\sigma_x - \sigma_y)^2 + 4\tau^2}$$

$$\sigma'_{\min} = \frac{\sigma_x + \sigma_y}{2} - \frac{1}{2} \sqrt{(\sigma_x - \sigma_y)^2 + 4\tau^2}$$

$$\tau'_{\max} = \frac{1}{2} \sqrt{(\sigma_x - \sigma_y)^2 + 4\tau^2}$$

$$\tan 2\theta_1 = - \frac{2\tau}{\sigma_x - \sigma_y}$$

101. Mohr's circle for obtaining principal stresses. Mohr's circle may be used to solve the problem discussed in Art. 99: namely, to find the maximum normal and shearing stresses at a point, in terms of the shearing stresses on any two planes at right angles to each other, and the normal stress on one of the two planes. This may be done as follows: In Fig. 306b, the vertical axis through the origin O represents shearing stress, and the horizontal axis represents normal stress. The "given" stresses as shown in Fig. 306a are σ and τ. The coordinates in Fig. 306a of the point E are $(\sigma, -\tau)$ and of A are $(0, +\tau)$. Mohr's circle must pass through the points A and E and must have its center on the σ axis. Therefore, the center of the circle is the point C, which is the intersection of the diameter AE with the σ axis. With C as a center and a radius equal to CA or CE, Mohr's circle is drawn. The center C is also at the midpoint of OB so that $OC = CB = \frac{1}{2}\sigma$.

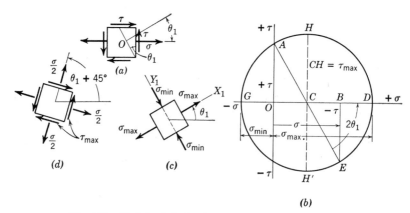

Fig. 306. Mohr's circle for determining principal stresses.

Since the coordinates of every point on the circumference of the circle represent the shearing and normal stresses in the body on some plane through the point where the "given" stresses in the body occur, the abscissas of the points D and G, respectively, represent the maximum and minimum values of the normal stresses: that is, the principal stresses. The abscissa σ_{max} of D is the maximum principal stress and acts on a plane perpendicular to the X_1 axis, as shown in Fig. 306c; the direction of the X_1 axis or the plane on which σ_{max} acts is found by making θ_1 in Fig. 306c equal to one half of $2\theta_1$ in Fig. 306b. The abscissa σ_{min} of G is the minimum principal stress and acts on a plane perpendicular to the Y_1 axis, as shown in Fig. 306c. Since the ordinates of D and G are zero, the shearing stresses are zero on the planes on which the principal stresses σ_{max} and σ_{min} act, as was noted in Art. 99.

The maximum shearing stress is given by the ordinate to the uppermost point H of the circle. Thus, the maximum shearing stress τ'_{max} is equal to the radius of Mohr's circle, and, from Fig. 306b, its value is

$$\tau'_{max} = CH = CA = \sqrt{\left(\frac{\sigma}{2}\right)^2 + \tau^2} = \frac{1}{2}\sqrt{\sigma^2 + 4\tau^2} \quad (204)$$

By use of Fig. 306b and Eq. 204, the principal stresses σ_{max} and σ_{min} are found to be expressed algebraically as follows:

$$\sigma_{max} = OD = OC + CD = \frac{\sigma}{2} + \sqrt{\left(\frac{\sigma}{2}\right)^2 + \tau^2} = \frac{\sigma}{2} + \frac{1}{2}\sqrt{\sigma^2 + 4\tau^2} \quad (205)$$

$$\sigma_{min} = OG = OC - CG = \frac{\sigma}{2} - \sqrt{\left(\frac{\sigma}{2}\right)^2 + \tau^2} = \frac{\sigma}{2} - \frac{1}{2}\sqrt{\sigma^2 + 4\tau^2} \quad (206)$$

$$\tan 2\theta_1 = \frac{BE}{CB} = \frac{-2\tau}{\sigma} \quad (207)$$

These equations are the same as Eqs. 190, 193, 194, and 197.

The maximum shearing stress τ_{max}, as shown by Fig. 306d, acts on a plane making the angle $\theta_1 + 45°$ with the planes on which the given stress σ acts, since, as shown in Art. 100, the maximum shearing stress lies on each of two planes, making 45° with the planes on which the principal stresses act. It should be noted that, on the plane on which the stress τ'_{max} acts, there is also a normal stress $\sigma/2$, which is equal to the abscissa of the point H.

It should be noted also that the angle θ_1 in Fig. 306c is measured in a counterclockwise direction from the direction in which the stress σ_1 acts. Furthermore, the angle 2θ, in Fig. 306b, is measured counterclockwise from the radius CE to the radius CD. The direction in which θ_1 should be measured, as a rule, may be determined easily by inspection by noting that, if the shearing stresses τ were the only stresses acting, the maximum principal stress would be on one of the 45° planes, which may be determined easily by inspection in any case, and, if σ were the only stress acting, it would be the maximum principal stress, and hence θ_1 would be zero. Therefore, if both τ and σ act, the plane of the maximum principal stress will be between the plane on which σ acts and the 45° plane. The use of Mohr's circle when principal stresses are given follows.

102. Mohr's circle; principal stresses given. Mohr's circle furnishes a convenient graphical representation of the relation between principal stresses at a point and the shearing and normal stresses at the same point on planes inclined to the planes of principal stresses.

Mohr's circle will be used to determine the normal and shearing stress at a point on any plane, in terms of the principal stresses at the point. Let the two principal stresses be σ_1 and σ_2, as shown in Fig. 298a, and let it be required that Mohr's circle be used for the solutions of Eqs. 199 and 202.

Mohr's circle is constructed as follows. In Fig. 307a let ordinates represent shearing stress and abscissas normal stress on any plane making an angle θ with the direction of the plane on which principal stress σ_1 acts (Fig. 307b). Lay off the principal stresses σ_1 and σ_2

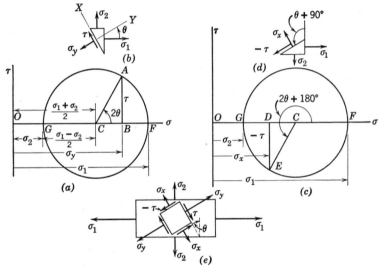

Fig. 307. Mohr's circle constructed from known principal stresses.

represented by OF and OG. It is customary to consider tensile stresses as positive and to lay them off to the right, whereas compressive stresses are considered to be negative and laid off to the left. Construct a circle having its center C on the σ axis and its diameter GF; that is, the center C is at a distance $\frac{1}{2}(\sigma_1 + \sigma_2)$ from the origin, and the circle has a radius equal to $\frac{1}{2}(\sigma_1 - \sigma_2)$. If a radius CA is drawn, making an angle 2θ with the σ axis, the coordinates of the point A on the circumference represent the shearing and normal stresses acting on the plane, making an angle θ (Fig. 307b) with the plane on which σ_1 acts.

Proof. From Fig. 307a and Eqs. 199 and 202, the following equations are obtained:

$$AB = AC \sin 2\theta = \frac{\sigma_1 - \sigma_2}{2} \sin 2\theta = \tau \qquad (208)$$

$$OB = OC + CB = \frac{\sigma_1 + \sigma_2}{2} + \frac{\sigma_1 - \sigma_2}{2} \cos 2\theta = \sigma_y \qquad (209)$$

If, in Fig. 307c, a radius CE is drawn, making an angle $2\theta + 180°$ with the σ axis, the coordinates of the point E on the circumference represent the normal and shearing stresses, respectively, on a plane, making an angle of $\theta + 90°$ with the plane on which σ_1 acts, as indicated in Fig. 307d. For, from Fig. 307c and from substitution of $(\theta + 90°)$ for the angle θ in Eqs. 199 and 202, respectively, the equations obtained are

$$DE = CE \sin (2\theta + 180°) = -\frac{\sigma_1 - \sigma_2}{2} \sin 2\theta = -\tau \qquad (210)$$

$$OD = OC - CD = \frac{\sigma_1 + \sigma_2}{2} - \frac{\sigma_1 - \sigma_2}{2} \cos 2\theta = \sigma_x \qquad (211)$$

Figure 307e shows the stresses σ_x, σ_y, and τ at the given point in the stressed body, which act on two perpendicular planes through the given point, the planes making an angle θ with the planes on which the principal stresses σ_1 and σ_2 act.

Determining Principal Stresses and Maximum Shears for Combined Loads. In the preceding articles we have dealt mainly with the problem of determining, under elastic behavior of the member, the principal stresses and maximum shearing stresses for a given combination of σ and τ stresses at a point in the member. The real problem, as a rule, is to relate the maximum stresses to the given loads on a member. The solutions given in the following illustrative problems show how this is done.

Illustrative Problems for Arts. 99 to 102

Problem 308. If in Fig. 308 the axial tensile load P is equal to 45,000 lb, the twisting moment Qq is equal to 30,000 lb-in., and the diameter d is equal to 3 in.,

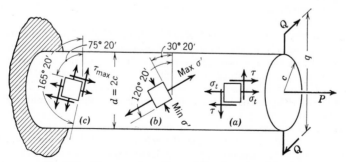

Fig. 308. Stresses caused by axial and torsional loads.

find the maximum normal and shearing stresses and the directions of the planes on which these stresses occur. Assume that the bar acts elastically.

Solution. The stress σ_t (Fig. 308a) caused by the load P if acting alone is

$$\sigma_t = \frac{P}{a} = \frac{45,000}{\pi(3)^2/4} = 6360 \text{ lb per sq in.}$$

and the maximum shearing stress τ (on the outer fibers) caused by the torsional moment T or Qq if acting alone is

$$\tau = \frac{Tc}{J} = \frac{30,000 \times 1.5}{\pi(3)^4/32} = 5660 \text{ lb per sq in.}$$

The planes on which these stresses occur at an outer fiber of the shaft are shown in Fig. 308a.

The principal stresses (max σ'_t and min σ'_t) and the maximum shearing stresses τ' at the point and the planes on which they act may be found as follows (or Mohr's circle may be used):

$$\text{Max } \sigma' = \tfrac{1}{2}\sigma_t + \tfrac{1}{2}\sqrt{\sigma_t{}^2 + 4\tau^2} = \tfrac{1}{2}\sqrt{(6360)^2 + 4(-5660)^2} \quad +\tfrac{1}{2}\,\sigma_t$$

$$= 3180 + 6480 = 9660 \text{ lb per sq in. tensile stress}$$

$$\text{Min } \sigma' = \tfrac{1}{2}\sigma_t - \tfrac{1}{2}\sqrt{\sigma_t{}^2 + 4\tau^2} = -3300 \text{ lb per sq in. compressive stress}$$

$$\tau' = \pm\tfrac{1}{2}\sqrt{\sigma_t{}^2 + 4\tau^2} = 6480 \text{ lb per sq in.}$$

and the planes on which the principal stresses occur make the angles θ_1 with the plane on which the stress σ_t occurs, the values of θ_1 being found as follows:

$$\tan 2\theta_1 = -\frac{2\tau}{\sigma_t} = \frac{(-2)(-5660)}{6360} = 1.78$$

Hence,

$$2\theta_1 = 60°40' \text{ or } 240°40' \quad \text{and} \quad \theta_1 = 30°20' \text{ or } 120°20'$$

as indicated in Fig. 308b. Further, the angle θ_2 that the planes of maximum shear make with the plane on which σ_t occurs are

$$\theta_2 = \theta_1 + 45° = 75°20' \text{ and } 165°20'$$

These planes are shown in Fig. 308c. Normal stresses (not shown) less than the maximum normal stress at the point also act on the planes on which the maximum shearing stresses act.

Problem 309. A pressure P of 10,000 lb on the crankpin of the steel crankshaft shown in Fig. 309a is required to turn the shaft at constant speed when the shaft is subjected to a constant resisting torque Qq. If the diameter d of the shaft is 4 in., find the maximum normal and shearing stresses at the section AB. The direction of P is perpendicular to the axis of the pin and to the crank. Neglect the stress concentration caused by the bearing, and assume that the crankshaft acts elastically.

Solution. If we consider a free-body diagram of the part of the shaft to the right of section AB, it is evident that the only external force acting on this part is P, and hence the internal forces at section AB are caused by P and must be such as to hold P in equilibrium. By the introduction of two equal, opposite, and collinear forces P_2 and P_3, each equal to P, at H (Fig. 309b), P is resolved into a bending

(margin, handwritten, rotated): SKETCH A A MOHRS CIRCLE

load P_3 and a torsional couple P, P_2; and these three forces cause the same stresses on the section AB as does the original single force P. Thus the shaft to the right of the section AB is subjected to combined bending and torsional loads that cause at the point C the state of stress shown in Fig. 309c.

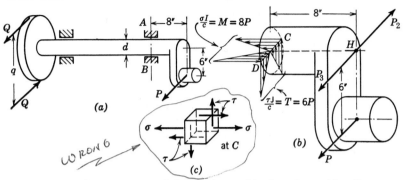

Fig. 309. Stresses in a crankshaft under combined torsion and bending.

The bending moment at section AB due to the load P_3 is $8P$ and is held in equilibrium by the resisting moment $\sigma I/c$ on the section AB, as shown in Fig. 309b. Thus, the tensile stress σ at C on this section (or the compressive stress at D) is

$$\sigma = \frac{Mc}{I} = \frac{8 \times 10{,}000 \times 2}{\pi(4)^4/64} = 12{,}730 \text{ lb per sq in.}$$

The twisting moment due to the forces P and P_2 is $6P$ and is held in equilibrium by the shearing resisting moment $\tau J/c$ on section AB, as shown in Fig. 309b. Thus the shearing stress τ at C (or at D) on section AB is

$$\tau = \frac{Tc}{J} = \frac{6 \times 10{,}000 \times 2}{\pi(4)^4/32} = 4770 \text{ lb per sq in.}$$

The maximum normal (principal) stress at C, then, is

$$\sigma' = \tfrac{1}{2}\sigma + \tfrac{1}{2}\sqrt{\sigma^2 + 4\tau^2} = \tfrac{1}{2} \times 12{,}730 + \tfrac{1}{2}\sqrt{(12{,}730)^2 + 4(4770)^2}$$
$$= 6365 + 7935 = 14{,}300 \text{ lb per sq in.}$$

The maximum shearing stress at C and at D is

$$\tau' = \tfrac{1}{2}\sqrt{\sigma^2 + 4\tau^2} = 7935 \text{ lb per sq in.}$$

Or Mohr's circle may be used for determining the values of σ' and τ'.
   Check on Value of τ'_{max}. From Eq. 201, we have

$$\tau'_{max} = \tfrac{1}{2}(\sigma_{max} - \sigma_{min})$$

But

$$\sigma_{max} = 14{,}300 \text{ lb/in.}^2 \quad \text{and} \quad \sigma_{min} = \frac{\sigma}{2} - \sqrt{\sigma^2 + 4\tau^2} = 6365 - 7935$$
$$= -1570 \text{ lb/in.}^2$$

Hence,

$$\tau'_{max} = \tfrac{1}{2}(14{,}300 + 1570) = \tfrac{1}{2} \times 15{,}870 = 7935 \text{ lb/in.}^2$$

Problems for Arts. 99 through 102

310. A steel bar shown in Fig. 310a is held fixed at one end and has a wrench, indicated by AB, attached at the other end; a force P is applied as shown to the handle of the wrench. Assume the following values: $P = 150$ lb, $p = 20$ in., $l = 24$ in., $d = 2$ in. The tensile-stress-strain diagram for the material is shown in Fig. 310b. Calculate the maximum elastic principal tensile stress and the elastic

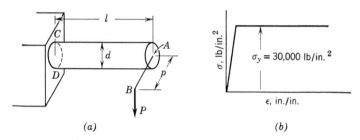

$\sigma_y = 30,000$ lb/in.^{2}

σ, lb/in.^{2}

ϵ, in./in.

(a)   (b)

Fig. 310. Cylindrical member under combined torsional and bending loads.

maximum shearing stress developed in the bar, neglecting the stress concentration caused by the gripping of the bar at the fixed end. State where in the bar the tensile principal stress occurs, and justify the assumption that the bar acts elastically.   *Ans.* At C, $\sigma'_{max} = 5270$ lb/in.^{2} (tensile stress); $\tau'_{max} = 2980$ lb/in.^{2}

311. Solve Prob. 310 graphically by use of Mohr's circle.

312. A solid cylindrical steel ship-propeller shaft 6 in. in diameter transmits 400 hp at a speed of 120 rpm. If the thrust (compressive axial force) of the propeller is 80,000 lb, calculate the maximum principal (normal) stress and the maximum shearing stress in the shaft; assume that bending of the shaft is prevented, that stress concentrations are negligible, and that the shaft acts elastically.

     Ans. $\sigma'_{max} = +3755$ lb/in.^{2} (tension); $\sigma'_{min} = -6585$ lb/in.^{2} (compression); $\tau'_{max} = 5170$ lb/in.^{2}

313. Solve Prob. 309 graphically by use of Mohr's circle.

314. Solve Prob. 301 graphically by use of Mohr's circle.

315. Solve Prob. 308 graphically by use of Mohr's circle.

316. A cylindrical shaft made of aluminum is 2 in. in diameter and is subjected to a twisting moment of 2500π lb-in. and an axial tensile load of 4000π lb. Calculate the maximum principal (normal) stress and the maximum shearing stress in the shaft. Draw a sketch indicating approximately the direction of the planes on which the stresses act. Would the solution be changed if the shaft were made of steel? Assume that both shafts act elastically.

317. A cylindrical shaft made of an aluminum alloy (see Table 1) is 3 in. in diameter and 6 ft long. A twisting moment only is applied at each end of the shaft. The value of the moment is 100,000 lb-in. Calculate the maximum and minimum (normal) principal stresses, and show by a sketch where in the shaft they act. It is assumed that the elastic limit of the material is not exceeded.

318. Two pulleys, A and B, are mounted on a shaft as shown in Fig. 311. The driving pulley A transmits 15 hp to the shaft and the driven pulley B. It turns the shaft at 120 rpm. The smaller belt tension T_2 is 250 lb, the diameter d of the

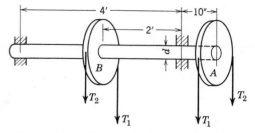

Fig. 311.   Shaft subjected to combined torsional and bending loads.

shaft is $2\frac{1}{2}$ in., and the diameter of each pulley is 2 ft.   Find the maximum normal and shearing stresses in the shaft.

Ans. $\sigma_{\max} = 8390$ lb/in.^{2}; $\tau_{\max} = 4600$ lb/in.^{2}

319. The crankpin pressure P (Fig. 312) in a direction perpendicular to the crank is 2000 lb when the shaft is turned against a constant resisting moment Qq.   The

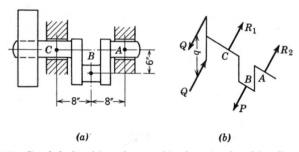

(a)   (b)

Fig. 312.   Crankshaft subjected to combined torsional and bending loads.

$Qq = 12,000 \ \# / in$ $R_1 = R_2 = 1000 \ \#$

diameter of the shaft at A, B, and C is 2 in.   Find the reactions R_1 and R_2 of the bearings and also the maximum normal and shearing stresses at B.

320. In Fig. 313 a shaft 2 in. in diameter is supported in flexible bearings at A and D, and two gears B and C are keyed to the shaft.   The gears are acted on by

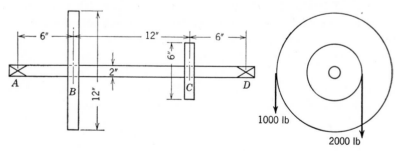

Fig. 313.   Combined torsional and bending loads acting on shaft.

tangential forces, as shown by the end view in Fig. 313.   Calculate the maximum principal tensile stress and the maximum shearing stress, and show in a sketch approximately where in the shaft they occur. Neglect stress concentrations, and assume that the shaft acts elastically.

321. In Fig. 313 let the 1000-lb force act at the top of the gear B in the horizontal direction to the left, instead of acting vertically downward as shown in the figure, and calculate the maximum principal and shearing stresses in the shaft.

Ans. $\sigma' = 12,760$ lb/in.^{2}; $\tau' = 6950$ lb/in.^{2}

322. A steel shaft 4 in. in diameter is subjected to an axial end thrust of 9 tons and also a bending moment of 6000 lb-ft and a twisting moment of 10,000 lb-ft. Calculate the maximum normal and shearing stresses in the shaft. Assume that the shaft acts elastically.

103. Mode of failure. Working loads. Design.

As in previous chapters, the term failure of a member, as here used, means the condition that renders the load-resisting member unfit for resisting further increase in loads. It was noted in Art. 97 that, in general, a member fails by inelastic deformation (yielding) if it is made of ductile material or by fracture (rupture or breaking) if the material is brittle.

It was also pointed out in Art. 97 that, if the member is considered to fail when inelastic deformation *starts* at the most stressed point in the member, we obtain one limit (the lower limit) of the loads that may be applied to the body without causing it to fail; this load is called the elastic-limit load. If the loads are increased appreciably above the lower limiting value, the member will begin to yield, provided that it is made of ductile material, or it will fracture if made of truly brittle material.

The stress analysis given in Arts. 99 and 100 furnishes the means of designing a member subjected to combined loading when the member fails, as indicated in the preceding paragraph, provided that we know what causes the beginning of inelastic deformation or of fracture. The logical method of obtaining this information would be to test the material under the same state of stress that exists in the member to be designed; this was done in the earlier chapters in which the state of stress was uniaxial (in Chaps. I and III), and hence was the same as that occurring in the specimen in a simple tension test. However, it is not feasible (even if possible) to make tests under complex states of stress. In fact, most of the properties of materials are obtained from the simpler tests such as the tension test, and hence we must adopt some method of using the results of the tension test for more complex states of stress, such as biaxial and triaxial states of stress. This is done by adopting a so-called theory of failure.

One commonly used theory of failure is the maximum shearing-stress theory * (sometimes called Coulomb's theory or Guests' law). It

---

* See our *Advanced Mechanics of Materials* for other theories of failure.

states that, for ductile material, inelastic action at any point in a body at which any state of stress exists begins only when the maximum shearing stress on some plane through the point reaches a value equal to the maximum shearing stress in a tension specimen when inelastic action starts. This means that the shearing elastic limit (or yield point) τ_y must be not more than one half of the tensile elastic limit (or yield point) σ_y, since the maximum shearing stress in a tension specimen (on a 45° oblique plane) is one half of the maximum tensile stress in the specimen.

Working Stress and Working Load. The working stress for the ductile material is found by dividing the shearing yield point by a factor of safety ($\tau_w = \tau_y/N$), or the loads acting on the member may be multiplied by the factor of safety N and the working shearing stress be assumed to be τ_y.

For an ideal brittle material (which is assumed to act elastically until the material fractures), the member fails by fracture when the maximum principal (tensile) stress at the point where any state of stress exists reaches a value equal to the tensile ultimate (breaking) stress in a specimen in the tension test. It is known that this theory of failure (called the maximum principal stress theory) leads to somewhat conservative results when applied to so-called brittle materials.

The method of designing a member under combined loading if failure occurs when inelastic deformation at any point in a ductile member *begins,* or when fracture of a brittle member occurs, is indicated in the following illustrative problem.

Illustrative Problem

Problem 323. A cylindrical steel shaft is subjected to a constant bending moment of $M = 80,000$ lb-in. throughout its length and to a constant twisting moment of $T = 60,000$ lb-in. A tensile test of the material gives a tensile yield point $\sigma_y = 40,000$ lb/in.^{2} (See Fig. 310b for shape of stress-strain diagram.) Determine the minimum diameter of the shaft if it is specified that the shaft will fail when the material at any point receives an inelastic deformation and that a factor of safety of 2 shall be used.

Solution. The maximum-shearing-stress theory of failure will be used. The working stress τ_w is

$$\tau_w = \frac{\tau_y}{N} = \frac{0.5 \times 40,000}{2} = 10,000 \text{ lb/in.}^2$$

The maximum shearing stress $\tau' = \frac{1}{2}\sqrt{\sigma^2 + 4\tau^2}$ caused by M and T must not exceed $\tau_w = 10,000$. Thus,

$$10,000 = \frac{1}{2}\sqrt{\sigma^2 + 4\tau^2}$$

in which

$$\sigma = \frac{Mc}{I} = \frac{32M}{\pi d^3} \quad \text{and} \quad \tau = \frac{Tc}{J} = \frac{16T}{\pi d^3}$$

Hence,

$$10,000 = \frac{16}{\pi d^3} \sqrt{M^2 + T^2}$$

Therefore,

$$d^3 = \frac{160}{10\pi} \sqrt{8^2 + 6^2} = 51.0 \text{ in.}^3$$

Hence,

$$d = 3.71 \text{ in.}$$

This is the upper limiting value for d. The lower limiting value will be found from the results in the next article.

Problems

324. The cylindrical bar in Fig. 310a is made of a brittle material having an ultimate strength of $\sigma_u = 100,000$ lb/in.^{2}, as found from a tensile test. Determine the diameter d that the shaft should have if it is specified that the shaft fails by fracture. Assume that it is further specified that the maximum-principal-stress theory shall be used with a factor of safety of 3. Let $P = 150$ lb, $p = 20$ in., $l = 24$ in. Neglect any stress concentrations that may be caused at points of load applications and of reactions.

325. In the steel crankshaft in Fig. 309, assume that the tensile yield point of the material is 40,000 lb/in.^{2} and that the shaft will be considered to fail when inelastic deformation at the most stressed point starts. Calculate the diameter of the shaft to satisfy the conditions that the maximum-shearing-stress theory of failure shall be used with a factor of safety of 2.5. Let $P = 10,000$ lb.

326. Calculate the working (or allowable) value of the load P for the steel bar in Prob. 310 (also Fig. 310), if it is specified that the bar will be considered to have failed when the maximum stress in the most stressed point exceeds the elastic limit (or yield point) of the material. Assume that the maximum-shearing-stress theory of failure applies and that a factor of safety of 2 shall be used. The tensile yield point, as found from the tension test, was $\sigma_y = 36,000$ lb/in.^{2}

§ 2   Inelastic Behavior

104. Fully plastic load. As noted in Art. 97, the fully plastic load may represent the upper limit of loads that can be applied to a ductile member. The fully plastic load does not cause objectional inelastic deformation of the member as a whole, but the local yielding, resulting in plastic hinges, soon leads to general yielding (and hence failure) of the member if loads somewhat larger than the fully plastic load are applied.

It is our purpose in § 2 to present a method of determining the fully plastic values of the loads on a circular cylindrical member that is subjected to a combination of bending and twisting loads. As in the case of combined bending and axial tension in Chapter V and of combined bending and axial compression in Chapter VI, interaction curves are used to solve these problems.

105. Interaction curve for combined bending and twisting. Let a circular cylindrical member, either solid or tubular, of ductile material be subjected to a combination of bending and twisting loads, as shown in Fig. 314a, and let $M = Pl$ be the maximum bending moment and $T = Qq$ the maximum twisting moment, both M and T

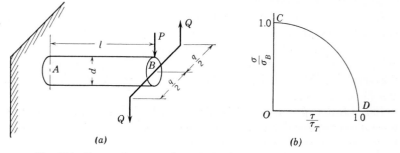

Fig. 314.   Interaction curve for combined torsional and bending loads.

occurring at the fixed end A.   Let M and T represent the combination of moments that must be applied to cause the fully plastic condition at the cross section A.   In the expressions $\sigma = Mc/I$ and $\tau = Tc/J$, σ and τ represent stresses only when the member acts elastically.   If then values of σ and τ are computed by letting M and T be substituted into the elastic-stress formulas, the resulting values, designated as σ_B and τ_T, may be thought of as fictitious stresses (see Art. 75 and Eq. 139), but nevertheless they serve a useful purpose.

Let σ_B be the so-called bending stress, as computed from $\sigma_B = Mc/I$, when the twisting moment $T = 0$: that is, when $Q = 0$ in Fig. 314a and the bar is subjected to bending only.   Let τ_T be the so-called torsional stress as computed from $\tau_T = Tc/J$ when the bending moment $M = 0$: that is, when $P = 0$ in Fig. 314a and the bar is subjected to pure twisting.   If we form the ratios σ/σ_B and τ/τ_T of the foregoing so-called stresses, we may write * the following interaction equation:

* The theoretical derivation of this interaction curve (Eq. 212) is given in a paper by R. Hill and M. P. L. Siebel "On the Plastic Distortion of Solid Bars by Combined Bending and Twisting," *Journal of Mechanics and Physics of Solids*, vol. no. 3, Apr. 1953.   Experimental verification of Eq. 212 is given by R. E. Harvout, "Allowable Shear from Combined Bending and Torsion in Round, Elliptical, and Streamlined Tubes and Allowable Normal Stress from Bending of Thin-Walled Tubes," Air Corps Information Circular 669, Washington, U. S. Government Printing Office, 1932.

$$\left(\frac{\sigma}{\sigma_B}\right)^2 + \left(\frac{\tau}{\tau_T}\right)^2 = 1 \qquad (212)$$

Equation 212 is represented graphically in Fig. 314b by the curve CD which is a circle. The point C represents the condition of bending only ($Q = 0$ in Fig. 314a), and the point D represents twisting only ($P = 0$ in Fig. 314a). The fully plastic conditions for each of these cases has been discussed previously; see Art. 53 in Chapter III and Art. 31 in Chapter II; the values of σ_B and τ_T may be determined from the equations given in these articles.

Interaction Curves for Other Combinations of Loads. Interaction curves for round tubes subjected to combined bending, torsion, and direct compression and for bolts subjected to combined direct shear and axial tension are given on pages 49–51 of ANC-5 Bulletin, 1955, "Strength of Metal Aircraft Parts," Government Printing Office, Washington, D. C.

106. Limiting values of loads. In § 1 of this chapter, methods were discussed for determining the relation between the loads, where they occur in combinations such as torsion with tension or torsion with bending, and the maximum elastic principal stress and the maximum shearing stress. These relationships may be used for such members up to the elastic-limit values of the loads, which is one important limiting value of the loads. However, in § 2 is given a method of determining a second (and higher) limiting value: namely, the fully plastic value of the loads when some inelastic behavior of the (ductile) material (such as a plastic hinge) does not cause failure of the member.

A comparison of the values of the elastic-limit load and the fully plastic load for a given member is usually of importance in determining the safety factor for the member. The illustrative problem that follows will demonstrate the method of computing the fully plastic value of combined twisting and bending loads.

Illustrative Problem

Problem 327. Determine the value of the maximum twisting moment T that must be combined with the maximum bending moment $M = 100,000$ lb-in. to cause the fully plastic condition in a shaft if $d = 3$ in. and $\sigma_y = 60,000$ lb/in.^{2}

Solution. We use Eq. 212 for which we compute the values of σ_B and τ_T. The value of σ_B is found by the substitution in $\sigma_B = Mc/I$ of the fully plastic bending moment M for a beam of circular cross section, which is found, from Art. 53 and Table 4, to be $1.7\sigma_y I/c$. Hence,

$$\sigma_B = (1.7\sigma_y I/c)c/I = 1.7\sigma_y = 102,000 \text{ lb/in.}^2$$

In like manner τ_T is found from $\tau_T = Tc/J$ and from Art. 31 to be

$$\tau_T = \tfrac{4}{3}\tau_y = \tfrac{4}{3}(\tfrac{1}{2}\sigma_y) = 40,000 \text{ lb/in.}^2$$

Furthermore,

$$\sigma = \frac{32M}{\pi d^3} = \frac{32 \times 100,000}{27\pi} = 37,700 \text{ lb/in.}^2$$

and

$$\tau = \frac{16T}{\pi d^3} = \frac{16T}{27\pi}$$

Hence,

$$\left(\frac{37,700}{102,000}\right)^2 + \left(\frac{16T}{27\pi \times 40,000}\right)^2 = 1$$

Therefore, $T = 197,000$ lb-in.

This result shows, when compared with the value $T = 124,000$ lb-in., which is the twisting moment at which inelastic strains will start in this shaft, that the twisting moment T is 1.59 times greater at the fully plastic condition of the cross section than at the start of inelastic behavior at the point of maximum shearing (elastic) stress in the section. This fact indicates that there is a significant difference in the elastic-limit load and the fully plastic loads on this shaft. A knowledge of the values of both of these loads usually is of importance to a designer.

Problems

328. In Fig. 314a let $d = 2$ in., $l = 10$ in., $q = 15$ in., and $Q = 2000$ lb. If the bar AB is a steel shaft whose tensile and compressive yield point is $\sigma_y = 40,000$ lb per sq in., determine the value of the load P that will cause the cross section at A to be fully plastic. *Ans.* = 3700 lb.

329. The crankshaft in Fig. 309 has a diameter $d = 4$ in. and is made of steel having a tensile and compressive yield point of 40,000 lb per sq in. Determine the value of the load P that will cause the fully plastic condition to occur at section AB. *Ans.* $P = 38,600$ lb.

330. Determine the value of the load P for the bar in Prob. 310 that will cause the fully plastic condition at section CD of the bar. Let $\sigma_y = 36,000$ lb/in.^{2} Compare the answer to this problem to that of Prob. 326, and discuss the significance of the difference in values of P. *Ans.* $P = 1370$ lb.

Chapter IX

REPEATED LOADS. FATIGUE OF METALS

107. Introduction. *Definitions.* A repeated load is a force that is applied many times to a member, causing stress in the material that continually varies, usually through some definite range. If a stress is developed in a member and is then released, the member is said to have been subjected to a *cycle of stress*. Further, if a tensile stress has been developed, and when it is released, a compressive stress is developed, and this stress then is released, the member is said to have been subjected to a *reversed cycle of stress* or, briefly, to a *reversal of stress*; the reversal of stress is said to be *complete* if the opposite stresses are of equal magnitudes.

The term "life of a member" denotes the accumulated time during which the member is, or is expected to be, in satisfactory use: that is, the time during which the member is subjected to the repeated loads before failure occurs. For example, the crankshaft of an airplane engine is subjected to approximately 20,000,000 cycles of reversed bending stress in its life; a railroad-car axle is subjected to about 50,000,000 complete reversals of bending stress in its normal "life"; a bandsaw in a normal service of about 2 months is subjected to about 10,000,000 cycles of stress, the stress in each cycle ranging from approximately zero to a maximum, etc.

The name *fatigue* strength of a material is often used to indicate its strength in resisting repeated stress. Early in the study of strength of materials (especially of metals), it was found from experience and experiment that members usually failed (fractured) under *repeated* loads that were considerably smaller than similar *static* loads that were required to cause failure. This fact led to the misleading idea that the material suffered some sort of fatigue in the repeated stressing process. Although the terms fatigue strength and fatigue of metals, etc. are still used, the original idea of fatigue of the material has been abandoned, as will be emphasized in the following article.

The Problem Defined. The general problem considered in this chapter is the same as that considered in each of the preceding chapters: namely, to obtain a relation between the loads acting on a member and the significant response (or quantity, usually a stress) in the member which will reach a value, as the loads increase, that will cause the member to fail and hence to limit the maximum load that may be applied; for repeated loads, this value is often called the fatigue strength for this material. In addition, methods must be found for determining the fatigue strengths for various materials. As pointed out in the previous chapter and especially in Art. 97, the first step in the solution of the general problem is to investigate the mode of failure of the member under the conditions considered.

108. Mode of failure; progressive fracture. The mode of failure of a ductile member caused by repeated loads is a gradual or progressive fracture. The fracture seems to start at some point in the member at which the stress is highest, usually at a point where the stress is concentrated or highly localized by the presence of a fillet, groove, or hole, or some other abrupt discontinuity, such as an internal flaw in the material. As the loads are repeated, a small crack may start and gradually spread until the member ruptures without measurable yielding of the member as a whole.

For example, in Fig. 315a is shown the section of a ruptured shaft that failed after being subjected to many repetitions of a completely reversed bending load P (Fig. 315b). The failure (crack) started at the fillet where high localized stress (stress concentration) occurred, and spread inwardly. The lighter-colored (outer) portion of the fractured cross section in Fig. 315a shows the area over which the crack spread, and the darker (central) portion shows the area of rupture over which the material fractured suddenly.

Fractures of various machine members due to repeated stress frequently have occurred in service; crankshafts in airplane engines and various parts of the airplane structure, railway-car axles, valve rods and springs in automobiles, etc., give much trouble in this respect. For example, in the operation of Liberty ships during a period of 3 years, about one hundred ship propellers were lost at sea as a result of fatigue failures.

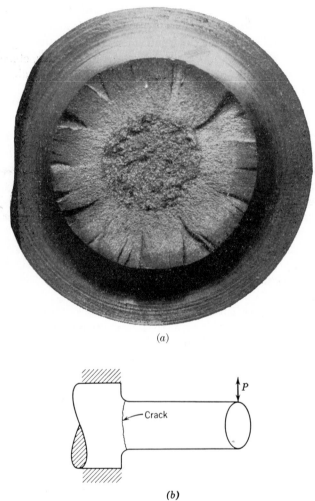

(a)

(b)

Fig. 315. A fatigue fracture.

Localized-stress Theory of Failure. From the engineering viewpoint, probably the most satisfactory theory of a fatigue failure is the localized-stress theory. The main features of this theory may be explained briefly as follows:

In determining the relation between stresses and *static* loads as expressed by the equations $\sigma = P/a$, $\sigma = Mc/I$, $\tau = Tc/J$, etc., developed in the preceding chapters it was assumed:

1. That the material and member were continuous and homogeneous: that is, there existed no discontinuities in the material such as minute internal flaws, no sudden or abrupt changes in the external form of the member, and no changes in the properties of the material from point to point throughout the material.

2. And, therefore, that, on any section of a stressed member, the stress varied gradually; in other words, the stress distribution could be represented by a smooth curve. For example, in a beam, the stresses at points on a transverse section varied directly as the distances of the points from the neutral axis. Thus, it was assumed that the stress at any one point could not attain a value greatly in excess of the stress at neighboring points.

It is known, however, that the assumed gradual variation of stress distribution never exists in structural members; metals, for example, are composed of crystalline grains whose strength and stiffness vary, and in various portions of members there are local concentrations of stress that may be much larger than the calculated values based on the assumed gradual variation of stress. These localized stresses are due (1) to *internal discontinuities* consisting of small internal flaws, fissures, nonmetallic inclusions, etc., at the edges of which high stresses exist, and variations in the strength and stiffness of the crystalline grains from those assumed for the material as a whole, and (2) to *external discontinuities*, resulting mainly from abrupt changes in section where the stress may be highly localized. Both types of discontinuities frequently are called *stress raisers*, and lead to fatigue fractures.

Under *static* loads, a ductile-metal member that contains stress raisers is not seriously damaged by the localized stresses, since the metal yields at the small regions of stress concentration when the localized stress reaches the yield point of the material, without causing structural damage to the member as a whole, and this local yielding prevents the stress concentrations from continuing to increase as the loads are increased appreciably.

The assumption that the stress distribution can be represented by a smooth curve and expressed mathematically by a relatively simple equation therefore leads, in general, to reliable results for ductile metals and static loads. But, when the load is applied a very large number of times, these localized stresses, if above the fatigue strength, may be accompanied by the formation of minute cracks which gradually spread as the stress is repeated until the whole member breaks.

The first experimental evidence of the gradual spread of the area of rupture was obtained by Ewing, Humphrey, and Rosenhain.* They found that, when the localized stress in certain crystals becomes sufficiently large, the crystals yield by sliding along many planes. These planes are called *slip planes*, and their traces on a polished section of the member are seen under the microscope as dark lines, called *slip lines* or *slip bands* (see Fig. 316). For example, slip lines were detected

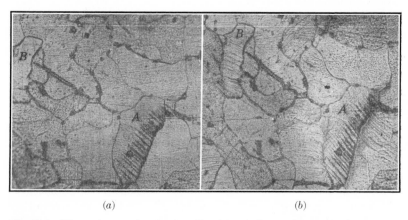

(a)   (b)

Fig. 316. Photomicrographs showing slip planes in low-carbon steel when repeatedly stressed near to the yield point (magnification = ×220). In (a), crystal A was the only crystal in the group in which slip planes were developed. In (b), after the repeated load was increased somewhat, slip planes were produced also in crystal B.

in some of the crystals of a Swedish iron specimen when subjected to a few complete reversals of stress of ±20,000 lb per sq in., although the static yield point and ultimate strength of the material were 31,600 and 52,800 lb per sq in., respectively; after more reversals of stress were applied, additional slip lines appeared, and the original ones broadened. Finally, various groups of slip lines united, forming a visible crack, which gradually extended until rupture occurred.

109. Relationship of loads and localized stress. Stress-concentration factor. Having adopted a (somewhat oversimplified) mode of failure, we may now logically discuss the relationship between the loads and the significant (localized) stress.

Since a localized stress (stress concentration) is considered to be associated with the formation (or initiation) and progressive spreading of a fatigue crack, and hence is associated with the fatigue failure

* *Philosophical Transactions of Royal Society A*, vol. 200 (1903), p. 241.

(fracture), a relationship must be found between the repeated loads and a localized stress in the member; this relationship must, of course, also contain the dimensions of the section of the member.

In calculating the significant (localized) stress in a member that contains some form of an abrupt change in section and that resists repeated loads, the formulas developed in the preceding chapters are used. For example, the equations for axial, torsional, and bending loads, respectively, are

$$\sigma = k\frac{P}{a}, \qquad \tau = k\frac{Tc}{J}, \qquad \text{and} \qquad \sigma = k\frac{Mc}{I} \qquad (213)$$

where k is a stress-concentration factor. The stress distribution at an abrupt change in section in a tension and a flexural member may be pictured approximately as in Fig. 317.

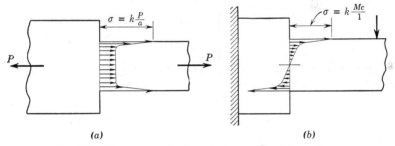

Fig. 317. Stress concentration at abrupt change in section.

It is assumed throughout this chapter that the repeated loads are not applied with impact and that the member is at ordinary (room) temperature. If a member is subjected to repeated impact loads, some additional allowance must be made for the effect of the impact, depending on the conditions of the problem.

In order to make intelligent use of the foregoing equations, we must know the following two quantities:

1. The maximum value of the repeated stress that the material of which the member is made can resist without being structurally damaged: that is, without permitting a crack to start and progressively spread. This maximum value of this stress is called the *fatigue strength* of the material. It may be used for determining the ultimate load for the member or, by applying a factor of safety to it, an allowable or working value of the stress may be found for use in Eq. 213 for design.

2. The value of the stress-concentration factors for the material and form of the member.

These two quantities are considered in the following article.

110. Fatigue strength. The fatigue strength of a material, there-fore, may be defined to be the maximum stress that can be repeated, through a definite cycle or range of stress, a large number of times, without causing the material to rupture by progressive fracture. When the term fatigue strength is used without any qualifying statement as to range of stress, it will be understood to be the fatigue strength with

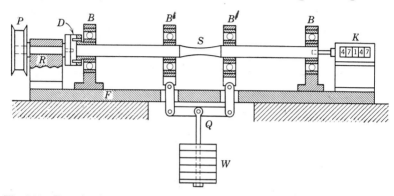

Fig. 318.　Rotating-beam repeated-stress testing machine.　This machine produces complete reversals of bending stress by the use of a rotating-beam specimen.　The specimen S is supported on ball bearings B and is driven by a pulley P.　Weights are hung from a second set of ball bearings B', and these weights cause bending stresses in the specimen.　The bending stress in the upper fibers of the specimen is compression and in the lower fibers tension.　As the specimen is rotated, the stress for any fiber changes from compression to tension, and the stress is completely reversed.　The maximum stress for both tension and compression can be computed from the amount of weights W applied, the dimensions of the specimen, and the distances between bearings; the bending moment is constant for all sections between the two center bearings.　A counter K indicates the number of reversals of stress given to the specimen, and, when the specimen breaks, the counter automatically stops.

completely reversed cycles of stress. The fatigue strength may be found from an S–N diagram as follows:

S–N Diagrams. If several specimens are cut from the same bar of steel and are subjected to repeated complete reversals of stress (see Fig. 318 for description of a repeated-stress testing machine), it will be found that, when a specimen is stressed nearly to the static ultimate strength of the material in each cycle of stress, the specimen will rup-ture (fracture) after being subjected to a small number of cycles of stress; if a second specimen is tested in the same way but stressed slightly less than the first, a larger number of reversals of stress will be required to cause the specimen to fracture. If a series of such experi-ments are carried out, the maximum stress in any specimen being somewhat less than in the preceding specimen, the relation between the value of the completely reversed stress and the number of cycles of reversals of stress required to rupture the specimen will be found to be represented by a curve similar to that shown in Fig. 319, in which stresses are plotted as ordinates and numbers of reversals as abscissas.

The curve in Fig. 319 is called an S–N diagram where S stands for stress and N for number of repetitions of stress required to cause fracture. When S is a tensile (or compressive) stress, its value will be designated by σ and, when a shearing stress, by τ, as in previous chapters. The fatigue strength of the material corresponding to any given num-

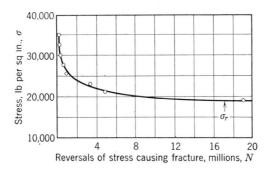

Fig. 319.   An S–N diagram for steel subjected to completely reversed cycles of bending stress.

ber of repetitions of the load or stress is obtained by entering the S–N diagram from the N axis.   For example, for 2,000,000 cycles of stress in Fig. 319, the fatigue strength is about 24,000 lb per sq in.

If the S–N curve becomes approximately horizontal as in Fig. 319, the ordinate σ_r to the horizontal portion is called the fatigue limit or the endurance limit.   Thus the fatigue limit σ_r obtained from the curve in Fig. 319 is approximately $\pm 19{,}000$ lb per sq in.   That is, this material will rupture when subjected, in bending, to cycles of completely reversed stress if the maximum stress in each cycle is slightly greater than 19,000 lb per sq in.

A more convenient way of obtaining an S–N curve and the fatigue limit is to plot values of the logarithms of S and N (or the equivalent of these: namely, to plot values of S and N on logarithmic paper). When this is done, the S–N curve for steel (Fig. 320) is an approximately straight sloping line until it changes its slope rather abruptly and becomes almost horizontal.   The stress at which the change of slope occurs is taken as the measure of the fatigue limit σ_r.   Logarith-

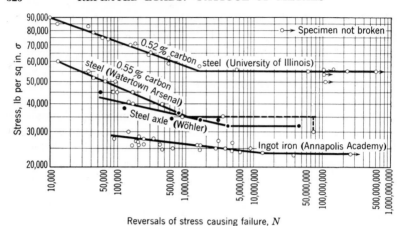

Fig. 320. Logarithmic S–N diagrams for steel subjected to completely reversed cycles of bending stress.

mic plotting makes it possible to show a large range of values on paper of convenient size.

Another convenient method of obtaining an S–N curve and the endurance limit is to plot the stresses as ordinates and the logarithms of the numbers of reversals as abscissas, sometimes called semilogarithmic plotting.

As shown in Fig. 320, wrought ferrous metals, if subjected to com-

TABLE 7

NUMBER OF REPETITIONS IN "LIFETIME" OF MEMBERS

Part of Structure or Machine	Approximate No. of Repetitions of Stress in "Lifetime" of Structure or Machine
Automobile rear-axle gears	100,000
Automobile transmission gears	300,000
Automobile truck rear axle	500,000
Railroad bridge, chord members	2,000,000
Elevated railroad structure, floor beams	40,000,000
Railroad rail, locomotive-wheel loads	500,000
Railroad rail, car-wheel loads	15,000,000
Airplane engine, crankshaft	20,000,000
Car axles	50,000,000
Automobile engine, crankshaft	120,000,000
Line shafting in shops	360,000,000
Steam engine, piston rods, connecting rods, and crankshafts	1,000,000,000
Steam-turbine shafts	15,000,000,000
Steam-turbine blades	250,000,000,000

plete reversals of stress, usually will fracture after resisting 1,000,000 to 5,000,000 cycles of stress, when the maximum stress in each cycle is slightly above the fatigue limit. (Compare these values with the probable number of repetitions of stress in the "lifetime" of various members as given in Table 7.)

111. Stress-concentration factors. The values of these factors depend mainly on two conditions: namely, (1) the form of the member or nature of the discontinuities that give rise to the stress concentrations, and (2) the properties of the material that modify the damaging influence of the stress concentrations. The stress-concentration factor resulting from the first condition only is called the theoretical factor and is denoted by k_t (or merely k); and that resulting from both conditions jointly is frequently called the effective stress-concentration factor and is here denoted by k_f.

The values of k_t are usually found either entirely by mathematical methods of elastic-stress analysis or by experimental methods (models) for solving the equations resulting from the mathematical analysis; some values of k_t are given in tables and curves of Chapters I, II, and III. Values of k_f are found by use of tests of the actual materials. One such method is the repeated-stress method discussed in the next paragraph. For various experimental methods of determining both k_t and k_f, see *Handbook on Experimental Stress Analysis* (John Wiley & Sons, 1950).

Repeated-stress Method for Determining k_f. The minimum repeated load that will cause fracture found by testing a series of specimens free from stress raisers is larger than the similar load found from tests of specimens that contain a given stress raiser; it is assumed that the dimensions of the cross section where the stress raiser occurs is the same as that of the specimens free from the stress raiser. But it is assumed also that a fatigue fracture starts (a crack starts and gradually spreads) in each type of specimen at the same stress (at the fatigue strength or endurance limit of the material.)

These conditions are interpreted to mean that the stress-concentration factor k_f for the given stress raiser and given material is the ratio of the load corresponding to the fatigue strength of the specimens free from the stress raiser to the load corresponding to the fatigue strength of the specimens that contain the given stress raiser. For example, if the minimum repeated load that will cause a fatigue fracture in the specimens free from the stress raisers is 3000 lb and the minimum load that will cause a fatigue fracture in specimens that contain the stress raiser is 1500 lb, the stress-concentration factor k_f is considered to be 2 for the given stress raiser and material.

Problems

331. A steel bar having a constant diameter of 2 in. is to be subjected to several million complete reversals of bending stress. The bar is turned with a lathe, which gives a surface for which the stress-concentration factor is $k_f = 1.2$. What is the maximum allowable repeated bending moment that should be applied to the shaft if the bar is made of a heat-treated steel, for which the yield strength is 65,000 lb per sq in. and the fatigue limit is $\sigma_r = 48,000$ lb per sq in.? Use a value of 3 for the factor of safety N.   *Ans.* $M_w = 10,450$ lb-in.

332. A rectangular bar having a cross section 1.5 in. deep by 4 in. wide is used as a simple beam, as indicated in Fig. 321. The beam contains a hole $\frac{3}{4}$ in. in diameter, as shown in the figure. The bar is made of steel having a yield point of 50,000 lb per sq in., a static tensile ultimate strength of 80,000 lb per sq in., and a fatigue limit for completely reversed bending stress of 40,000 lb per sq in. Find the maximum allowable completely reversed repeated load. Assume a factor of safety of 3 based on the fatigue limit. Assume also that $k_f = 2.2$.

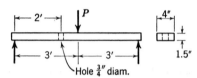

Fig. 321. A beam containing a stress raiser (hole) subjected to repeated loads.

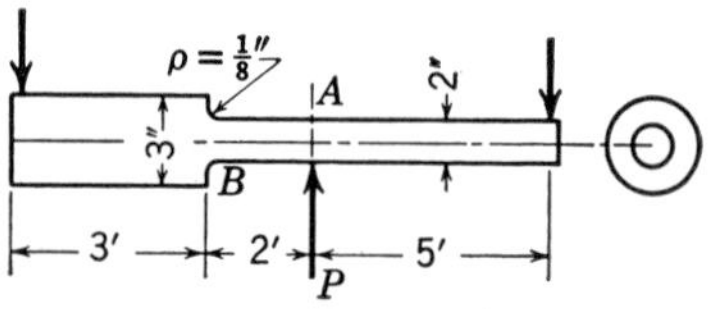

Fig. 322. A beam containing a stress raiser (fillet) subjected to repeated loads.

333. The steel in the cylindrical beam shown in Fig. 322 has a yield point of 40,000 lb per sq in., a tensile ultimate strength of 75,000 lb per sq in., and a percentage of elongation of 30 in 8 in. The fatigue limit of hot-rolled steel for completely reversed bending stress is approximately one half of the tensile ultimate strength. Estimate the maximum allowable completely reversed load P that can be applied to the beam. Use a factor of safety of 2.5 based on the fatigue limit. See Table 3 in Art. 46 for value of k.

334. An aluminum-alloy 7075-T6 bar of constant square cross section 1 in. on a side is used as a component part of an airplane structure. The part is expected to resist 100,000 cycles of completely reversed cycles of bending stress. The fatigue strength for this material at 100,000 complete reversals of stress is found from an S–N diagram to be 42,000 lb per sq in. Use a value of 1.5 for the factor of safety, and calculate the maximum allowable value of the bending moment M.

112. Further consideration of stress–concentration factors and of fatigue strength.

We now need to consider further (I) the modifying influence of the adjustments of the actual material on the theoretical (mathematical) value of the stress-concentration factor, and (II) the effect of the range of repeated stress (other than completely reversed stress) on the fatigue strength of the material.

I. *Relation between k and k_f.* The value of k_f as found by the repeated-stress test method is usually somewhat smaller than the value of k_t, as determined by the mathematical (or equivalent experimental) methods.   At an abrupt change of section such as a fillet, hole, or groove in a member, the stress developed in the member by the repeated load may be assumed to be equal to the sum of two parts: (1) the nominal value of stress given by the ordinary stress equations ($\sigma = P/a$, $\sigma = Mc/I$, etc.), and (2) some proportion (1/4, 1/2, 3/4, say) of the increase in the theoretical stress ($\sigma = kP/a$, $\sigma = kMc/I$, etc., in which k is the mathematically determined (theoretical) value of the stress concentration) caused by the abrupt change in section.   This means that the nominal stress plus some proportion of the increase in stress caused by the abrupt change of section is considered effective in causing damage to the member.   For example, if the abrupt change in section is caused by a small hole in the center of a plate subjected to an axial load, and if one half of the difference between the nominal stress $\sigma = P/a$ and the maximum theoretical value of the localized stress $\sigma = 3P/a$ is used, then the value of k_f would be $k_f = 1 + \frac{1}{2}(3 - 1) = 2$.   Thus, the formula for use, if the axial load on the plate is completely reversed repeatedly, would be $\sigma = 2P/a$.

Notch-sensitivity Index.   The principle used in the foregoing example can be stated in a general form as follows: Let q represent the proportion of the increase in the theoretical localized stress above the nominal stress.   Then, following the foregoing example, we have

$$k_f = 1 + q(k - 1) \tag{214}$$

or, solving Eq. 214 for q, we have

$$q = \frac{k_f - 1}{k - 1} \tag{215}$$

The name frequently given to q as defined by Eq. 215 is the *notch-sensitivity index* of the material for the given form of abrupt change of section and for the given type of loading.   For example, if $q = 0$, $k_f = 1$ and the material and member are said to be insensitive to the effects of the stress concentration; whereas, if $q = 1$, $k_f = k$ and the member is said to be fully sensitive to the effects of the stress concentration.   The values of k_f (and hence of q) must be determined from repeated load tests, as described previously.

The results of many repeated load tests that have been made for determining the value of k_f and q for steel specimens containing a groove have shown that the values of q and the root radius of the groove

are related, as indicated by the curves in Fig. 323. Additional * tests
show that, for steel specimens containing a fillet or a hole, these same
curves that were obtained for a groove may be used for a fillet or hole.

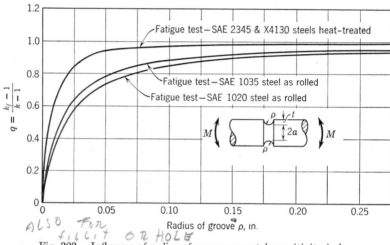

Fig. 323.   Influence of radius of groove on notch-sensitivity index.

II. *Effect of Range of Stress on Fatigue Strength.*   The early investigations of A. Wöhler (1870) and the supplementary work of Bauschinger
showed that the fatigue strength of materials depends on the range of
stress.

Goodman Diagram.   For example, the fatigue limit of a typical low-
carbon steel under completely reversed tension–compression is approximately 30,000 lb per sq in. If the same steel is subjected to cycles of
stress from zero to a maximum tension, the fatigue limit is approximately 40,000 lb per sq in. The results of many repeated load tests of
metals can be represented in a diagram frequently called a Goodman or
Goodman-Johnson diagram, shown in Fig. 324a where the ordinates to
the line *BOC* represent the minimum stresses σ_{min}, or lower limits of
the various ranges of stress $\Delta\sigma$, and the ordinates to the line *CAD* represent the maximum stresses σ_{max} of the range $\Delta\sigma$. For any range $\Delta\sigma$,
such as *GH*, between the lines *BOC* and *CAD*, no progressive fracture
will occur, even if an indefinitely large number of cycles of this range
of stress is applied. Note that *BD* represents the completely reversed
range of stress when σ_r is the fatigue strength of the material for completely reversed cycles, *OA* the fatigue strength under cycles from zero

* See p. 10 of R. E. Peterson's *Stress Concentration Design Factors*, John Wiley
& Sons, 1953, for further discussion of notch-sensitivity index.

to maximum, and the ordinate to C the static ultimate tensile strength of the material.

Steady-stress and Alternating-stress Components. A different method of introducing the effect of range of stress is as follows: A range of stress may be thought of as a steady or mean stress, on which is superimposed a completely reversed (alternating) stress. From this point of view, the test data referred to in the preceding paragraph can be represented in Fig. 324b as abscissas and ordinates to the points on line AB. For example, let OC represent a mean or steady stress σ_m. Then

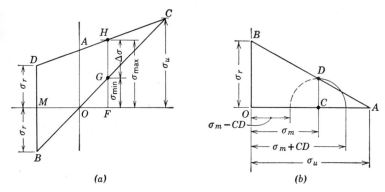

Fig. 324. Two methods of indicating the effect of range of stress.

CD represents the maximum value of alternating stress σ_a that can be completely reversed (superimposed) on σ_m without causing fatigue fracture. In this example $\sigma_m - CD$ is the minimum stress in the range and $\sigma_m + CD$ is the maximum stress in the range.

This method of representing the effect of range of stress has the following advantage in applying the fatigue stress-concentration factor k_f. There is considerable evidence * indicating that the damaging effect of the stress concentration in a repeated cycle of stress is associated only with the completely reversed (alternating) stress of the cycle and not with the maximum stress in the cycle. Thus, the stress-concentration factor k_f for the particular notch is applied only to the alternating stress σ_a and is the same as that found for completely reversed-stress cycle (where $\sigma_m = 0$) tests or from Fig. 323.

* *Transactions American Society of Mechanical Engineers, Applied Mechanics,* vol. 1, no. 3, July–Sept. 1933, APM-55-16. See also *University Illinois Engineering Experiment Station Bulletin 334.*

Illustrative Problem

Problem 335. Find the maximum allowable or working axial load P_w that should be applied to an SAE 1035 steel bar shown in Fig. 325; assume the load to be a completely reversed repeated load. The tensile yield point of the material is 50,000 lb/in.², the static tensile ultimate strength is 85,000 lb/in.², and the fatigue limit for completely reversed bending stress is 42,000 lb/in.² Use a factor of safety of 3.5 based on the fatigue limit.

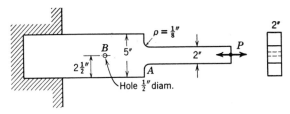

Fig. 325.   Member subjected to repeated axial load.

Solution. The significant (localized) stress σ is either at A or at B, and its value may be found as follows:

If at A: $\sigma_w = k_f P_w/a$. The value of k_f is found from Eq. 215. But first the value $k_t = 2.40$ is found from Art. 15, and the value $q = 0.9$ is found from Fig. 323, by reading the ordinate to the curve labeled SAE 1035 steel at $\rho = 0.125$ in. Hence, $k_f = 1 + 0.9(2.40 - 1) = 2.26$. Furthermore,

$$\sigma_w = \frac{\sigma_r}{N} = \frac{42,000}{3.5} = 12,000 \text{ lb/in.}^2$$

Then,

$$12,000 = 2.26 P_w/a \quad \text{or} \quad P_w = 21,200 \text{ lb}$$

If at B: $\sigma = k_f P/a_1$, in which the value $k_f = 2.65$ for the hole is found from Art. 15, and, from Fig. 323, $q = 0.93$. Therefore, $k_f = 1 + 0.93(2.65 - 1) = 2.53$. Hence,

$$P_w = \frac{12,000 \times 4.5 \times 2}{2.53} = 42,700 \text{ lb}$$

Therefore, the repeated stress at A is the significant stress, and the maximum allowable load is 21,200 lb.

Problems

336. Estimate the maximum allowable or working load P_w for the steel cantilever beam shown in Fig. 326; assume the load to be a completely reversed repeated load, and the factor of safety to be 2.5, based on the fatigue limit which is 42,000 lb per sq in. See Art. 46 for values of k_t.

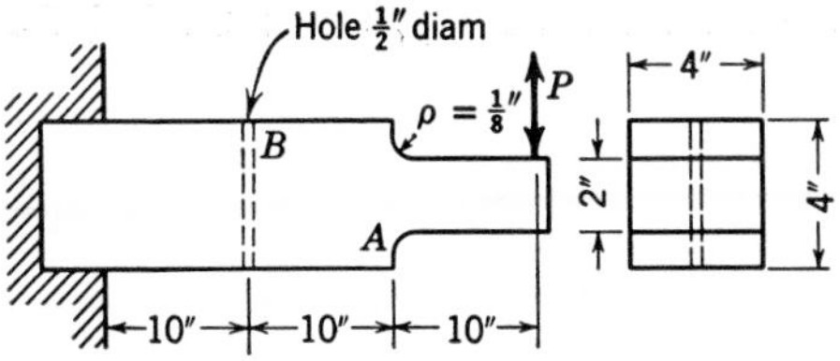

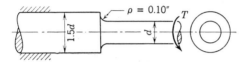

Fig. 326.   Member subjected to repeated bending load.

337. What should be the diameter d of the steel shaft shown in Fig. 327 if the shaft is subjected to a completely reversed repeated twisting moment of $T = 6000$ lb-in.?   The fatigue limit of the material for completely reversed bending stress is

Fig. 327.   Member subjected to repeated torsional load.

48,000 lb per sq in., and the fatigue limit for completely reversed torsional shearing stress is approximately one-half that for bending stress.   Assume a factor of safety of 4, which is considered to be sufficient to allow for some impact.   Also assume that Fig. 323 applies to torsion.   See Art. 29 for values of k_t in torsion.

338. The fatigue limit for a certain grade of steel, as found from specimens subjected to completely reversed bending stress, is 36,000 lb per sq in.   The tensile yield point of the steel, as found by the usual static test, is 45,000 lb per sq in. An axle made of this steel has a square shoulder (abrupt change of section) at the section of maximum moment, for which the stress-concentration factor k_f is 2.0, and the section modulus of the shaft at the dangerous section is 12.0 in.³   If in service the axle will be subjected to many millions of reversals of bending stress, calculate a working value of the maximum bending moment to which the shaft should be subjected; use a factor of safety of 3 based on the endurance limit.   See Art. 46 for values of k_t in bending.   *Ans.*   72,000 lb-in.

339. A steel cylindrical rod is subjected to a supposedly axial load P, which causes completely reversed cycles of stress.   V threads are cut round the rod, the diameter at the root of the threads being $\frac{1}{2}$ in.   If the rod is subjected to many millions of cycles of completely reversed stress, determine a working value of P.   The value of the fatigue limit of the material, as found from tests of specimens subjected to completely reversed bending stress, is 41,000 lb per sq in.   Assume $k_f = 3.0$.

340. A hardened and tempered chrome-nickel crankshaft of a gas engine is subjected to many repeated applications of a torsional shearing stress, which varies approximately from zero to a maximum; bending stresses may be neglected.   If the shaft is 2 in. in diameter, what maximum torque should be allowed?   The fatigue limit in completely reversed torsion is $\tau_r = 40,000$ lb per sq in., and the ultimate torsional static strength is $\tau_u = 120,000$ lb per sq in.   Neglect stress concentrations.

341. A simple beam has a span of 20 in. and is made of hardened and tempered chrome-nickel steel.   This steel has a fatigue limit of $\sigma_r = 68,000$ lb per sq in. for complete reversals of bending stress and a static ultimate tensile strength of σ_u = 138,000 lb per sq in. It is loaded at the center of the span with a concentrated load, which varies repeatedly from 1000 to 3000 lb. Use a factor of safety of 4 and estimate, by the method illustrated in Fig. 324b, an allowable range of stress for the material.   *Ans.* Allowable range = 8580 to 25,720 lb/in.[2]

113. Methods of reducing harmful effects of stress concentration.

The problem that frequently arises in engineering is to reduce the value of a stress concentration below the minimum value that will cause a fatigue fracture to occur or to raise the fatigue strength of the material so that fracture is avoided rather than to calculate the stress

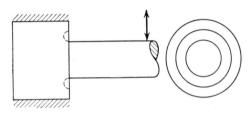

Fig. 328.   One method of increasing fatigue strength, by removing material so that stress concentration is decreased.

concentration. Some of the ways that have been employed in an attempt to overcome the damaging effects of localized stresses are listed as follows:

1. Reducing the abruptness of the change in cross section of the member by use of fillets, etc., either by adding small amounts of material or by removing small amounts of material as suggested in Fig. 328.

2. Reducing the value of the stress concentration by making the portion of the member in the neighborhood of the stress concentration less stiff; this sometimes may be done by substituting a member made of material with a lower modulus of elasticity, such as replacing a steel nut on a steel bolt by a bronze nut for reducing the stress concentration at the threads of the steel bolt.

3. Increasing the fatigue strength of the material by cold-working the portions of the members where the stress concentrations occur: for example, by the cold rolling of fillets and of bearing surfaces on axles, by the shot blasting or shot peening of surfaces of machine parts. The increased fatigue strength of a member caused by local cold working of the metal at the region of stress concentration in some cases may be due primarily to residual compressive stresses set up in the cold-worked

metal by the surrounding elastic material as this elastic material attempts to return to its original position when the cold-working tool is removed.

4. Increasing the fatigue strength of the material by alloying and heat treating of portions of steel members that resist high stress, by case hardening, nitriding, flame hardening, etc.

Chapter X

DYNAMIC LOADS

114. Introduction. In the preceding chapters, it was assumed that the loads acting on a member were applied gradually (without impact), and that the member was in stable equilibrium (not accelerated) at each instant or stage of the loading. Thus it was assumed that the time during which the load was applied had negligible influence on the value of the load and on the properties of the material involved in the response of the member to the loads.

Dynamic Load. A load caused by a moving body is usually called a dynamic load, for the reason that such a body usually will not satisfy the conditions of equilibrium stated in the foregoing paragraph. The force applied to the resisting member by the moving body is frequently called an impact load.

Some dynamic loads, however, act on the resisting member over a considerable time interval, during which the loads accelerate the member, such as the air pressure on an airplane while it is traveling in a curved path.

A dynamic load, whether applied rapidly as an impact load or less rapidly as an accelerating load, produces higher stresses in the resisting member than would be produced by the same maximum force gradually applied while maintaining the condition of equilibrium.

Effect of Time. From the foregoing statement it is evident that time is an important factor in the response of a member to loads. One extreme condition occurs when the time of applying the load is very long,

336

leading to slowly increasing deformation called *creep*, especially at elevated temperatures. The opposite extreme condition exists when the load is applied during an extremely short period of time (often called high-velocity impact), such as the force of a shell from a long-range gun when the shell strikes the armor plate of a ship, etc. The stresses developed and the general behavior of the material under these conditions may bear little resemblance to those caused by gradually applied loads. High-velocity impact will not be discussed in this book.

Low-velocity Impact. If, however, the time during which the load is applied is sufficient to enable the material in the resisting member to exhibit substantially the same properties as are involved in response to so-called static (gradually applied) loads, the impact is frequently called low-velocity impact. Under these conditions, the impact effect of the load may be considered to be equivalent to an additional static load, as is discussed in the next article. The difference in the two types of impact, however, is not dependent alone on the velocity of impact. It depends also on the relative masses of the two bodies (Art. 121) involved in the impact, and on their connections to other bodies in the structure; likewise, it depends on the properties of the material in the bodies.

Vibrational Effect of Dynamic Loading. In addition, the dynamic load applied by the moving body may cause a vibration of the resisting member, and, if the period or frequency of the impulses of the dynamic load is nearly the same as the natural frequency of vibration of the resisting member, a condition, called *resonance*, is established, which causes excessive deflection, and which usually soon leads to complete failure or destruction of the resisting member. Several suspension bridges under the influence of wind pressure (aerodynamic loading) have been destroyed in this fashion. Many machine parts and airplane parts also are likely to be subjected to resonant vibration if special care is not exercised to avoid such conditions. Vibration of load-resisting members is discussed briefly in Chapter XVI, and only nonvibrational, low-velocity dynamic loads will be considered in the present chapter.

115. Equivalent static-load method. As previously noted, members of engineering structures and machines are often required to resist nonvibrational dynamic loads in the form of low-velocity impact or accelerating loads. The usual method of determining the stresses and deformations caused by such loads is first to estimate the maximum pressure or force exerted by the moving body on the resisting body; this load is then considered to be a static load (a so-called equivalent static load), and is used in the equations developed in the preceding chapters.

Thus the load caused by a moving train on a bridge, by a moving crowd of people in a stadium, by the blast pressure of a bomb explosion on a building, by the pressure of the earth on the wheels of an airplane as it lands on the runway, by an earthquake force on buildings, by pressure on gear teeth in gear-driven machinery, by wind pressure on a building, etc., may often be assumed to be equivalent to a static load composed of the weight of the moving body (usually called the live load), plus a static load assumed to be equivalent (in producing stress) to the dynamic or impact effect of the live load.

The total equivalent static load, then, may often consist of the weight of a resisting member or structure (called dead load), such as the weight of a bridge, plus the live load, such as the weight of a train moving on the bridge, plus the product of an impact factor and the live load.

116. Impact factors. As already noted, if the body that applies a load to a member or structure is in motion when it comes in contact with the resisting body, the stresses caused in the member are larger than would be produced by the same load at rest. The increase in the static load required to cause the same stress that the dynamic load produces is called the impact effect or merely the impact load. It is usually found by multiplying the moving (live) load by an *impact factor*.

The impact factor is different for each different type of dynamic loading, and the value for the factor never can be considered to be more than a rough approximation to the actual dynamic effect of the moving load. For, in spite of much experimental work in this field on actual structures, as well as on laboratory models, the behavior of the structure cannot be predicted accurately; the conditions influencing the action of the member under dynamic loading are always numerous and uncertain.

Values for impact factors have been proposed in codes for certain service conditions by various technical societies and government agencies, such as the American Railway Engineering Association (AREA), the subcommittee on Air Force–Navy–Civil Aircraft Design Criteria of the Munitions Board, Aircraft Committee, designated as ANC-5 Bulletin on *Strength of Metal Aircraft Elements*, American Society of Civil Engineers (ASCE), American Society of Mechanical Engineers (ASME), City Government Building Codes.

117. Importance of ability of member to absorb energy. The equivalent static-load method of treating problems in nonvibrational, low-velocity impact frequently needs supplementary information in order to obtain an acceptable design. This additional information comes from a study of the conditions that allow as much as possible of the kinetic energy of the moving body to be absorbed by the resisting body. For, it will be shown, in the following articles, *that the dimensions of the resisting member and the properties of the material in the member that give it maximum capacity to absorb energy may be quite different from those that give it maximum resistance to a static load.*

Importance of Relative Stiffness. It should be noted also that, often in problems involving loads applied by moving bodies, the main objective is not to determine the maximum (equivalent static) load and the resulting maximum stresses, but rather to select the shape and material for the member, and to adjust the relative stiffness of the member *and its connections with other parts or bodies,* so that the energy delivered by the moving body to the resisting body will be distributed as widely as possible to all parts of the member and its connecting bodies. Such a distribution of energy is usually achieved by proportioning the dimensions (and shape) so that the stresses are distributed as evenly as possible throughout the member. Damage to a member from impact usually results from the absorption of an excessive amount of energy at small portions where the stress is high, for the reason that the elastic energy stored in material varies as the square of the stress in the material, as will be shown later.

In fact, the stiffness of the member relative to that of the connections of the member to other members in the structure is often of prime importance in avoiding damage from impact loading; this statement applies to conditions involving only elastic behavior and to conditions in which some (small) plastic behavior is permissible in members of the structure (see § 2 of this chapter).

§ 1   Elastic Behavior under Impact Loads

118. Relation between energy stored and stress in member. *Axial Load.* Let a low-velocity impact load P be applied to a bar of constant cross section so that the bar is subjected to an axial tensile stress, as shown in Fig. 329a. Let the elastic energy that is absorbed by the resisting body be U. The energy absorbed by the resisting member is sometimes called an energy load. The relation between U and the stress σ in the bar may be expressed as follows: The assumption is made that a material, when resisting a low-velocity impact load, acts in the same way as when resisting a gradually applied (static) load; namely, stress is proportional to strain until the proportional limit is reached. Hence, the elastic energy U stored in the bar when the stress in the bar is σ (which is equal to the work w done on the bar in causing the stress σ) may be expressed as the average force $P/2$ times the total deformation e (see Fig. 329d). Thus, $U = w = \frac{1}{2}Pe$, in which

P is the final value of the gradually applied load. But, $\sigma/\epsilon = E$, and $\sigma = P/a$ where a is the cross-sectional area of the bar. Hence,

$$U = \tfrac{1}{2}(\sigma^2/E)(al) \quad \text{or} \quad \sigma = \sqrt{2UE/al} \qquad (216)$$

in which σ must not exceed the proportional limit of the material. If U is expressed in inch-pounds, E in pounds per square inch, a in square inches, and l in inches, σ will be expressed in pounds per square inch.

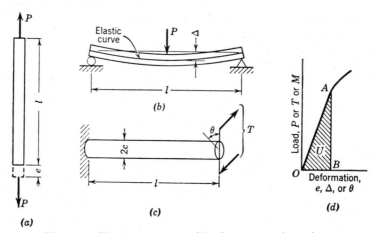

Fig. 329.   Elastic energy stored in three types of members.

Equation 216 shows that the energy absorbed per unit volume of the material, when stressed to the proportional limit σ_e is $(\tfrac{1}{2}\sigma_e{}^2/E)$; this value is represented by the area OAB in Fig. 329d and is called the _modulus of resilience_ of the material.

The ideal material, then, for resisting low-velocity impact loads in service, in which the material must not incur permanent distortion, as, for example, in springs, is one having a high modulus of resilience: that is, one having a high proportional limit and a low modulus of elasticity.   (See Table 8.)

Simple Beam with Concentrated Load at Center.   Let it be required to find the maximum stress caused by a low-velocity impact load P at the center of a simply supported beam as in Fig. 329b. It is assumed that the maximum stress does not exceed the proportional limit of the material. It is also assumed that the elastic energy that can be stored in a beam is the same when subjected to a gradually applied load as when subjected to a low-velocity impact load. The expression for the elastic energy U that can be absorbed by the beam may be found in the same manner as for the axial load. The relation between the load P and the deflection Δ of the beam is shown by Fig. 329d. The energy U that can be absorbed by the beam (which is equal to the work done on the beam as a gradually applied load increases from zero to the value P) may be found from the expression,

$$U = \tfrac{1}{2}P\Delta \tag{217}$$

And, in accordance with Chapters III and IV, P and Δ may be obtained from the equations

$$M = \frac{Pl}{4} = \frac{\sigma I}{c} \quad \text{and} \quad \Delta = \frac{1Pl^3}{48EI}$$

Therefore,

$$U = \frac{1}{6}\frac{I}{c^2}\frac{\sigma^2}{E}l \tag{218}$$

But $I = ar^2$ (Art. 157), in which r is the radius of gyration of the cross-sectional area with respect to the neutral axis. Hence,

$$U = \frac{1}{6}\frac{r^2}{c^2}\frac{\sigma^2}{E}al \quad \text{or} \quad \sigma = \frac{c\sqrt{6}}{r} \cdot \sqrt{\frac{UE}{al}} \tag{219}$$

If U is expressed in inch-pounds, E in pounds per square inch, a in square inches, and r, c, and l in inches, σ will be expressed in pounds per square inch.

Since the numerical value of the ratio r^2/c^2 is always the same for similarly shaped sections, the amount of energy that a horizontal rectangular beam will absorb without exceeding the elastic limit when the short dimension is vertical will be the same as that absorbed when the long dimension is vertical. On the contrary, the static loads necessary to cause the elastic-limit stress for these two arrangements of the beam are not equal.

Torsional Energy Load. If one end of a solid cylindrical shaft of length l, radius c, and area of cross section a is fixed at one end, and a low-velocity impact twisting moment T is applied to the other end (Fig. 329c) by means of a moving body (such as a flywheel connected to the shaft by a clutch), the maximum shearing stress developed in the shaft in terms of the energy absorbed by the shaft may be found as follows:

The elastic work done on the shaft by a gradually applied twisting moment, whose final value is T, is $\tfrac{1}{2}T\theta$, where θ is the angle of twist (in radians) of the free end of the shaft. If it is assumed, as in the preceding paragraphs, that the relation between stress and strain is the same under low-velocity impact as under static load, the energy U absorbed by the shaft when stressed within the proportional limit is (referring to Chap. II)

$$U = \frac{1}{2}T\theta = \frac{1}{2}\frac{T^2l}{GJ} = \frac{\tau^2Jl}{2c^2G} = \frac{\tau^2\pi c^2l}{4G} = \frac{\tau^2}{4G}al \qquad (220)$$

Hence,

$$\tau = 2\sqrt{\frac{UG}{al}} \qquad (221)$$

Problems

342. A structural-steel bar and an oak stick used as direct-tension members are required to absorb the energy of a falling weight. The cross-sectional area of the steel and oak bars are 2 and 3 sq in., respectively; the lengths are 3 ft for the steel bar and 5 ft for the oak. The modulus of elasticity of the oak is $\frac{1}{15}$ of that of steel. The proportional limit of the oak is $\frac{1}{10}$ of that of steel. Which bar can resist the greater energy load without causing inelastic action in the bar?

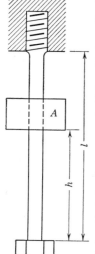

343. The piston rods of the forging hammers in a certain steel plant frequently broke, and, when they were finally replaced by a higher-carbon steel, the trouble ceased. If the proportional limit of the low-carbon steel was 32,000 lb per sq in. and that of the higher-carbon steel was 60,000 lb per sq in., how much more energy could the higher-carbon steel rod absorb without being stressed above the proportional limit?

Ans. The higher-carbon steel rod will absorb 3.51 times as much elastic energy as the lower-carbon steel rod.

344. A body A (Fig. 330) having a weight of 15 lb falls a height h of 5 ft when it comes in contact with the end of a rod having a length l of 8 ft. (a) If the rod is made of steel having a proportional limit of 60,000 lb per sq in., what cross-sectional area should the rod have in order to prevent the stress from exceeding the proportional limit? *Ans.* 0.156 in.²

345. A steel bar having a length of 15 in. and a cross section of 1.0 sq in. has a low-velocity axial load applied to it. The work done on, and energy absorbed by, the bar when the body is brought to rest is 9 ft-lb. Find the maximum stress developed in the bar.

Fig. 330. Axial impact load caused by falling body.

346. A low-carbon steel bar 20 in. long and an aluminum-alloy (7075-T6) bar, each $\frac{1}{2}$ in. in diameter, are subjected to equal low-velocity impact loads causing axial stress. If it is specified that the energy absorbed by each bar per unit volume is one third of the modulus of resilience of the material, what should be the length of the aluminum-alloy bar? (Consult Table 8 of this chapter.)

347. Two steel bars, each 20 in. long, are coupled together to form a bar 40 in. long. It is to be subjected to an axial low-velocity impact load. One of the bars is a solid cylindrical bar 1 in. in diameter, and the second bar is a circular tube whose inner diameter is 1 in. Determine the outer diameter of the tube so that it will absorb the same amount of elastic energy as the solid cylinder.

348. A hickory timber beam is 6 ft long, 6 in. deep, and 2 in. wide, and is simply supported at its ends. A 50-lb weight is to be dropped from a height h above the midpoint to strike the beam. If the maximum stress must not exceed 5000 lb per sq in., compute the maximum value of h. $E = 2,000,000$ lb per sq in.

Ans. 12 in.

349. Show that, if the beam has a rectangular cross section, Eq. 218 reduces to

$$U = \frac{1}{18} \frac{\sigma^2}{E} al = \frac{1}{9} \left(\frac{1}{2} \frac{\sigma^2}{E} \right) al$$

which shows that the elastic energy that this beam can resist is only one ninth as large as the energy it could resist if it were used as a tension member and stressed to the same maximum value σ.

350. Show that, if the beam has a circular cross section, Eq. 218 reduces to

$$U = \frac{1}{24} \frac{\sigma^2}{E} al = \frac{1}{12} \left(\frac{1}{2} \frac{\sigma^2}{E} \right) al$$

Interpret this expression as was done in the preceding problem.

351. Refer to Fig. 207 and Art. 61, and note that in any beam the work done on, or the elastic energy stored in, a beam is given by the expression

$$U = \frac{1}{2} \int M \, d\theta = \frac{1}{2} \int \frac{M^2 \, dx}{EI}$$

Show that this expression reduces to Eq. 219 for a simple beam with the load applied at the center of the beam.

352. Show that

$$U = \frac{1}{240} \frac{w^2 l^5}{EI} = \frac{4}{15} \frac{r^2}{c^2} \frac{\sigma^2}{E} al$$

for a simple beam with a uniformly distributed load. *Hint.* Use $U = \int \frac{1}{2} \frac{M^2 \, dx}{EI}$.

353. If a round structural-steel bar having a given value of a and l is to be used to absorb energy without acquiring plastic deformation, would it be better to use the bar as a torsion member or as an axially loaded tension member? (Consult Table 1, Chap. I.) *Ans.* It will absorb 2.22 times as much in tension as in torsion.

119. Comparison of effect of static and impact loads.

The elastic resistance offered by a bar to a *static* load P depends only on the maximum stress developed, which may occur on only one cross section and perhaps at only one point in the cross section. On the other hand, the resistance of the bar to an impact load, as indicated by Eq. 216, depends not only on the maximum stress σ but also on two additional conditions: (1) The evenness or uniformity of stress distribution throughout the body, since the elastic energy absorbed per unit volume is $\frac{1}{2}\sigma^2/E$, and hence depends on the degree to which each unit of volume is stressed to the maximum stress σ. Hence, the body absorbs a maximum amount of energy when every unit of volume is subjected to the maximum stress σ. Therefore (2) under these conditions, the more units of volume (al) of material in the bar, the more energy is absorbed. The influence of these two factors may be shown as follows.

Effect of Distribution of Stress in Axially Loaded Bar. The static strengths of the two cylindrical bars shown in Fig. 331 when subjected

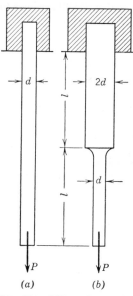

to axial loads are equal, since the smallest cross sections are equal, and hence the static loads P required to produce a given stress σ in the bars are equal ($P = a\sigma$). The low-velocity impact loads required to produce a given elastic stress in the two bars, however, are very different; the bar having the constant diameter, and hence a uniform distribution of stress σ throughout the length of the bar, is able to absorb the greater amount of elastic energy. For example, if the diameter of the upper half of the bar shown in Fig. 331b is reduced from $2d$ to d, the area a (and also volume al) thereby will be decreased to one fourth of the original area (and volume), and hence the stress will be increased to four times the original value. Therefore, the energy absorbed per unit volume ($\sigma^2/2E$) by this upper half will be 16 times greater than that absorbed per unit volume when the diameter is $2d$. Thus, in the expression ($\sigma^2/2E$)al for the upper half

Fig. 331. Effect of removing material on energy stored in member.

of the bar, the factor $\sigma^2/2E$ has been increased more than the factor al has been decreased. The total energy absorbed by the upper half of the bar has been increased to four times its original value by reducing the diameter of the upper half from $2d$ to d.

Effect of Distribution of Stress in Beam. In Fig. 332a, b, and c are shown two cantilever beams each of which is subjected to the same static load P. The beam of Fig. 332a has a constant rectangular section of depth h and width b, and the beam of Fig. 332b and c has the same constant depth h and the same width b at the fixed end as the first beam but is tapered (see Fig. 332c) so that its width at any distance x from the free end is $(b/l)x$. The maximum bending stress ($\sigma = Mc/I$) in each beam is $\sigma = 6Pl/bh^2$. In Fig. 332a this stress occurs only at the fixed end, and the maximum bending stress gradually decreases to a value of zero at the free end, but in the tapered beam (Fig. 332b) the stress σ occurs at every section of the beam, since at

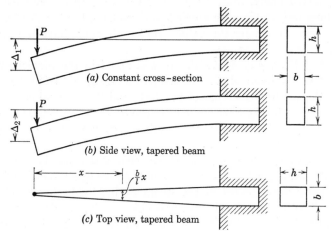

Fig. 332.   Effect of shape of member on energy stored in member.

any section a distance x from the left end the maximum bending stress is given by the equation

$$\sigma = \frac{Mc}{I} = \frac{Px(h/2)}{\dfrac{1}{12}\left(\dfrac{b}{l}\,x\right)h^3} = \frac{6Pl}{bh^2} \tag{222}$$

We may conclude, therefore, that the given static load P produces the same maximum bending stress σ in each of the two beams. The energy absorbed by the two beams is not equal, however, as we might observe from the difference in distribution of the maximum bending stress along the length of the beams.

To show this fact quantitatively, we compute the energy absorbed by each of the beams. In Fig. 332a the energy absorbed is equal to the work done by the force P; this work is $\frac{1}{2}P\Delta_1$ and in the tapered beam it is $\frac{1}{2}P\Delta_2$. By making use of the methods of Chapter IV, we find $\Delta_1 = \frac{1}{3}Pl^3/EI = 4Pl^3/Ebh^3$ and $\Delta_2 = 6Pl^3/Ebh^3$. Therefore, the energy absorbed in the tapered beam is one and one-half times the energy absorbed in the beam of constant cross section. Hence, we may conclude that, if equal low-velocity impact loads are applied to the two beams (for example, if a body of weight W is dropped from the same height h above the end of each beam), the maximum bending stress in the tapered beam will be less than that in the beam of constant cross section. The same conclusion would be true of the axially loaded bars of Fig. 331: namely, that, if equal low-velocity impact loads (such as the falling weight W) were applied to these bars, the bar of Fig. 331a with constant diameter throughout its length would have the smaller stress.

Effect of Volume of Material. It was noted in the previous paragraphs that the removal of materials (reduction of $2d$ to d in the upper half of the axially loaded bar of Fig. 331b and the removal of material by tapering as in Fig. 332b and c from the beam of Fig. 332a) increased the capacity of the member to absorb energy without exceeding the elastic limit of the material.

This method of increasing the elastic energy that can be applied to an axially loaded bar was brought forcibly to the attention of engineers in the early development of the steam engine by Professor John E. Sweet. The bolts in the connecting-rod head when made in the usual form with full-sized shanks and threaded ends as in Fig. 333a fre-

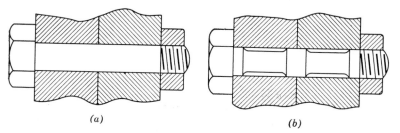

(a)   (b)

Fig. 333.   Effect of removing material of bolt.

quently broke * in service, owing to the energy delivered by the reciprocating parts of the engine. By turning down the bolts (removing material) so that the area of cross section of the shank was equal to that at the roots of the threads, as shown in Fig. 333b, the difficulty was removed, since the energy that the bolts were required to absorb was absorbed mainly by the shanks of the bolts, and the amount absorbed at the roots of the thread was thereby greatly reduced with a corresponding reduction in the localized stress developed at the roots of the threads. It should be noted that, although the removal of material from the bolt increased the stress on the sections where the bolt diameter was thus reduced, this fact results in a great decrease in the

* F. A. Halsey, "Materials and Constructions for Resisting Shock," *American Machinist*, Sept. 9, 1915, p. 459.

stress at the root of the threads, since a better distribution of energy absorption over a greater volume of material has been achieved.

An example of distributing the energy absorption over a greater volume by adding material was illustrated in the early development of rock drills.* The cylinder heads of the rock drills were attached to the

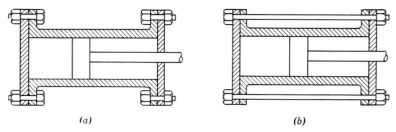

(a)   *(b)*

Fig. 334. Effect of increasing length of bolts.

cylinder, as shown in Fig. 334a, and, since, in the operation of the drill, it is impossible to avoid occasional sharp blows of the piston on the cylinder head, the bolts were subjected to rather severe impact loads and, as a consequence, broke. The trouble was remedied by using bolts long enough to extend through both cover plates as shown in Fig. 308b.

Examples of good distribution of stresses in beams for large energy absorption are given in Figs. 335 and 336. Figure 335 shows a beam

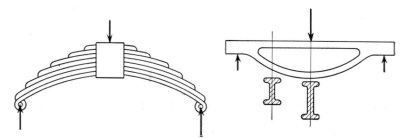

Fig. 335. Shape of beam for storing large amount of energy.   Fig. 336. Shape of beam for storing large amount of energy.

consisting of leaf springs. If the leaves are made of gradually decreasing length, so that the moment of inertia of the cross sections decreases toward the supports approximately in proportion to the bending moment, the resulting distribution of stress is approximately the same as

* *Ibid.*

for the tapered beam of Fig. 332b and c. Incidentally, it is well to note that a leaf spring absorbs a considerable amount of energy, owing to friction between the leaves.

Figure 336 shows a simple beam with an I section made so that the cross-sectional area decreases toward the supports, as is sometimes done in forged axles, etc.; the energy resistance of the beam is very much greater than that of a beam having a constant cross section that would have the same static strength as the beam with the variable cross section.

Effect of Localized Stress. Abrupt changes in section should be avoided in members subjected to impact loads, especially in members composed of brittle material. Even in ductile material, the localized stresses at such abrupt changes of section cause very high values of energy to be absorbed per unit volume of the highly stressed material, which may cause the material to fracture before the energy (and hence stress) can be distributed to other portions of the member. The influence of abrupt changes in section is likely to be even more damaging under elastic impact loads than under elastic static loads, for the reason that the energy is expressed in terms of the square of the stress.

Problems

354. Figure 337a and b represent rectangular flat plates of the same size and thickness. The holes in the first plate have diameters that are equal to the width of the slot in the second plate. If each plate is to be subjected to an axial impact (energy) load, which plate will resist (absorb) the greater amount of energy if the elastic-limit stress must not be exceeded?

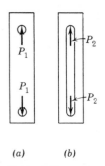

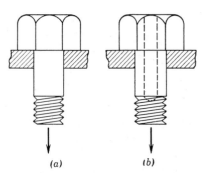

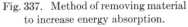

(a)   (b)   (a)   (b)

Fig. 337. Method of removing material   Fig. 338. Method of removing material
to increase energy absorption.   to increase energy absorption.

355. Which of the two steel bolts of Fig. 338 is the better for resisting an axial impact load: the solid one (Fig. 338a), or the one with an axial hole drilled to the root of the threads? Why?

120. Special cases of impact loads. *Impact Load Due to Falling Weight.* It is convenient frequently to express the stress caused by a low-velocity impact load, due to a falling weight W, in terms of the stress that would be caused by the force W when gradually applied. Similarly, the deflection caused by a falling weight W may be expressed in terms of the deflection that would be caused by a load W gradually applied. This may be done as follows:

If a body having a weight W falls from a height h and strikes a member such as the simply supported beam of Fig. 329b, the maximum deflection Δ of the beam will be proportional to the maximum stress σ developed, and the ratio of σ to Δ is assumed to be the same, within the proportional limit, as that of the stress σ_1 to the deflection Δ_1 caused by a static load equal to W: thus,

$$\frac{\Delta}{\Delta_1} = \frac{\sigma}{\sigma_1} \tag{223}$$

provided the proportional limit of the material is not exceeded.

Furthermore, if Q is a static load that causes a deflection Δ equal to that caused by the impact load, the work done by Q, which is $\frac{1}{2}Q\Delta$, will be equal to the energy supplied or given up by the falling body, and, since the assumption is made here that all the energy of the falling body $W(h + \Delta)$ is absorbed in stressing the beam, then $\frac{1}{2}Q\Delta$ will be equal to the energy absorbed by the beam. Hence,

$$W(h + \Delta) = \tfrac{1}{2}Q\Delta \tag{224}$$

But the static loads are proportional to the stresses they develop, and hence

$$\frac{\Delta}{\Delta_1} = \frac{\sigma}{\sigma_1} = \frac{Q}{W} \tag{225}$$

By combining Eqs. 224 and 225, we obtain

$$\sigma = \sigma_1 + \sigma_1\sqrt{1 + \frac{2h}{\Delta_1}} \quad \text{and} \quad \Delta = \Delta_1 + \Delta_1\sqrt{1 + \frac{2h}{\Delta_1}} \tag{226}$$

in which σ and Δ are the stress and deflection, respectively, due to the falling body, and σ_1 and Δ_1 are the stress and deflection, respectively, due to a static load equal to the weight of the falling body. Equations 226 apply to a falling body striking a member so as to produce an axial load, a bending load, or a torsional load. Expressions for σ_1 and Δ_1 are given in Chapters I through IV. Equations 226 show that a body whose weight W is applied as a static load to a beam causes a relatively small stress and deflection, and may cause a large stress and deflection if allowed to drop on the beam through a relatively short distance.

Impact Factor. From the definition of impact factor in Art. 116, it will be noted that in Eqs. 226 this factor is given by the quantity $\sqrt{1 + (2h/\Delta_1)}$. This value of the impact factor usually is somewhat too large, since some of the energy due to an impact load is absorbed in the bodies that support the member or by the falling body itself (see Art. 121).

Sudden Load. If the value of h in Eqs. 226 is zero, that is, if the load W is a sudden load, the values of σ and Δ due to the sudden load are

$$\sigma = 2\sigma_1 \quad \text{and} \quad \Delta = 2\Delta_1 \tag{227}$$

Therefore, a sudden load applied to a beam will cause twice the stress and twice the deflection that will be caused by the same load gradually applied.

Illustrative Problem

Problem 356. The proportional limit for hickory timber may be taken at 3000 lb per sq in., and its modulus of elasticity at 1,500,000 lb per sq in. (*a*) Will a weight of 20 lb falling 6 in. on the center of the span of a hickory beam 4 in. square cause a stress above the proportional limit, if the beam has a span of 3 ft? (Assume that the supports of the beam are rigid and that all the energy delivered by the falling weight is absorbed by the beam.) (*b*) How many inches will the beam deflect? (*c*) What should be the length of the span to make the stress equal to 3000 lb per sq in.?

Solution. (*a*) *First Method.* The deflection of the beam will be neglected in comparison with 6 in., and hence the energy U delivered to the beam is

$$U = Wh = 20 \times 6 = 120 \text{ in.-lb}$$

The stress caused by this energy load is (see Prob. 349)

$$\sigma = \sqrt{\frac{18UE}{al}} = \sqrt{\frac{18 \times 120 \times 1,500,000}{4 \times 4 \times 36}} = 2370 \text{ lb per sq in.}$$

(*a*) *Second Method.* If the deflection of the beam is not neglected, the maximum stress σ developed in the beam is

$$\sigma = \sigma_1 + \sigma_1 \sqrt{1 + \frac{2h}{\Delta_1}}$$

The stress σ_1 due to a static load of 20 lb at the center of span is

$$\sigma_1 = \frac{Mc}{I} = \frac{1}{4} Pl \cdot \frac{c}{I} = \frac{1}{4} \times 20 \times 36 \times \frac{2}{\frac{1}{12}(4)^4} = 16.9 \text{ lb per sq in.}$$

The maximum deflection Δ_1 of the beam caused by the 20-lb static load is

$$\Delta_1 = \frac{1}{48}\frac{Pl^3}{EI} = \frac{1}{48}\frac{20 \times (36)^3}{1,500,000 \times \frac{1}{12}(4)^4} = 0.000608 \text{ in.}$$

Hence,

$$\sigma = 16.9 + 16.9\sqrt{1 + \frac{2 \times 6}{0.000608}}$$

$$= 16.9 + 2365 = 2382 \text{ lb per sq in.}$$

and hence the error introduced in the first method of solution by neglecting the deflection of the beam is very small.

(b) The maximum deflection of the beam is

$$\Delta = \Delta_1 + \Delta_1\sqrt{1 + \frac{2h}{\Delta_1}} = 0.000608 + 0.000608 \times 140$$

$$= 0.000608 + 0.0853 = 0.0859 \text{ in.}$$

(c) The deflection may be neglected in determining the stress, and, hence,

$$\sigma = \sqrt{\frac{18UE}{al}} = 3000 \text{ lb per sq in.}$$

Therefore,

$$l = \frac{18UE}{a \times (3000)^2} = \frac{18 \times 120 \times 1,500,000}{16 \times (3000)^2} = 22.5 \text{ in.}$$

Problems

357. Three steel beams, A, B, and C, all of the same dimensions, are arranged as shown in Fig. 339 similar to one type of draft gear. Each beam is 3 in. square and has a span of 12 in. (a) What static load applied at the midspan will cause a

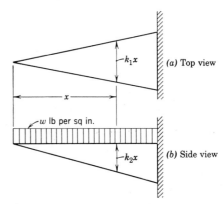

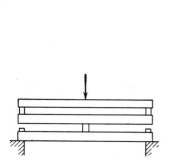

Fig. 339. Method of increasing energy absorption by adding material.

Fig. 340. Method of increasing energy absorption by variable cross section.

maximum elastic stress of 20,000 lb per sq in.? (b) Will all the beams when arranged as shown in Fig. 339 resist a greater static load than any one of the beams alone? (c) What is the weight of a body which, when allowed to fall a height h of 8 in., will cause a stress of 20,000 lb per sq in.? (d) Assume that all of the energy of the falling body is absorbed by the resisting member. What stress would the weight in (c) cause if it were resisted by only one of the three beams?

Ans. (a) 30,000 lb; (b) no; (c) 30 lb; (d) 34,700 lb per sq in.

358. A tapered cantilever beam (Fig. 340) has a width k_1x and a depth k_2x where x is the distance from the free end, and k_1 and k_2 are constants. Show that, if the beam is subjected to a uniformly distributed load w lb per sq in. as shown in the figure, the maximum bending stress on all sections is constant, and hence that the energy absorption per unit volume is constant. Note that many aircraft wings have approximately a double taper such as in Fig. 340.

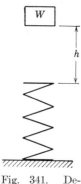

359. In Prob. 344, determine the maximum elastic elongation of the free end of the bar (Fig. 330) when the body A strikes the end; assume that the cross-section area is 0.156 in.[2]

360. A steel bar, 3 in. in diameter and 3 ft long, remains in a horizontal position as it falls a distance of 3 ft and strikes rigid supports at its ends. If all the energy is absorbed by the beam, what stress is developed in the beam, if it is assumed that the proportional limit is not exceeded, and that steel weighs 490 lb/ft[3]? (See Prob. 352.)

361. A high-carbon steel shaft has a diameter of 2 in. It is used as a simple beam with a span of 4 ft. The proportional limit of the material is 70,000 lb per sq in. If a moving body strikes the beam at midspan, and two thirds of the energy of the moving body is absorbed by the beam, how much energy does the body possess if it produces a stress equal to the proportional limit?

Fig. 341. Deflection of spring caused by falling body.

362. A coil spring (Fig. 341) has a weight $W = 20$ lb dropped vertically on it from a height $h = 3$ in. If the spring deflects elastically 1 in. when a static axial force of 10,000 lb is applied to it, compute the maximum deflection that occurs.

121. Reduction in energy absorbed due to inertia of resisting member.

It was stated previously that the value of the energy load U, as used in this chapter, is the energy that actually is absorbed by the resisting member and that one of the ways in which the energy of the moving body is dissipated is in causing local yielding of the resisting member. The energy dissipated in this way may be relatively large if the weight W of the resisting member is large compared to the weight P of the moving body. If, then, a third body of weight W_1 is attached to the resisting member, the energy load U absorbed by the member thereby will be decreased.

This principle is recognized in the design of structures and machines by reducing the allowance made for impact as the ratios W/P and W_1/P increase. In accordance with this principle, a heavy floor on a suspension bridge decreases the stress due to impact in the vertical rods that connect the floor to the cables; for the same reason, the specifications for the drop test for steel rails specify, in addition to the height of drop, not only the weight of the striking tup but also that of the spring-supported anvil block to which the rail supports are attached.

By using the principle of conservation of momentum for the condition of inelastic impact, an expression for U may be found in terms of W/P, W_1/P, and E_k, where E_k is the energy of the moving body as it comes in contact with the resisting body; the expression is $U = nE_k$ in which n has the following values:

(a) For an axial low-velocity impact load on a bar (Art. 106):

$$n = \frac{1 + q_1 + \frac{1}{3}q}{(1 + q_1 + \frac{1}{2}q)^2} \quad \text{where} \quad q_1 = \frac{W_1}{P} \quad \text{and} \quad q = \frac{W}{P} \quad (228)$$

(b) For an impact load applied at the center of a simple beam (Art. 111), and with W_1 attached at the center of the span:

$$n = \frac{1 + q_1 + \frac{17}{35}q}{(1 + q_1 + \frac{5}{8}q)^2} \quad \text{where} \quad q_1 = \frac{W_1}{P} \quad \text{and} \quad q = \frac{W}{P} \quad (229)$$

The values of n found from the foregoing expressions should be regarded as relative rather than absolute values because of some of the assumptions made in the derivations. Waves of stress or vibrations caused by impact are here neglected.

§ 2   Inelastic Behavior with Axial Impact Loading

122. Significance of inelastic deformation.   Some members that are subjected to axial impact loads may be stressed somewhat above the elastic limit, especially at sections of high localized stress, such as occur at fillets or at holes where the member is connected to other parts of a structure, without their proper load-resisting function being destroyed. The energy absorbed per unit volume in causing inelastic deformation of ductile material is usually very large compared to the modulus of resilience, which is the energy absorbed per unit volume in stressing the material to the elastic limit, and hence ductile metals, in general, offer much greater resistance to energy loads than brittle materials.

Furthermore, even though a member is used in service in which it can be strained inelastically to only a small amount (of the same order of magnitude as the elastic-limit strain), the amount of energy absorbed per unit volume in causing the material to fracture under an impact load (called the ultimate energy resistance or *toughness* of the material) represents the reserve energy absorption of the material, which may be used in resisting total collapse of a member. For example, a train was derailed just as it started across a steel bridge. The members of the bridge in absorbing the large amount of energy of the train were given such large inelastic deformations that the structure could no longer function normally as a bridge, but the members in absorbing and dissipating the energy prevented the bridge from fracturing and falling into the river below.

123. Toughness. The property of *toughness* of a material, then, may be defined as the energy absorbed per unit volume in stressing the material to fracture, and this energy is considered to be equal to the work done on the material in stressing it to its ultimate strength. Hence toughness is measured by the area under the stress-strain diagram, and values of toughness, thus found, for several materials are given in Table 8. It is of importance in lessening the effects of localized stresses and in furnishing emergency reserve strength under low-velocity impact loading. Most of this work done in causing inelastic deformation is dissipated in heat and in causing permanent deformation of the material, and only a very small part is stored in the material as stress energy that can be recovered when the stress is released.

For example, the toughness of a material such as ductile steel that has a stress-strain diagram similar to that shown in Fig. 342 is repre-

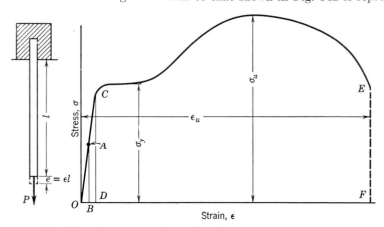

Fig. 342. Stress-strain diagram for ductile steel. Not to scale.

sented by the area under the curve and is given approximately by the expression $\dfrac{\sigma_y + \sigma_u}{2}\,\epsilon_u$ per unit volume, and hence the work done in

TABLE 8

AVERAGE VALUES OF MODULUS OF RESILIENCE AND TOUGHNESS

Material	Tensile Proportional Limit, lb per sq in., σ_e	Tensile Ultimate Strength, lb per sq in., σ_u	Tensile Modulus of Elasticity, lb per sq in., E	Ultimate Elongation per Inch of Length, in., ϵ_u	Tensile Modulus of Resilience, in.-lb per cu in., $\dfrac{1}{2}\dfrac{\sigma_e^{2}}{E}$	Toughness in Tension (Represented by Area under Stress-strain Diagram) in.-lb per cu in.
Low-carbon steel	30,000	60,000	30,000,000	0.35	15.0	15,700
Medium-carbon steel	45,000	85,000	30,000,000	0.25	33.7	16,300
High-carbon steel	75,000	120,000	30,000,000	0.08	94.0	5,100
Special-alloy steel (heat-treated)	200,000	230,000	30,000,000	0.12	667.0	22,000
Gray iron	6,000	20,000	15,000,000	0.005	1.2	70
Malleable iron	20,000	50,000	23,000,000	0.10	17.4	3,800
Rolled bronze	40,000	65,000	14,000,000	0.30	57.2	15,500
Timber (hickory)	5,500 *	10,000 *	2,400,000 *	—	6.32 *	—
Aluminum-alloy 7075-T6	70,000	86,000	10,300,000	—	238.0	—
Magnesium-alloy 0-1HTA	17,000	48,000	6,500,000	—	22.2	—

* In compression. The effectiveness of timber for resisting energy loads is greater than that indicated by the value of the resilience given in the table, due in part to the fact that timber may be stressed somewhat above its proportional limit without its usefulness being destroyed; that is, the properties of resilience and toughness are not sharply defined.

stressing the bar to fracture is approximately

$$U = \frac{\sigma_y + \sigma_u}{2}\, \epsilon_u \cdot al \tag{230}$$

in which σ_y and σ_u are the yield point and ultimate strength of the material, respectively, and ϵ_u is the ultimate strain. Values of the property of toughness of several materials, as well as of the modulus of resilience of the materials, are given in Table 8.

Problems

363. Figure 343 shows stress-strain diagrams for medium-carbon steel (about 0.30 per cent carbon) and for high-carbon steel (about 0.80 per cent carbon). (*a*) If a bolt of medium-carbon steel is stressed just to its proportional limit by an

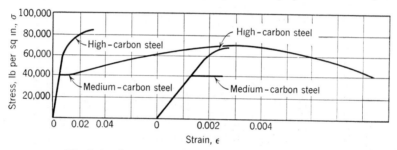

Fig. 343. Stress-strain diagrams for two grades of steel.

energy load of 25 ft-lb, how much energy will a bolt of the same size of the 0.80 per cent carbon steel resist when stressed to its proportional limit? (*b*) What will be the ratio of the amounts of energy that will cause rupture of the two bolts?

Ans. (*a*) 56.2 ft-lb; (*b*) 6.5 approx.

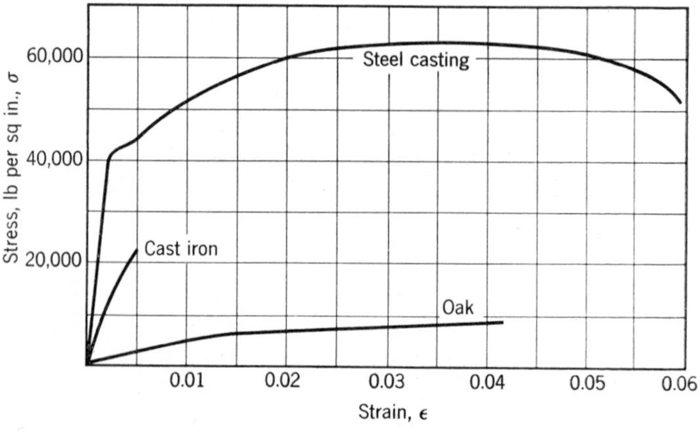

Fig. 344. Stress-strain diagrams of three materials that vary greatly in toughness.

364. In Fig. 344 are shown stress-strain diagrams from gray iron and for steel castings having about 0.20 per cent of carbon. Owing to the greater strength of steel, the cross-sectional area of a steel casting for railway service (car couplers for example) is made only 0.4 as great as that of a gray-iron casting. What will be the relative resistance to rupture, when subjected to an axial impact load, of the steel coupler and the gray-iron coupler if the lengths are the same? Since the service of a car coupler is not destroyed by permanent deformations, and since in railway service such deformations are very likely to occur, the ultimate rather than the elastic-impact loads are the governing factors. *Ans.* 18.4 times as great.

365. A tension member in a certain machine is subjected to an axial impact load. If the member can be given a permanent deformation without its usefulness being destroyed, and can be made of either gray iron or oak, which material should be used, provided that the strength of the member is the only factor to be considered? (Make use of Fig. 344.) *Ans.* Oak.

366. A rod of low-carbon steel is $\frac{1}{2}$ in. in diameter and 20 ft long. The following are tensile properties of the steel: yield point 30,000 lb per sq in., ultimate strength 60,000 lb per sq in., per cent elongation 30. Determine the total amount of energy that the rod can absorb under a tensile axial load before fracturing.

Part II

ADDITIONAL TOPICS

Chapter XI

COMPOSITE BEAMS.

REINFORCED-CONCRETE BEAMS

124. Composite (two-material) beam. In the derivation of the flexure formula $M = \sigma I/c$, it was assumed that the material of the beam was homogeneous. The formula, therefore, does not apply directly to a composite beam as, for example, a two-material beam such as a timber beam reinforced by steel plates, or a reinforced-concrete beam. It is sometimes convenient, however, to transform the section of such a beam to an equivalent section of a one-material (homogeneous) beam and to apply the flexure formula.

125. Timber beam reinforced by steel plates. *Plate on Both Tension and Compression Faces.* Let it be required to find the stress in the timber and in the steel plates at any section of the beam shown in Fig. 345, in which the thickness of the plates is small compared to the depth of the beam. The plates are attached to the timber so that the timber and plates act together as a unit. In other words, it is assumed that plane sections remain plane after bending, the same as in homogeneous beams, and hence the strains of the fibers vary directly as the distances of the fibers from the neutral axis, as indicated in Fig.

345b. Further, since the plates are thin, the strains of the steel plates and of the outer fibers of the timber at any section are nearly equal—denoted by ϵ in Fig. 345. The stress in the steel, however, is much

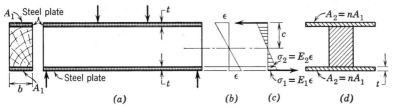

Fig. 345. A beam reinforced on top and bottom.

greater than that in the outer fibers of the timber, owing to the difference in the moduli of elasticity of the two materials. The stress in the steel is $E_1\epsilon$, and that in the outer fibers of the timber is $E_2\epsilon$, where E_1 and E_2 are the moduli of elasticity of the steel and timber, respectively.

The total internal force in each steel plate then is $E_1\epsilon A_1$, where A_1* is the area of cross section of one steel plate. If, now, the steel is replaced by timber so that the internal force in the added timber is equal to that in the steel and acts at the same distance from the neutral axis, the result will be a one-material or so-called homogeneous beam having the transformed section shown in Fig. 345d. The total internal force in each added timber area A_2 is $E_2\epsilon A_2$; hence,

$$E_2\epsilon A_2 = E_1\epsilon A_1 \quad \text{or} \quad A_2 = \frac{E_1}{E_2} A_1 = nA_1 \tag{231}$$

Thus the area of the timber to be added in place of the steel is n times the area replaced, where n is the ratio of the modulus of elasticity of the material replaced to that of the material added. The flexure formula may now be applied to the homogeneous beam having this transformed section. The solution of this simple problem, however, may be reached more conveniently perhaps by use of Fig. 345c rather than by the method of the transformed section.

Illustrative Problem

Problem 367. Let the beam in Fig. 345a be a simple beam with a span of 12 ft, supporting a concentrated load of 4000 lb at the center of the span instead of two loads as shown in the figure. Let the width of the beam be 4 in. and its depth

* The symbol A (rather than a) is used in this chapter to conform with the usual practice in dealing with reinforced concrete beams (Art. 126).

$6\frac{1}{4}$ in., and let the thickness of each steel plate be $\frac{1}{8}$ in. Calculate the maximum stress in the steel and in the timber. The moduli of elasticity of the timber and steel are 10^6 and 30×10^6 lb/in.^{2}, respectively; therefore $n = 30$.

Solution. σ_1 = stress in steel, σ_2 = stress in outer fiber of timber, $\sigma_1 = n\sigma_2 = 30\sigma_2$.

Bending moment = resisting moment

$$2000 \times 72 = \frac{\sigma_2 I}{c} + \sigma_1 A_1 \times 6\tfrac{1}{8}$$

$$= \frac{\sigma_2 \frac{1}{12} \times 4 \times 6^3}{3} + 30\sigma_2 \times 4 \times \frac{1}{8} \times 6\tfrac{1}{8}$$

$$= 24\sigma_2 + 91.8\sigma_2 = 115.8\sigma_2$$

Therefore, $\sigma_2 = 1240$ lb/in.^{2}, and $\sigma_1 = 30\sigma_2 = 37{,}200$ lb/in.^{2} Or, instead of obtaining the resisting moment in the timber from $\sigma_2 I/c$, it may be found as the moment $T_2 \times \frac{2}{3}d$ (or $C_2 \times \frac{2}{3}d$) of the couple T_2 and C_2, as indicated in Fig. 346,

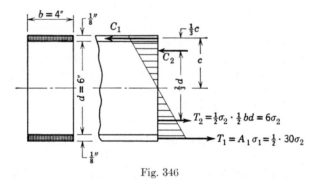

Fig. 346

where T_2 is the total tensile force in the timber below the neutral axis. Thus the moment in the timber is

$$(\tfrac{1}{2}\sigma_2 \times \tfrac{1}{2}bd) \times \tfrac{2}{3}d = \tfrac{1}{6}\sigma_2 bd^2 = 24\sigma_2$$

Problems

368. Solve Prob. 367 by the method of the transformed cross section.

369. A rectangular timber member having a width of 6 in. and a depth of 10 in. is used as a horizontal cantilever beam having a free length of 8 ft. Steel plates $\frac{1}{4}$ in. thick are firmly attached to the top and bottom faces of the beam. The beam supports a uniformly distributed load. If the maximum stress in the timber is 1000 lb/in.^{2}, what is the maximum stress in the steel, and what is the total load on the beam? The modulus of elasticity for the timber is 2×10^6 and for steel 30×10^6 lb/in.^{2} *Ans.* 6890 lb.

370. If in Prob. 367 steel plates $\frac{1}{4}$ in. thick are attached to the vertical sides of the timber beam instead of to the top and bottom faces, what will be the maximum stress in the steel and in the timber? The steel plates cover the sides of the beam completely, and the composite beam acts as a unit.

371. Let the working stress be 600 lb/in.^{2} for the timber beam of Prob. 367 and determine the proper thickness of the steel plates. Use $n = 30$.

Ans. $t = 0.285$ in.

Steel Plate on Tension Side Only. Let it be required to determine the maximum bending stress in the steel plate and in the outer fibers of the timber at any section of the beam shown in Fig. 347. Since the timber and steel are assumed to act together as a beam, the strains of the fibers vary directly as the distances of the fibers from the neutral axis of the

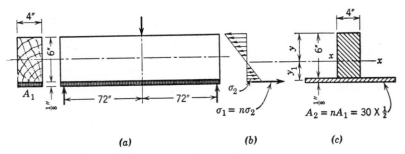

(a)   (b)   (c)

Fig. 347. A beam reinforced on bottom face only.

beam. But the location of the neutral axis is not known; it may be found conveniently by locating the centroidal axis of the transformed section since the neutral axis and centroidal axis are coincident in a homogeneous beam (Art. 40).

The transformed section is obtained by replacing the area A_1 of the steel by an area A_2 equal to nA_1, as previously discussed, where n is the ratio of the modulus of elasticity of the material replaced to that of the material added. The transformed section is shown in Fig. 347c. The stress in the beam with this section may be found from the flexure formula.

Illustrative Problem

Problem 372. In Prob. 367 let it be assumed that the steel plate is removed from the top face of the beam, leaving the beam reinforced only on the bottom or tension face. Let it be required to find the maximum moment the beam can resist without causing an elastic stress in the timber greater than 1000 lb/in.^{2} What will be the corresponding stress in the steel?

Solution. The transformed section is shown in Fig. 347c. The neutral axis XX of the beam is the centroidal axis of this area and is at the distance y from the top of the beam. By taking moments of areas about the top of the section,

y may be found as follows:

$$(24 + 15)y = 24 \times 3 + 15 \times 6.06; \qquad \text{hence,} \quad y = 4.18 \text{ in.}$$

$$I_x = \tfrac{1}{12} \times 4 \times 6^3 + 24 \times (1.18)^2 + 15(6.06 - 4.18)^2$$

$$= 72 + 33.5 + 53.1 = 158.6 \text{ in.}^4$$

$$M = \frac{\sigma I_x}{y} = \frac{1000 \times 158.6}{4.18} = 38,000 \text{ lb-in.}$$

Stress in added timber area is $\sigma_2 = \dfrac{y_1}{y}\sigma = \dfrac{1.88}{4.18} \times 1000 = 450 \text{ lb/in.}^2$

Therefore, the stress in the steel is $\sigma_1 = 450 \times 30 = 13,500 \text{ lb/in.}^2$

126. Reinforced-concrete beams. Concrete is weak in tension and relatively strong in compression; therefore, when a beam is made of concrete, steel bars usually are embedded near the surface of the tension side of the beam, in order to resist the tensile stress, thereby making possible the effective use of the compressive strength of concrete. Such a concrete beam is called a reinforced-concrete beam, and the bars are called reinforcing bars. These bars may be either plain or deformed; a deformed bar is one having projections along the bar (produced by special rolling), which provide mechanical anchorage in addition to the ordinary adhesion or "bond" between the steel and concrete.

127. Stress in steel and in concrete. Figure 348 represents a rectangular reinforced-concrete beam in which the steel is assumed to resist all the tensile stress; when the beam is subjected to small loads,

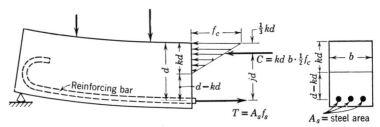

Fig. 348.   Stresses in reinforced-concrete beam.

the concrete will offer tensile resistance, but, when the beam is subjected to larger loads, the concrete will crack on the tensile side of the beam, and practically all the tensile stress will then be carried by the steel bars. Hence, it is customary to neglect the tensile resistance of the concrete in calculating the strength of the beam.

Let the depth of the center line of the bars below the top surface of the beam be denoted by d (Fig. 348), and let the depth of the neutral axis (unknown as yet) below the top surface be denoted by kd where k

is less than unity; further, let the moment arm of the resisting couple be jd where j is less than unity. The meaning of k and j are very important in the study of this subject; values for them are determined in the following.

The cross section of the beam is considered to be bd; the concrete below the center line of the reinforcement is neglected in the computations. Let the total cross-sectional area of the steel bars be denoted by A_s, and let the ratio A_s/bd be denoted by p; this ratio is called the steel ratio or the percentage of steel. Thus, $p = A_s/bd$. Let the ratio of the modulus of elasticity E_s of the steel to that of the concrete E_c be denoted by n. Thus, $n = E_s/E_c$.

It is assumed that the compressive stress in the concrete varies directly as the distance from the neutral axis; this assumption is approximately true for stresses that do not exceed the working stress, although for stresses near the ultimate strength of the concrete it is largely in error.

The stress * in the steel and in the concrete now may be expressed as follows: Since the beam (Fig. 348) is in equilibrium, the total compressive force C is equal to the total tensile force T. But

$$T = \text{area of steel} \times \text{stress in steel} = A_s f_s$$

and

$$C = \text{compressive area} \times \text{avg stress in concrete} = bkd \cdot \tfrac{1}{2} f_c$$

Hence,

$$A_s f_s = bkd \tfrac{1}{2} f_c \tag{232}$$

in which f_s is the stress in the steel and f_c is the stress in the outer fibers of the concrete. Also from equilibrium it is known that the internal or resisting moment M_r must equal the external or bending moment M; that is, $M = M_r$, in which M_r is the moment of the couple formed by the compressive force C and the tensile force T; the moment of the couple is $C \cdot jd$ or $T \cdot jd$. Furthermore, since the action line of C is at a distance of $\tfrac{1}{3}kd$ from the top surface of the beam (see Fig. 348),

$$jd = d - \tfrac{1}{3}kd \quad \text{or} \quad j = 1 - \tfrac{1}{3}k \tag{233}$$

If the value of T or of C is substituted in the preceding expression for the resisting moment and it is noted that $A_s = pbd$, the equation

* The symbol f is used to denote stress in this and the following articles of this chapter, in conformity with the usual practice of treating stresses in reinforced concrete; and the subscripts s and c are used to denote the stress in the steel and concrete, respectively.

$M = M_r$ becomes

$$M = A_s f_s jd = p f_s jbd^2 \quad \text{or} \quad f_s = \frac{M}{pjbd^2} \tag{234}$$

when the stress in the steel governs the strength of the beam, and

$$M = \frac{1}{2} f_c kjbd^2 \quad \text{or} \quad f_c = \frac{M}{\frac{1}{2}jkbd^2} \tag{235}$$

when the stress in the concrete governs.

Location of Neutral Axis. But k (and therefore j also) is unknown, and hence the position of the neutral axis must be found before the preceding equations can be used for determining the stress in the steel and the concrete. The neutral axis may be found by determining the centroidal axis of the transformed section, as was done in the preceding article.

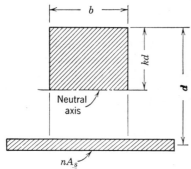

The transformed section is shown as the cross-hatched area in Fig. 349 in which the tensile area of the concrete below the neutral axis is neglected and the steel area A_s is replaced by an area of concrete equal to nA_s, where n is the ratio of the modulus of elasticity of the replaced material (steel) to that of the added material (concrete).

Fig. 349.   Transformed cross section.

In any numerical problem the value of kd may be easily computed by locating the centroidal axis of the transformed section, or a literal expression for it may be obtained as follows: Since the moment of the cross-hatched areas (Fig. 349) about the neutral axis must be equal to zero, the following equation may be written:

$$bkd \times \tfrac{1}{2}kd = nA_s \times (d - kd) = npbd(d - kd)$$

or

$$k^2 + 2pnk - 2pn = 0$$

Hence,

$$k = \sqrt{2pn + (pn)^2} - pn \tag{236}$$

Value of n. The Building Code of the American Concrete Institute (ACI) recommends the following formula for values of n with concrete having the various 28-day ultimate compressive strengths f'_c specified (in pounds per square inch): $n = \dfrac{30{,}000}{f'_c}$. Thus, if

$$f'_c = 2000 \qquad n = 15$$

$$f'_c = 2500 \qquad n = 12$$

$$f'_c = 3000 \qquad n = 10$$

$$f'_c = 4000 \qquad n = 8$$

$$f'_c = 5000 \qquad n = 6$$

Values of k and j. For well-designed rectangular beams having tension reinforcement only, the values of k and j vary but little from $k = \frac{3}{8}$ and $j = \frac{7}{8}$. By using these values in Eq. 235, approximate but reliable results may be found. Thus,

$$bd^2 = \frac{M}{\frac{1}{6}f_c} = \frac{6M}{f_c} \tag{237}$$

After bd^2 has been determined from the foregoing equation and values have been assigned to b and d, the stress in the steel and the required steel area may be found from

$$T = \frac{M}{\frac{7}{8}d} \quad \text{and} \quad A_s = \frac{T}{f_s} \tag{238}$$

Working Stress. The ACI Building Code specifies a value for the working stress in the extreme fiber of the concrete equal to 0.45 of the ultimate compressive strength of a test cylinder of the concrete $(0.45f'_c)$ when 28 days old. Thus, the working stress in the extreme fiber of a beam made of concrete having an ultimate compressive strength, at 28 days, of 2000 lb per sq in. is 900 lb per sq in. The working stress in the steel usually is taken to be 18,000 to 20,000 lb per sq in.

Steel Ratio. The amount of reinforcement required to develop given working stresses in the concrete and the steel may be found by equating the expression for the bending moment based on the stress in the steel to that for the bending moment based on the stress in the concrete; that is, by equating values of M given by Eqs. 234 and 235. The value of p thus found is

$$p = \frac{kf_c}{2f_s} \tag{239}$$

Also, p may be expressed in terms of the working stresses and the ratio of the moduli of elasticity.   Thus, from Eqs. 236 and 239,

$$p = \frac{\frac{1}{2}}{\frac{f_s}{f_c}\left[\frac{f_s}{nf_c} + 1\right]} \tag{240}$$

The value of p given by Eqs. 239 and 240 is commonly termed the percentage for *balanced reinforcement*; if the reinforcement used is less than the percentage for balanced reinforcement, the beam may be said to be *underreinforced*, and its strength is governed by the resisting moment of the steel.   On the other hand, if the beam is *overreinforced*, its strength is governed by the resisting moment of the concrete.   It is well to note that the value of p for balanced reinforcement depends only on the values of the working stresses and n: that is, it is independent of the dimensions of the beam.

Problems

373. A concrete beam, 12 in. wide and 20 in. deep, is reinforced with four steel bars $\frac{3}{4}$ in. in diameter.   The center of the steel area is $1\frac{3}{4}$ in. from the tension surface of the beam.   The modulus of elasticity of the concrete is 2,000,000 lb per sq in., and that of steel is 30,000,000 lb per sq in.   How far from the compressive surface of the beam is the neutral axis when the beam is subjected to its working load?   *Ans.   kd = 7.05 in.*

374. Let the value of E_c in the preceding problem be 2,500,000, and find the value of the kd.

375. A reinforced-concrete beam is 10 in. wide and 16 in. deep to the center of the steel area; the area of the steel is 1.40 sq in. $E_s = 30,000,000$ lb per sq in., and $E_c = 2,000,000$ lb per sq in.   Find the maximum bending moment that the beam can resist if the following values of working stresses are not to be exceeded: $f_c = 800$ lb per sq in., and $f_s = 18,000$ lb per sq in.

376. The width of a reinforced-concrete beam is 8 in., and the depth to the center of the steel area is 10 in.   The beam is used with a span of 10 ft and is subjected to a uniformly distributed load of 650 lb per ft; the area of the steel is 1.0 sq in.   Calculate the stress in the steel and the maximum stress in the concrete, using a value of 15 for n.   *Ans. $f_s = 11,500$ lb per sq in.; $f_c = 635$ lb per sq in.*

377. What should be the cross-sectional area of the steel bars for a reinforced-concrete beam having a width of 12 in. and a depth of 18 in. to the center of the steel area, if the values of f_c and f_s are 900 and 18,000 lb per sq in., respectively, and $E_c = 2,500,000$ lb per sq in.?   *Ans. $A_s = 2.02$ sq in.*

378. A reinforced-concrete beam has a width of 10 in.   The beam is used on a span of 16 ft and is subjected to a total uniformly distributed load of 15,000 lb, including the weight of the beam.   The ultimate compressive strength of the concrete is 3000 lb per sq in.   What should be the depth of the beam, and what area of steel is required?   Use $f_s = 18,000$ lb/in.^{2} and $n = 10$. $A_s = 1.92$ in.^{2}
          Ans.   d = 12.0 in.

379. What should be the dimensions of a reinforced-concrete beam to resist a bending moment of 40,000 lb-ft if $E_c = 2,000,000$ lb per sq in.; the working values of the stresses are $f_c = 900$ lb per sq in., $f_s = 20,000$ lb per sq in., and $n = 15$? What should be the area A_s of the steel?

Inelastic Bending of Reinforced-concrete Beams. It is well known that concrete is very brittle when subjected to tensile stresses (or to direct-shearing stresses), but under compressive stresses it will withstand considerable inelastic strain before failure by fracture will occur. This fact has led to much effort to obtain an analysis for the inelastic behavior of reinforced-concrete beams. For a treatment of this topic the reader is referred to "Ultimate Strength of Reinforced Concrete Beams as Related to the Plasticity Ratio of Concrete," by V. P. Jensen, *University Illinois Engineering Experiment Station Bulletin 345,* 1944.

Chapter XII

UNSYMMETRICAL BENDING

128. Introduction. One of the assumptions on which the flexure formula, $M = \sigma(I/c)$, is based is that the neutral axis for any cross

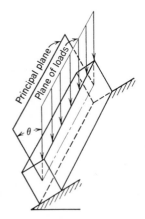

Fig. 350. Unsymmetrically loaded beam.

section of the beam is perpendicular to the plane of the loads. But, as shown in the next article, this condition requires that the plane of the loads shall contain one of the principal * axes passing through the shear center † of the section; such a plane is called a principal plane. Since an axis of symmetry is always a principal axis, bending caused by loads that do *not* lie in a plane containing a principal axis of each cross section usually is called unsymmetrical bending.

Some beams, such as roof purlins, are subjected to loads whose planes make large angles with principal planes, as indicated in Fig. 350, whereas many beams in structures and machines are subjected to loads whose planes are inclined only slightly to principal planes, but even small inclinations of loading may be of importance for sections of cer-

---

* For a discussion of principal axes, see Appendix I.
† See Chapter III, Art. 50.

tain shapes. For example, the shape of most of the steel-rolled sections, such as I sections and channel sections, that are used for beams
is such as to give maximum resistance to bending, on the assumption
that the stresses developed are in accordance with the flexure formula,
$\sigma = \dfrac{M}{I/c}$; in other words, the shape of the cross section is made so that
I/c is as large as its practicable. It is shown in this chapter, however,
that a section that is well designed to resist elastic bending due to
symmetrical loading may be poorly designed to resist bending due to
unsymmetrical loading, even though the plane of the loads deviates
only slightly from a plane of symmetry.

**129. Elastic stress in beam subjected to unsymmetrical load-
ing.** In the following discussion, it is assumed that the plane of the
loads contains the bending axis of the beam, and hence the beam is not
subjected to torsion; it is assumed also that the loads are perpendicular
to the bending axis of the beam, and hence the bending is not accompanied by axial tension or compression.

In Fig. 351 is represented a straight beam having a constant cross
section with two axes of symmetry (assumed rectangular for conven-

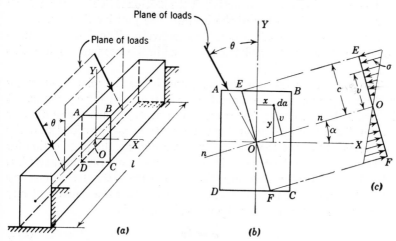

Fig. 351. Stresses in unsymmetrically loaded beam.

ience only), subjected to loads that pass through the geometric (bending) axis of the beam and lie in a plane making an angle θ with a plane
designated as the Y plane; this plane is not necessarily a plane of symmetry (principal plane), although later it will be so specified.

Figure 351b represents (enlarged) the cross section $ABCD$ in the central portion of the beam. Let nn represent the neutral axis and let α

denote the angle between the neutral axis and the axis OX. Let it be required to determine the direction of the neutral axis and the magnitude of the stress at any point in the cross section; that is, let it be required to find the values of α and σ.

The same procedure will be used as in obtaining the flexure formula (Art. 40). If a free-body diagram is drawn (not shown) of the portion of the beam to the left of section $ABCD$, and the equations of equilibrium are applied to the forces acting on this portion of the beam, the equations obtained are

$$\int \sigma \, da = 0 \tag{241}$$

$$M_x = \int y\sigma \, da \tag{242}$$

$$M_y = \int x\sigma \, da \tag{243}$$

in which M_x and M_y are the moments about the x and y axes, respectively, of the external forces that lie to one side of the section $ABCD$, and $\sigma \, da$ is an internal force acting at the section $ABCD$ on the area da of each longitudinal fiber of the beam. The positive directions for x and y are to the right and upward, respectively. The sign conventions to be used later for M_x and M_y are stated in the last paragraph of this article.

The stress σ varies over the area, and hence the relation among σ and x and y must next be found for use in the foregoing equations. It is assumed that, on any cross section, σ at any point varies directly as the distance of the point from the neutral axis, provided that the proportional limit of the material is not exceeded; the justification for this assumption is the same as in the case of symmetrical loading (Art. 40). Figure 351c then indicates the distribution of the stress along any line EF perpendicular to the neutral axis. Thus the stress σ at any point at the distance v from the neutral axis nn is

$$\sigma = kv \tag{244}$$

where k is a constant. But, since the direction of the neutral axis is as yet unknown, it will be convenient to express v in terms of a set of rectangular axes OX and OY (not necessarily principal axes as shown in Fig. 351). From the geometry of the figure, it may be seen that

$$v = (y - x \tan \alpha) \cos \alpha \tag{245}$$

$$= y \cos \alpha - x \sin \alpha \tag{246}$$

and hence Eq. 244 becomes

$$\sigma = k(y \cos \alpha - x \sin \alpha) \tag{247}$$

This equation with Eqs. 242 and 243 furnishes three equations from which the three unknown quantities σ, k, and α may be found. Equations 242 and 247 give

$$M_x = M \cos \theta = \int k(\cos \alpha \, y^2 \, da - \sin \alpha \int xy \, da)$$

$$= k \cos \alpha \int y^2 \, da - k \sin \alpha \int xy \, da \tag{248}$$

But $\int y^2 \, da$ is the moment of inertia of the cross-sectional area of the beam about the axis OX and is denoted by I_x, and $\int xy \, da$ (denoted by I_{xy}) is the product of inertia of the same area with respect to the axes OX and OY (see Appendix I). However, the product of inertia of an area is equal to zero with respect to principal axes. Therefore, if the axes OX and OY are specified to be principal axes, Eq. 248 may be written

$$M_x = k \cos \alpha \, I_x \tag{249}$$

Similarly, Eqs. 243 and 247 give

$$M_y = k \cos \alpha \, I_{xy} - k \sin \alpha \, I_y \tag{250}$$

and for principal axes this equation reduces to

$$M_y = -k \sin \alpha \, I_y \tag{251}$$

Direction of Neutral Axis. By dividing Eq. 251 by Eq. 249, the following equation is found:

$$\frac{M_y}{M_x} = -\frac{I_y}{I_x} \tan \alpha$$

But $M_y/M_x = \tan (90 + \theta) = -\tan \theta$, in which θ is measured from the y axis. Thus,

$$\tan \alpha = \frac{I_x}{I_y} \tan \theta \tag{252}$$

in which x and y refer to principal axes, and θ is measured from the Y principal axis, whereas α is measured from the X principal axis. Equation 241 requires that the neutral axis shall pass through the centroid of the cross-sectional area of the beam; the proof of this fact is given in Art. 40. Equations 241 and 252, therefore, make it possible to locate the neutral axis if θ and the dimensions of the area are known.

Equation 252 may be interpreted as follows: If the plane of the loads is rotated about the bending axis of the beam through an angle θ from one principal plane, the neutral plane will rotate from the other principal plane in the same direction about the longitudinal centroidal axis of the beam through an angle α. It should be noted that the plane of

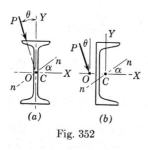

(a)   (b)

Fig. 352

the loads rotates about the bending axis, which passes through the shear center O of each cross section, and the neutral plane rotates about the centroidal axis of the beam, which passes through the centroid C of each cross section.

This fact is illustrated in Fig. 352a for an I section having two axes of symmetry in which the shear center O and the centroid C of the section are coincident, whereas, in Fig. 352b, θ and α are shown for a section having one axis of symmetry for which the shear center and centroid are not coincident.

Elastic Stress at Any Point in Cross Section. By solving Eq. 249 for $\cos \alpha$ and Eq. 251 for $\sin \alpha$ and substituting these values in Eq. 247, the following equation is found:

$$\sigma = \frac{M \cos \theta\, y}{I_x} + \frac{M \sin \theta\, x}{I_y} = \frac{M_x y}{I_x} + \frac{M_y x}{I_y} \qquad (253)$$

Equations 252 and 253 are valid only when α, θ, x, y, I_x, and I_y refer to principal axes; these axes are frequently convenient axes to use, since axes of symmetry are principal axes, and the properties of the commonly rolled sections with respect to axes of symmetry are given in handbooks.

Equation 253 shows that the stress at any point in the cross section may be found as follows: Calculate the bending moment about each of the principal axes; then calculate the stress due to each of these component moments separately, by use of the flexure formula, and add (algebraically) the stresses thus found.

Sign Convention. In Eq. 253 the sign of M_x is to be considered positive if it produces a tensile stress (and negative if it produces a compressive stress) at points that lie on the positive side of the X principal axis, and similarly for M_y. In many problems the sign of each of the two parts of the right-hand side of Eq. 253 (whether it is a tensile or a compressive stress) can be determined easily from inspection, but, if the preceding sign conventions for M_x and M_y are followed and the proper signs given to the coordinates x and y of the points, σ will be a tensile stress when positive and a compressive stress when negative.

Illustrative Problems

Problem 380. The rectangular beam shown in Figs. 351 and 353 is 6 in. wide and 8 in. deep; it is used as a simple beam on a span of 16 ft. Two loads of 800 lb each are applied to the beam, each load being 4 ft from an end of the span; the plane of the loads makes an angle of 30° with the vertical plane of symmetry. Find the direction of the neutral axis and the stress at A.

Solution.

$$I_x = \tfrac{1}{12}bh^3 = \tfrac{1}{12} \times 6(8)^3 = 256 \text{ in.}^4, \qquad I_y = \tfrac{1}{12}hb^3 = 144 \text{ in.}^4$$

$$\tan \alpha = \frac{I_x}{I_y}\tan \theta = \frac{256}{144} \times 0.577 = 1.028$$

Hence,

$$\alpha = 45°51' \quad \text{as shown in Fig. 353}$$

All points in the area above the neutral axis nn (Fig. 353) are subjected to compressive stresses, and all points below to tensile stresses. The stress at the corner

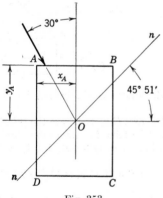

Fig. 353

A, which is the maximum stress in the beam, is

$$\sigma_A = \frac{M_x y_A}{I_x} + \frac{M_y x_A}{I_y}$$

It is evident from inspection that each component moment causes compressive stress at A, and hence σ_A is found by adding the two parts of the right-hand member of the equation; however, the signs of x, y, M_x, and M_y will cause the equation to yield the correct results. Thus, $x_A = -3$ in., $y_A = +4$ in., $M_x = -(800$

$\times 4 \times 12 \times 0.866) = -33,300$ lb-in., and $M_y = +(38,400 \times 0.5) = +19,200$ lb-in. Therefore,

$$\sigma_A = \frac{-33,300 \times 4}{256} + \frac{+19,200 \times (-3)}{144}$$

$$= -518 - 400 = -918 \text{ lb per sq in. compression}$$

Problem 381. An 8-in.-by-8-in.-by-$\frac{3}{4}$-in. angle beam is loaded as shown in Fig. 354, the total load P being 10,000 lb. Find the direction of the neutral axis. Also calculate the values of the fiber stresses at A, B, and C; compare these values with those found by assuming (erroneously) that the neutral axis is perpendicular to the plane of the loads and using the ordinary flexure formula. To prevent the end portions of the beam from twisting as the beam bends, the loads should be applied through the bending axis as in Fig. 356, but the twisting is relatively unimportant in this problem and will be neglected.

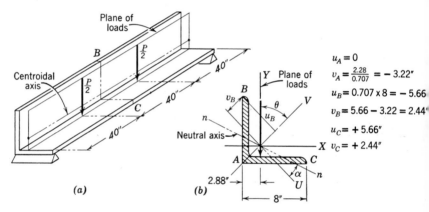

Fig. 354.   Unsymmetrically loaded angle beam.

Solution. The U and V axes (Fig. 354b) are the principal axes since the V axis is an axis of symmetry. The following values are obtained from a steelmaker's handbook: $a = 11.44$ sq in., $x_A = y_A = 2.28$ in., $I_x = I_y = 69.7$ in.^{4}, $r_u = 1.57$ in. Hence,

$$I_u = ar_u^2 = 11.44 \times (1.57)^2 = 28.2 \text{ in.}^4$$

Also,

$$I_u + I_v = I_x + I_y \quad \text{(see Appendix I)}$$

Hence,

$$I_v = 2(69.7) - 28.2 = 111.2 \text{ in.}^4$$

Therefore,

$$\tan \alpha = \frac{I_u}{I_v} \tan \theta = \frac{28.2}{111.2} \tan 45° = \frac{28.2}{111.2} \times 1 = 0.254$$

$$\alpha = 14°20' \quad \text{as shown in Fig. 354b}$$

The central portion of the beam is subjected to a bending couple having a moment of $M = 5000 \times 40 = 200,000$ lb-in. Furthermore, the magnitude of M_u

and M_v is

$$M_u = M_v = 200,000 \times 0.707 = 141,400 \text{ lb-in.}$$

Stress at A, B, and C.

$$\sigma_A = \frac{M_u v_A}{I_u} + \frac{M_y u_A}{I_v}$$

$$= \frac{(-141,000) \times (-3.22)}{28.2} = 16,200 \text{ lb per sq in. tension}$$

$$\sigma_B = \frac{(-141,000) \times 2.44}{28.2} + \frac{(141,000) \times (-5.66)}{111.2}$$

$$= -19,300 \text{ lb per sq in. compression}$$

$$\sigma_C = \frac{(-141,000) \times 2.44}{28.2} + \frac{(141,000) \times (5.66)}{111.2}$$

$$= -5100 \text{ lb per sq in. compression}$$

The values for σ at A, B, and C, as found from the flexure formula, if it is assumed (erroneously) that the x axis is the neutral axis, are

$$\sigma_A = \sigma_C = \frac{M y_A}{I_x} = \frac{200,000 \times 2.28}{69.7} = 6550 \text{ lb per sq in. tension}$$

$$\sigma_B = \frac{200,000 \times 5.72}{69.7} = 16,400 \text{ lb per sq in. compression}$$

Since the stress at B would govern the allowable moment or load, the value of the allowable load for this angle beam, as found from the flexure formula, if it is assumed that the x axis is the neutral axis, would be about 15 per cent too large.

Problems

382. A timber beam, 10 in. wide by 12 in. deep by 14 ft long, is used as a simple beam on a span of 12 ft. It is subjected to a concentrated load of 6000 lb at the midsection of the span. If the plane of the load makes an angle of 45° with the vertical axis of symmetry (similar to θ in Fig. 351), find the direction of the neutral axis and the maximum stress in the beam.

Ans. $\alpha = 55°15'$; $\sigma = 1400$ lb per sq in.

383. A 6-in. 8.2-lb channel beam is used as a purlin for a roof. If the pitch of the roof is 1/4 (that is, the roof rises $\frac{1}{2}$ ft per horizontal foot; thus the total rise is 1/4 of the span) and the span is 10 ft, find the maximum stress caused by a uniformly distributed vertical load of 100 lb per ft of span; the plane of the load contains the bending axis of the beam.   *Ans.* $\sigma = -16,500$ lb per sq in.

384. In Fig. 355, let $b = 2$ in., $h = 6$ in., and $l = 20$ in. If the maximum elastic bending stress caused by P is 2000 lb per sq in., calculate the value of P.

385. In Fig. 356, let $b = 8$ in., $h = 8$ in., $t = \frac{3}{4}$ in., $l = 50$ in., and $P = 4000$ lb. Calculate the elastic bending stresses at A and C. Neglect any stress concentration at A and C.

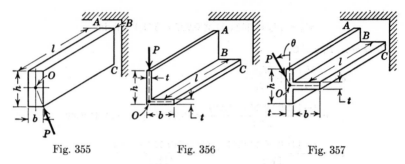

Fig. 355   Fig. 356   Fig. 357

386. In Fig. 357, let $b = 6$ in., $t = 2$ in., $h = 6$ in., $l = 40$ in., $P = 6000$ lb., and $\theta = 30°$. Calculate the elastic bending stress at A, and determine the location of the neutral axis. Neglect any stress concentration at A.

130. Change in slope of neutral axis and increase in elastic stress in rolled sections due to a very small inclination of plane of loads to a principal plane. Equation 252 shows that α is large, even though θ is relatively small, provided that the cross section of the beam is of such a shape that I_x is much larger than I_y. Thus the neutral axis of I beams, channels, etc., is steeply inclined to the horizontal axis of symmetry when the plane of the loads deviates but little from the vertical plane of symmetry, and likewise the maximum fiber stress is increased considerably, as is indicated in Table 9 in which the plane of the loads is assumed to make an angle θ of one degree with a principal plane (Fig. 358).

TABLE 9

Percentage Increase in Stress and Change in Slope of the Neutral Axis, Caused by a One-degree Inclination of the Plane of the Loads to a Principal Plane

Legend	I Beam	$\dfrac{I_x}{I_y}$	Increase in Bending Stress, per cent	Change in Slope of Neutral Axis
	27-in. 90-lb	39.3	23.0	34°20′
	20-in. 65-lb	41.8	22.8	36°10′
	18-in. 55-lb	37.5	21.8	33°15′
	15-in. 42-lb	30.2	19.3	27°15′
	12-in. 31½-lb	22.7	16.5	21°35′
	10-in. 25-lb	17.7	14.4	17°14′
	8-in. 18-lb	15.0	13.1	14°40′
Fig. 358	6-in. 12¼-lb	11.8	11.5	11°40′

Table 9 indicates clearly that a section that is well proportioned to resist elastic bending due to loads in a plane of symmetry, such as I sections, may be poorly designed to resist elastic bending due to loads in a plane that makes only a very small angle with the plane of symmetry.

131. Eccentric load not in plane of symmetry. In Art. 73 the action line of the eccentric load lay in a plane containing an axis of symmetry (principal axis) of the area on which the stress was desired. Whereas in Fig. 359a, the load P does not lie in a plane containing an axis of symmetry; it may however be resolved into an axial load P_1 (equal to P) and a couple P and P_2 having a moment Pe, and this couple may be resolved further into two component couples in planes

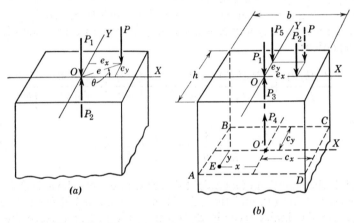

Fig. 359.   Eccentric load not in plane of symmetry.

containing the axes of symmetry or principal axes, OX and OY; the elastic stress due to each component couple then may be found from the ordinary flexure formula as in the preceding article. Thus, the moment of the component couple in the plane containing the axis OX is $Pe \cos \theta$ or Pe_x, the forces of this couple being represented by P_2 and P_3 in Fig. 359, and the moment of the component couple in the plane containing OY is Pe_y, and the forces of this couple are P_4 and P_5. These five forces, each equal to P, will produce the same stress at any point in the section $ABCD$ as the original force P, and the normal stress at any point in the section is the algebraic sum of the stresses produced by the axial load P_1 and the two bending couples P_2, P_3, and P_4, P_5.

The maximum compressive stress occurs at C and is

$$\sigma = \sigma_1 + \sigma_2 + \sigma_3 = \frac{P}{a} + \frac{Pe_x c_x}{I_y} + \frac{Pe_y c_y}{I_x}$$

For other points in the area a, either the second or the third term or both may be negative. Thus, the stress at a point E in the quadrant $O'A$ (Fig. 359), for which x and y are negative, is

$$\sigma = \frac{P}{a} - \frac{Pe_x x}{I_y} - \frac{Pe_y y}{I_x} \tag{254}$$

Kern of a Section. It is evident that the least numerical value of the compressive elastic stress σ will occur at A, and its value will be given by Eq. 254 in which the numerical values of x and y are $x = b/2$ and $y = h/2$. The stress σ will be a tensile stress if the sum of the last two terms is greater than P/a. If a tensile stress is to be avoided, therefore, the values of e_x and e_y cannot be greater than those found from the equation:

$$\frac{Pe_x(b/2)}{I_y} + \frac{Pe_y(h/2)}{I_x} = \frac{P}{a} \quad \text{or} \quad \frac{e_x(b/2)}{\frac{1}{12}hb^3} + \frac{e_y(h/2)}{\frac{1}{12}bh^3} = \frac{1}{bh}$$

Thus

$$\frac{e_x}{b} + \frac{e_y}{h} = \frac{1}{6} \quad \text{or} \quad \frac{e_x}{\frac{1}{6}b} + \frac{e_y}{\frac{1}{6}h} = 1 \tag{255}$$

which is the equation of a straight line that intersects the axis OX at a distance $b/6$ from 0, and the axis OY at a distance $h/6$ from O (Fig. 360). Similar limits occur in the other quadrants, and hence the re-

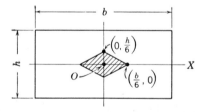

Fig. 360. Kern of a rectangular cross section.

sultant load on the member must pass within the shaded area shown in Fig. 360, if tensile elastic stress in the member is to be avoided.

The area within which the resultant load must pass to avoid tensile stress on a section frequently is called the *core, kernel,* or *kern* of the section. Thus, for a *rectangular section* the kern is a rhombus, the diagonals of which are the middle thirds of the principal axes of the section.

Problems

387. A short rectangular timber having a section 6 in. by 8 in. is subjected to a longitudinal eccentric compressive load of 10,000 lb. The action line of the load passes through a point in the section 3 in. from the 6-in. side and $2\frac{1}{2}$ in. from the 8-in. side. Find the stress at each corner.

$Ans.$ $\sigma_A = 52$ lb per sq in. T.; $\sigma_B = 156$ lb per sq in. C.;
$\sigma_C = 468$ lb per sq in. C.; $\sigma_D = 260$ lb per sq in. C.

388. The resultant normal pressure P on top of a concrete base (block) having a square cross section a acts at the center of one quadrant of the square. Will tensile stresses occur in the base? If so, find the maximum tensile and compressive stresses that will be developed, assuming the values of P and a to be 80,000 lb and 4 sq ft, respectively.

Chapter XIII

DOUBLE-INTEGRATION METHOD FOR

DEFLECTION OF BEAMS

132. Introduction. In Arts. 59 and 60, the problem of relating the loads on a beam to the deflection of the beam was discussed, and the elastic-curve equation for a beam subjected to loads was derived. This equation (Eq. 113) is

$$\pm \frac{d^2y}{dx^2} = \frac{M}{EI} \tag{256}$$

This is the equation (in terms of rectangular coordinates) of the elastic curve of an originally straight beam. In this equation, M is the bending moment at the section whose distance from the origin of the coordinates is x, and y is the deflection of the elastic curve at the same section, as shown in Fig. 361. The sign to be selected for the right-hand member of the equation is discussed in the following.

Signs of M and d^2y/dx^2. In using the preceding elastic-curve equation, it is important to understand the significance of the signs of M and d^2y/dx^2; E and I are essentially positive and may be regarded merely as magnitudes. The sign of M already has been discussed (Art. 42); it is positive for a horizontal beam when it produces tensile stress in the bottom fibers of the beam or when it causes the center of curvature to lie above the beam, and is negative when it causes compressive stress on the bottom fibers, etc. The sign of d^2y/dx^2, however, depends on the choice of the positive directions of the axes. For example, Fig. 361a represents a horizontal simple beam subjected to a positive bending moment. Let the origin of axes be chosen at the left end of the beam, and let the positive directions for the x and y axes be to the right and upwards, respectively.

The slope dy/dx at a point A on the curve is negative, whereas at a point B the slope is positive, and thus as x increases dy/dx increases.

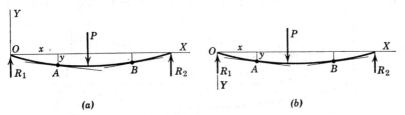

(a)   *(b)*

Fig. 361.   Effect of direction of axes on sign of d^2y/dx^2.

Therefore, the rate of change of dy/dx with respect to x (that is, d^2y/dx^2) is positive, and, since M is also positive, the equation may be written $M = EI(d^2y/dx^2)$.

If, however, the positive direction of the y axis is chosen downward, as shown in Fig. 361b, the slope at A is positive and decreases as x increases; thus d^2y/dx^2 is negative. But M is positive, and the right side of the equation then must also be positive, which requires that the equation shall be written $M = -EI(d^2y/dx^2)$. If, then, for any horizontal beam, the x axis is positive to the right and the positive direction of the y axis is chosen upward, the plus sign in Eq. 256 should be used since the sign of d^2y/dx^2 will be the same as that of M (for a cantilever with downward loads, both quantities will be negative), and, if the positive direction of the y axis is chosen downward, the negative sign should be used, since the sign of d^2y/dx^2 will be opposite to that of M. In the articles and problems in this chapter, the positive direction of the y axis is chosen upward for horizontal beams, and hence the positive sign in Eq. 256 is used.

133. Double-integration method.   In this method the bending moment M in the equation $EI(d^2y/dx^2) = M$ is expressed as a function of x, and then both sides of the equation are integrated twice to find the deflection. With each integration is added a constant of integration, the values for which are found by making use of the physical conditions imposed by the nature of the supports; these conditions are often called boundary conditions. This method is applied to several statically determinate beams in the following articles.

Applications of Double-integration Method

134. Deflection of simple beam, uniform load. Let it be required to determine, by the double-integration method, the equation of the elastic curve and the maximum deflection of a simple beam, having a span l, when subjected to a uniformly distributed load of w per unit length, as shown in Fig. 362, in which the elastic deflections are greatly exaggerated; the known quantities in addition to w and l

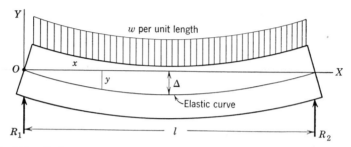

Fig. 362. Deflection of simple beam subjected to uniformly distributed load.

are the modulus of elasticity E and the moment of inertia I of the cross section of the beam.

Let the y axis be chosen positive upward, as shown in Fig. 362. The general elastic-curve equation, then, is $EI(d^2y/dx^2) = M$. But M varies with x and may be expressed in terms of x; thus, the bending moment at any section whose distance from the left support is x is

$$M_x = R_1 x - wx \cdot \left(\frac{x}{2}\right) = \frac{wl}{2} x - \frac{wx^2}{2}$$

The elastic-curve equation, therefore, is

$$EI \frac{d^2y}{dx^2} = \frac{wl}{2} x - \frac{wx^2}{2} \tag{257}$$

This differential equation may be transformed to an algebraic equation in x and y by being integrated twice. Equation 257 is prepared for integration by two steps as follows: First, replace $\dfrac{d^2y}{dx^2}$ by its equivalent $\dfrac{d}{dx}\left(\dfrac{dy}{dx}\right)$, that is

$$EI \frac{d}{dx}\left(\frac{dy}{dx}\right) = \frac{wl}{2} x - \frac{wx^2}{2} \tag{258}$$

Second, multiply both sides of Eq. 258 by dx, which gives

$$EI \, d\left(\frac{dy}{dx}\right) = \frac{wl}{2} x \, dx - \frac{wx^2}{2} dx \qquad (259)$$

Both sides of Eq. 259 are perfect differentials, and thus the first integration gives

$$EI \frac{dy}{dx} = \frac{wlx^2}{4} - \frac{wx^3}{6} + c_1$$

in which c_1 is a constant of integration. The value of a constant in an equation may be determined by substituting a pair of values of the variables; in this equation the variables are the slope dy/dx of the elastic curve and the distance x. One pair of values as found from inspection is $x = l/2$, $dy/dx = 0$. By substituting this pair of values in the preceding equation, we find the value of c_1 as follows:

$$c_1 = -\frac{wl^3}{16} + \frac{wl^3}{48} = -\frac{1}{24} wl^3$$

The preceding equation, then, becomes

$$EI \frac{dy}{dx} = \frac{wlx^2}{4} - \frac{wx^3}{6} - \frac{1}{24} wl^3 \qquad (260)$$

This equation shows that the slope dy/dx to the elastic curve at the left end of the beam (for $x = 0$) is $-\frac{1}{24}(wl^3/EI)$.

By multiplying both sides of Eq. 260 by dx, integrating, and evaluating the constant of integration, we find the equation expressing the relation between y and x. Thus,

$$EIy = \frac{wlx^3}{12} - \frac{wx^4}{24} - \frac{wl^3x}{24} + c_2$$

From inspection, we see that, when $x = 0$, $y = 0$, and hence $c_2 = 0$. Therefore, the equation of the elastic curve of a simple beam subjected to a uniformly distributed load is

$$EIy = \frac{wlx^3}{12} - \frac{wx^4}{24} - \frac{wl^3x}{24} \qquad (261)$$

Maximum Deflection. The maximum deflection Δ occurs at the midspan; that is, y in the foregoing equation becomes Δ when x is equal to $l/2$. Hence, the maximum deflection is

$$\Delta = \frac{1}{EI}\left(\frac{wl^4}{96} - \frac{wl^4}{384} - \frac{wl^4}{48}\right)$$

$$\Delta = -\frac{5}{384}\frac{wl^4}{EI} = -\frac{5}{384}\frac{Wl^3}{EI} \qquad (262)$$

The minus sign shows that the deflection is opposite to the positive direction of the y axis. It should be noted that the dimensions of the quantities in the right side of Eqs. 262 are such that Δ has the dimension of length.

135. Deflection of simple beam, concentrated load. When a concentrated load P acts on a beam, the expressions for M on opposite

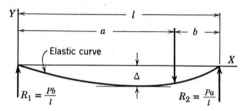

Fig. 363. Deflection of simple beam subjected to concentrated load at any section.

sides of the load are different, and hence there are two elastic-curve equations.

Figure 363 represents a simple beam subjected to a concentrated load P at the distance a from the left support and b from the right support, a being greater than b. Let it be required to find the equation of the elastic curve of the left portion of the beam and the maximum deflection by the double-integration method. Let the axes be chosen as shown in Fig. 363.

The bending moment at any section is given by the appropriate one of the following two equations:

For all points to the left of the load:

$$M = \frac{Pb}{l}x \qquad (263)$$

For all points to the right of the load:

$$M = \frac{Pb}{l}x - P(x - a) \qquad (264)$$

By the substitution of these expressions for M in Eq. 256 and integrating each equation once, we have the following equations:

$$EI \frac{d^2y}{dx^2} = \frac{Pb}{l} x \qquad (265)$$

$$EI \frac{d^2y}{dx^2} = \frac{Pb}{l} x - P(x - a) \qquad (266)$$

$$EI \frac{dy}{dx} = \frac{Pbx^2}{2l} + C_1 \qquad (267)$$

$$EI \frac{dy}{dx} = \frac{Pbx^2}{2l} - \frac{P(x - a)^2}{2} + C_3 \qquad (268)$$

Since the two elastic curves (to the left and to the right of the load, respectively) have a common tangent under the load, when x is made equal to a in both Eqs. 267 and 268, the value of dy/dx in Eq. 267 is equal to dy/dx in Eq. 268. Thus,

$$\frac{Pba^2}{2l} + C_1 = \frac{Pba^2}{2l} - \frac{P(a - a)^2}{2} + C_3$$

whence,

$$C_1 = C_3$$

The integration of Eq. 267 gives the following results:

$$EIy = \frac{Pbx^3}{6l} + C_1x + C_2 \qquad (269)$$

When $x = 0$, $y = 0$; hence $C_2 = 0$.

The substitution of $C_3 = C_1$ in Eq. 268 and the integration of this equation gives

$$EIy = \frac{Pbx^3}{6l} - \frac{P(x - a)^3}{6} + C_1x + C_4 \qquad (270)$$

Since the curves (Eqs. 269 and 270) have a common ordinate under the load, when $x = a$ the values of y in these equations are equal, and, hence,

$$\frac{Pba^3}{6l} + C_1a = \frac{Pba^3}{6l} + C_1a + C_4$$

$$C_4 = 0$$

Furthermore, when $x = l$ in Eq. 270, $y = 0$, and, hence,

$$C_1 = -\frac{Pbl^3}{6l^2} + \frac{P(l - a)^3}{6l} = -\frac{Pb}{6l}(l^2 - b^2) \qquad (271)$$

The substitution of C_1 from Eq. 271 in Eq. 269 gives the following elastic-curve equation for the left portion of the beam:

$$EIy = \frac{Pbx^3}{6l} - \frac{Pb(l^2 - b^2)x}{6l} \qquad (272)$$

The maximum deflection occurs at the point where the slope dy/dx of the elastic curve is zero: that is, where the tangent to the curve is horizontal (Fig. 363). However, the location of this point of tangency is unknown. The value of x that locates this point is found from Eq. 267, in which C_1 from Eq. 271 and $dy/dx = 0$ are substituted. Thus,

$$0 = \frac{Pbx^2}{2l} - \frac{Pb}{6l}(l^2 - b^2) \quad \text{or} \quad x^2 = \frac{l^2 - b^2}{3} = \frac{a(a + 2b)}{3} \qquad (273)$$

The substitution of the value of x from Eq. 273 into Eq. 272 gives the maximum deflection as follows:

$$\Delta = -\frac{Pb(l^2 - b^2)\sqrt{3(l^2 - b^2)}}{27EIl} \qquad (274)$$

or

$$\Delta = -\frac{Pba(a + 2b)\sqrt{3a(a + 2b)}}{27EIl} \qquad (275)$$

It should be noted that a in this article is *not* the area of cross section of the beam (as used elsewhere) but is the distance shown in Fig. 363.

If in the foregoing equations $a = b = l/2$, the load P acts at the midpoint of the span and the value of $\Delta = -\frac{1}{48}(Pl^3/EI)$, which is the value found in Art. 67.

Problems

389. By applying the general equation of the elastic curve, $EI(d^2y/dx^2) = M$, to the beam shown in Fig. 364, prove that

$$y = \frac{1}{EI}\left(\frac{Px^3}{12} - \frac{Pl^2x}{16}\right) \quad \text{and} \quad \Delta = -\frac{1}{48}\frac{Pl^3}{EI}$$

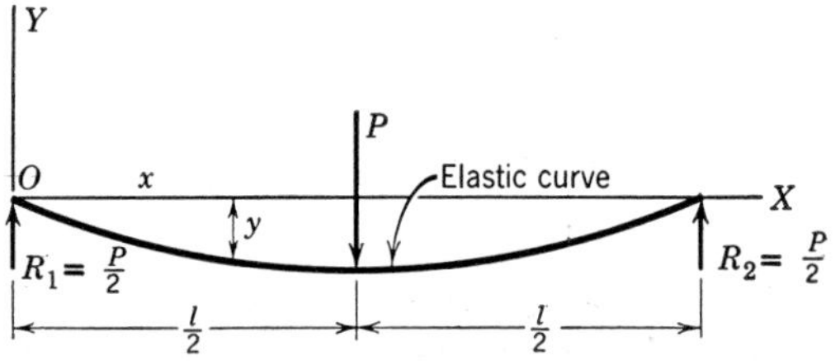

Fig. 364.   Deflection of simple beam with concentrated load at midspan.

The weight of the beam is assumed to be negligible. Also show by the use of this equation that the slope at the left end of the beam is $\theta_0 = -\frac{1}{16}Pl^2/EI$.

390. By applying the general equation of the elastic curve, $EI(d^2y/dx^2) = M$, to the beam shown in Fig. 365, in which w is the load per unit length of the beam, prove that

$$y = \frac{1}{EI}\left(-\frac{wx^4}{24} + \frac{wl^3x}{6} - \frac{wl^4}{8}\right) \quad \text{and} \quad \Delta = -\frac{1}{8}\frac{wl^4}{EI} = -\frac{1}{8}\frac{Wl^3}{EI}$$

What is the expression for the slope to the elastic curve at the free end?

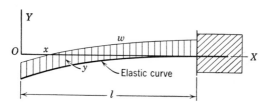

Fig. 365.   Deflection of cantilever beam with uniformly distributed load.

391. In Fig. 365 let the load $W = wl$ be removed, and let a downward load $P = W$ be applied at the free end. Show that

$$y = -\frac{P}{6EI}(x^3 - 3l^2x + 2l^3) \quad \text{and} \quad \Delta = -\frac{1}{3}\frac{Pl^3}{EI}$$

392. A cylindrical steel shaft 4 in. in diameter is used as a simple beam on a span of 8 ft. The beam is subjected to a uniformly distributed load of 200 lb per ft and a concentrated load of P lb at the center of the span. If the maximum deflection of the beam must not exceed 0.2 in. and the maximum bending stress must not exceed 16,000 lb per sq in., find the maximum value of P.

393. Find the deflection of the free end of the cantilever beam shown in Fig. 366, by choosing the origin at the fixed end and the axes as indicated in the figure. The known quantities are w, l, E, and I.

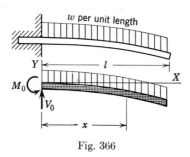

Fig. 366

394. A simple beam carrying a uniformly distributed load may be considered to be composed of two cantilever beams (see Fig. 367), each cantilever having a fixed end at the midspan section of the simple beam and being acted on by an upward concentrated load R_1 at the free end and a uniformly distributed downward load as indicated in Fig. 367b. Starting with the general equation of the elastic curve,

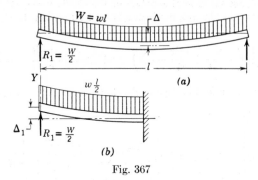

Fig. 367

and choosing axes as indicated in Fig. 367b, show that the maximum deflection Δ_1 of each cantilever beam is numerically the same as that of the simple beam

$$\Delta_1 = \Delta = \frac{5}{384} \frac{Wl^3}{EI}$$

395. Use the double-integration method to derive the equation of the elastic curve, and determine the location of and the value of the maximum deflection in terms of w, l, E, and I of a simply supported beam of constant cross section that

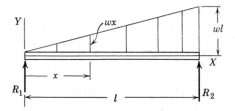

Fig. 368. Simple beam with nonuniformly distributed load.

supports a simply distributed load that varies linearly as the distance from the left end, as shown in Fig. 368.   *Ans.* $x = 0.519l$; $\Delta = -0.0065\ wl^5/EI$.

396. A cantilever beam has a couple M_0 applied at its free end as shown in Fig. 369. By applying the double-integration method, show that the change in slope

Fig. 369

to the elastic curve at the free end is $\theta = M_0 l/EI$ and that the deflection at the free end is $\Delta = -\frac{1}{2}M_0 l^2/EI$.

397. A cantilever beam is subjected to a load distributed as shown in Fig. 370. By applying the general elastic-curve equation, show that the deflection at the free end is $\Delta = -\frac{1}{30}wl^5/EI$.

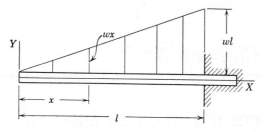

Fig. 370. Cantilever beam with nonuniformly distributed load.

Chapter XIV

CONJUGATE-BEAM METHOD

FOR DEFLECTION OF BEAMS

136. Conjugate beam defined. In Chapter IV, a procedure called the moment-area method for determining deflections of beams was developed and applied. In Chapter XIII, the double-integration method of finding deflections was derived, and its use demonstrated. A somewhat different method of accomplishing the same results, called the conjugate-beam method,* is discussed in this chapter. In the conjugate-beam method, the elastic deflection at any section of a beam (here called the "given" beam) is found by calculating the bending moment at the corresponding section of another beam called the substitute or conjugate beam, the conjugate beam being subjected to a distributed load such that the intensity of the load at any section is equal to the ordinate of the M/EI diagram of the given beam at that section. That is, the conjugate beam may be assumed to be loaded with sand, the depth of which over any section is, according to a chosen scale, the ordinate of the M/EI diagram of the given beam at the corresponding section. To describe this loading, the conjugate beam will be said to be loaded with the M/EI diagram of the given beam.

By definition, the conjugate beam is one that (a) has a length l' which is equal to the length l of the given beam, (b) is in equilibrium

---

* See "Deflection of Beams by the Conjugate Beam Method," by H. M. Wester-gaard, *Journal Western Society of Engineers*, vol. 26, Nov. 1921.

under the action of the loads and reactions (the nature of the reactions is discussed later), and (c) is so loaded that the bending moment M' at any section is equal to the deflection y at the corresponding section in the "given" beam. The defining equations then are:

From (a),

$$l' = l$$

from (b), since the loads and reactions constitute a parallel system of vectors,* there are two equations of equilibrium: namely,

$$\Sigma F' = 0 \quad \text{and} \quad \Sigma M' = 0$$

and, from (c),

$$M'_x = y_x$$

The last equation requires, as is shown in the following: (1) that the vertical shear V' for any section of the conjugate beam shall be equal to the slope at the corresponding point of the elastic curve of the "given" beam; that is,

$$V' = \frac{dy}{dx} = \theta \tag{276}$$

and (2) that the intensity w' of the distributed load on the conjugate beam at any section shall be equal to the M/EI for the corresponding section in the given beam; in other words, the conjugate beam is loaded with the M/EI diagram. Thus,

$$w' = \frac{M}{EI} \tag{277}$$

Proof of Eqs. 276 and 277. Let a straight beam be subjected to a distributed load only; the intensity of the load at the distance x from the left support is w, and the vertical shear and bending moment for this section are V and M.

The difference dV in the vertical shears for two sections the distance dx apart is

$$dV = w\,dx \quad \text{or} \quad w = \frac{dV}{dx} \tag{278}$$

But, from Art. 41,

$$V = \frac{dM}{dx} \tag{279}$$

---

* It will be found that the loads and reactions are not forces; that is, they are not expressed in pounds, tons, etc., but for convenience they may be called *elastic forces*, since they involve the elastic properties of the given beam.

and, hence,

$$\frac{dV}{dx} = \frac{d^2M}{dx^2} = w \tag{280}$$

The elastic-curve equation of the beam is (see Chap. IV)

$$\frac{d^2y}{dx^2} = \frac{M}{EI} \tag{281}$$

A comparison of the last two equations shows that the relation between w and M in Eq. 280 is the same as that between M/EI and y in Eq. 281. Therefore, if a substitute or conjugate beam is loaded with the M/EI diagram of the actual or "given" beam (and is provided with the proper reactions), *the bending moment M' in the conjugate beam represents the deflection y of the given beam.*

Further, since the slope θ of the elastic curve at any point is $\theta = dy/dx$, it follows that, if the conjugate beam is loaded so that $M' = y$, then, from Eq. 279,

$$V' = \frac{dy}{dx} = \theta$$

That is, the vertical shear for any section in the conjugate beam must be equal to the slope of the elastic curve at the corresponding section in the given beam.

It will be noted that, in the conjugate-beam method, the actual *elastic* beam is replaced by a *rigid* beam with the elastic properties of the actual beam introduced in the loads and reactions of the rigid beam.

Summarizing: The equations, then, that the *conjugate* beam for any *given* beam must satisfy are

$$l' = l, \qquad \Sigma F' = 0, \qquad \Sigma M' = 0, \qquad M' = y$$

$$V' = \theta, \qquad w' = \frac{M}{EI}$$

The application of these equations in finding the deflection of statically determinate beams is given in the following articles. In these applications the sign of the bending moment is determined as stated in Art. 132; the deflection y is positive in the downward direction, and x is positive to the right. Furthermore, the sign convention for M' is the same as that for M, and w' is a downward load for a positive M/EI. Likewise, the sign convention for V' will be the same as that for V; namely, upward forces to the left of the section produce positive shear. However, in many problems, the signs can be determined from inspection, and only the magnitudes need be determined mathematically.

Application of Conjugate-beam method

137. Simple beam; concentrated load at midspan. The beam is bent as shown in Fig. 371a. The bending-moment diagram (M diagram) is shown in Fig. 371b, and, since the beam has a constant cross section, the M/EI diagram will have the same form as the M diagram. The conjugate beam is shown in Fig. 371c; the bending moment at the midspan section of the conjugate beam is equal to the deflection of the

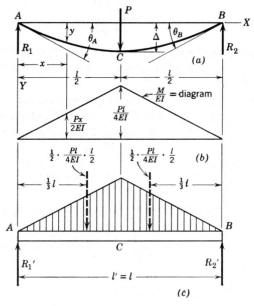

Fig. 371.   Conjugate beam method.   (a) Given beam; (b) M/EI diagram; (c) conjugate beam loaded with M/EI diagram.

midspan section (maximum deflection) of the given beam, provided that the conjugate beam is made to satisfy the equations of Art. 136. This may be done by selecting the beam as shown in Fig. 371c in which $l' = l$; the distributed load is the M/EI diagram; since $M' = y$, and since $y = 0$ at the ends of the "given" beam, the moment M' at the ends of the conjugate beam also must equal zero, and hence the ends of the conjugate beam are subjected to zero moments as shown in Fig. 371c; further, since $V' = \theta$ and since θ is not zero at the ends of the given beam, there must be vertical shears at the ends of the conjugate beam, and these could be produced by reactions R'_1 and R'_2 of supports at the ends. Thus, if the "given" beam is a simple beam, the conjugate beam also is a simple beam.

Since the conjugate beam is in equilibrium, the values of R'_1 and R'_2 may be found from the equations $\Sigma F' = 0$ and $\Sigma M' = 0$. From $\Sigma M' = 0$, or from the conditions of symmetry, it is evident that $R'_1 = R'_2$. And, from $\Sigma F' = 0$, the values of R'_1 and R'_2, are obtained. Thus,

$$\Sigma F' = 2R'_1 - \frac{1}{2}\frac{Pl}{4EI} \cdot l = 0; \quad \text{hence} \quad R'_1 = \frac{1}{16}\frac{Pl^2}{EI}$$

Therefore,

$$\theta_A = \frac{1}{16}\frac{Pl^2}{EI}$$

since R'_1 is equal to the vertical shear at the left end of the conjugate beam and hence is equal in magnitude to the slope of the "given" beam at the left end.

The maximum deflection Δ of the given beam occurs at the midspan section, and hence it is equal to the moment M'_c at the center of the conjugate beam, which is the moment of the couple shown in Fig. 371c. Thus,

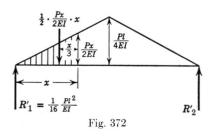

Fig. 372

$$\Delta = M'_c = \frac{1}{16}\frac{Pl^2}{EI} \cdot \frac{2}{3}\frac{l}{2} = \frac{1}{48}\frac{Pl^3}{EI}$$

Deflection at Any Point. The deflection y of the "given" beam at a distance x from the left support is equal to the bending moment M'_x of the conjugate beam which, as indicated in Fig. 372, is

$$y = M'_x = R'_1 x - \frac{1}{2}\frac{Px^2}{2EI} \cdot \frac{1}{3}x$$

$$= \frac{Pl^2 x}{16EI} - \frac{1}{12}\frac{Px^3}{EI} = \frac{P}{4EI}\left(\frac{l^2 x}{4} - \frac{x^3}{3}\right)$$

This is the equation of the elastic curve of the left half of the given beam.

138. Cantilever beam; concentrated load at end. The given beam is assumed to have a constant cross section; it bends as shown in Fig. 373a. The conjugate beam is shown in Fig. 373b; the distributed load on the conjugate beam is the M/EI diagram and is an upward load since M is negative. The end conditions of the conjugate beam are found by making the beam satisfy the fundamental equations of

Art. 136. Thus, since $M' = y$ and $V' = \theta$, and, further, since y and θ are not zero at the free end of the "given" beam, the moment M'_0 and the shear V'_0 at the left end of the conjugate beam are not zero. M'_0 and V'_0 may be produced by fixing the beam at the left end. On the other hand, since the θ and y at the right end of the "given" beam are zero, the M' and V' at the right end of the conjugate beam must be

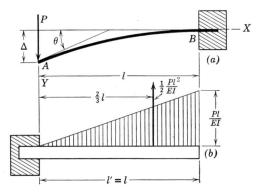

Fig. 373. Conjugate beam method. (a) Given beam; (b) conjugate beam loaded with M/EI diagram.

zero, and this condition will exist if the right end is free. Therefore the conjugate beam corresponding to a cantilever beam is another cantilever beam with the end conditions interchanged.

Since the maximum deflection Δ of the "given" beam is equal to the moment M'_0 at the left end of the conjugate beam, it may be expressed as follows:

$$\Delta = M'_0 = \frac{1}{2}\frac{Pl^2}{EI} \cdot \frac{2}{3}l = \frac{1}{3}\frac{Pl^3}{EI}$$

The slope θ at the free end of the given beam may be found, if desired, by calculating the shear V'_0 at the left end of the conjugate beam; the value found is

$$\theta = V'_0 = -\frac{1}{2}\frac{Pl^2}{EI}$$

The elastic-curve equation may be found in a manner similar to that used in the preceding article.

139. Simple beam; load distributed uniformly. The beam is assumed to have a constant cross section; it deflects as shown in Fig.

374a. The corresponding conjugate beam is shown in Fig. 374b; the distributed load is the M/EI diagram, the maximum ordinate of the diagram being $\frac{1}{8}wl^2/EI$.

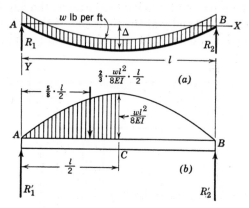

Fig. 374.   Deflection of simple beam found as the moment in the conjugate beam.

The maximum deflection is equal to the moment at the center of the conjugate beam, which is the moment of the couple shown in Fig. 374b. The deflection, therefore, is

$$\Delta = M'_c = \frac{2}{3} \cdot \frac{1}{8}\frac{wl^2}{EI} \cdot \frac{l}{2} \cdot \frac{5}{8}\frac{l}{2} = \frac{5}{384}\frac{wl^4}{EI} = \frac{5}{384}\frac{Wl^3}{EI}$$

140. Cantilever beam; load distributed uniformly. The beam has a constant cross section; it deflects as shown in Fig. 375a. The

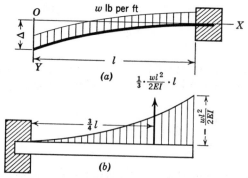

Fig. 375.   Deflection of cantilever beam.   (a) Given beam; (b) conjugate beam.

corresponding conjugate beam is shown in Fig. 375b. The maximum deflection Δ is equal to the moment M'_0 at the left end of the conjugate beam. Thus,

$$\Delta = M'_0 = \frac{1}{3} \cdot \frac{wl^3}{2EI} \cdot \frac{3}{4} l = \frac{1}{8} \frac{wl^4}{EI} = \frac{1}{8} \frac{Wl^3}{EI}$$

141. Simple beam; concentrated load at any point. Let the load act at a distance a from the left end and b from the right end; the deflected beam is shown in Fig. 376a. The M/EI diagram is shown in

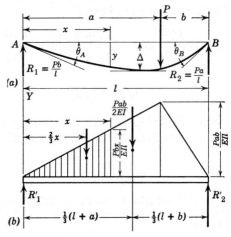

Fig. 376.   Deflection of simple beam at any point.

Fig. 376b as a distributed load acting on the conjugate beam; the "given" beam is assumed to have a constant cross section.

The total load is $\frac{1}{2}(Pab/EIl)\cdot l$, and its action line is at a distance of $\frac{1}{3}(l + a)$ from the left end. From the equations of equilibrium, $\Sigma F' = 0$ and $\Sigma M' = 0$, the values of R'_1 and R'_2 (and hence of θ_A and θ_B) are found to be

$$R'_1 = \frac{1}{3} \frac{l + b}{l} \frac{Pab}{2EI} \quad \text{and} \quad R'_2 = \frac{1}{3} \frac{l + a}{l} \frac{Pab}{2EI}$$

The deflection y at the distance x from the left end of the given beam is equal to the bending moment M'_x in the conjugate beam. Thus,

$$y = M'_x = R'_1 x - \frac{1}{2} \frac{Pbx^2}{EIl} \frac{1}{3} x$$

$$= \frac{1}{3} \frac{l + b}{l} \frac{Pab}{2EI} x - \frac{1}{6} \frac{Pbx^3}{lEI}$$

$$= \frac{Pbx}{6EIl} [a(l + b) - x^2] \tag{282}$$

which is the elastic-curve equation of that portion of the beam to the left of the load P.

The maximum deflection may be found as follows: The maximum moment in the conjugate beam is equal to the maximum deflection in the given beam, and the section of maximum moment in the conjugate beam is the section for which the vertical shear in the conjugate beam is zero. Thus, the value of x' in the following equation locates the point of maximum deflection in the given beam:

$$V'_x = R'_1 - \frac{Pbx^2}{2lEI} = 0 = \frac{1}{3}\frac{l+b}{l}\frac{Pab}{2EI} - \frac{Pbx^2}{2lEI} = 0$$

Hence,

$$x = \sqrt{\tfrac{1}{3}a(l+b)} \tag{283}$$

If this value of x is substituted in Eq. 282, the resulting value of y is the maximum deflection Δ (see Art. 135 for the value of Δ).

Problem

398. Find, from Eqs. 282 and 283, the maximum deflection of a simple beam subjected to a concentrated load at the center of the span, and compare the result with that given in Art. 67.

142. Simple beam; cross section not constant. Let a concentrated load act at the center of a simple beam, and let the moment of inertia for any section in the center half of the beam be I and for any section in the outer quarters $\frac{1}{2}I$, as indicated in Fig. 377a. The moment diagram is shown in Fig. 377b, and the M/EI diagram is shown in Fig. 377c acting as a load on the conjugate beam. The M/EI diagram may be divided into four triangles, I, II, III, and IV, as shown in Fig. 377c. From the equilibrium equation $\Sigma F' = 0$, the value of R'_1 is found to be

$$R'_1 = Q_1 + Q_2 = \frac{5}{64}\frac{Pl^2}{EI}$$

and the maximum deflection Δ which is equal to the bending moment M'_c at the center of the conjugate beam is

$$\Delta = M'_c = R'_1\frac{l}{2} - Q_1\frac{1}{6}l - Q_2\frac{1}{3}l$$

$$= \left(\frac{5}{128} - \frac{1}{96} - \frac{1}{192}\right)\frac{Pl^3}{EI} = \frac{3}{128}\frac{Pl^3}{EI}$$

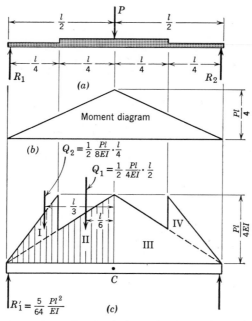

Fig. 377.   Conjugate beam for simple beam having a change in cross section.

Problem

399. A simple beam is subjected to a concentrated load P at the center of the span; the moment of inertia of the left half of the beam is I and of the right half is $\frac{1}{2}I$.   Derive the expression for the deflection of the center of the beam.

Ans. $\frac{1}{32}Pl^3/EI$.

Note.   The problems in Chapters IV and XIII also may be used in connection with this chapter.

Chapter XV

CONTINUOUS BEAMS.

THREE-MOMENT THEOREM

143. Introduction. Frequently a beam may be relatively long and may require more than two supporting reactions along its length. A beam that has more than two supports is called a continuous beam. Since there are more than two reactions on a continuous beam, such a beam is statically indeterminate. A method of solving for the reactions on statically indeterminate beams has been given in Chapter VII (see Arts. 90 and 91). This method is used in the article that follows to derive a method, known as the three-moment theorem, for finding the redundant moments (the bending moments at the supports) in a continuous beam. After the redundant moments are determined, the reactions are found by using the equations of equilibrium. When all the reactions at the supports are known, the shear and bending-moment diagrams for a continuous beam may be drawn, and the maximum values of the stresses and deflections may be found.

144. Theorem of three moments. Let Fig. 378a represent a continuous beam subjected to any combination of distributed and concentrated loads which cause stresses that do not exceed the elastic limit of the material; the beam has a constant cross section and rests on supports that are on the same level. A relationship between the bending moments over any three adjacent supports (called the three-

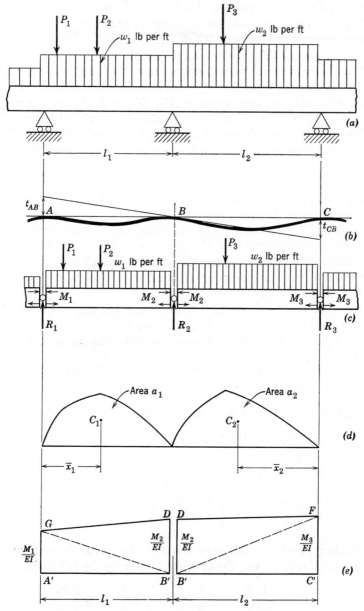

Fig. 378. Moment-area method used for deriving the three-moment theorem.

moment theorem) may be found as follows. The moment-area method (Chap. VII) for expressing the deflection of the beam is used, but the double-integration method (Chap. XIII) or the conjugate-beam method (Chap. XIV) may be used if desired.

The elastic curve of two adjacent spans of the beam is shown in Fig. 378b. If over the supports hinges are introduced, as indicated in Fig. 378c, then external end moments M_1, M_2, and M_3 are the values of the bending moments at the supports of the original beam. The values M_1, M_2, and M_3 are considered to be the redundant quantities, and, after they are found, these two spans become statically determinate.

Let Fig. 378d represent the bending moment diagram, as found by the method of parts (Art. 42), for the two spans l_1 and l_2. Thus, a_1 and a_2 represent the areas, respectively, under the moment diagrams of spans 1 and 2 when the fixed-end moments are removed; the points C_1 and C_2 are the centroids of the areas a_1 and a_2. Similarly, areas $A'GDB'$ and $B'DFC'$ represent the M/EI diagrams of spans 1 and 2 when the fixed-end moments are restored and the loads P_1, P_2, P_3, w_1, and w_2 are removed.

Let a tangent be drawn to the elastic curve at the support B (Fig. 378b); since the elastic curve is continuous over the support, the tangent to the elastic curve at B is common to the two curves of the adjacent spans l_1 and l_2.

From Theorem II of Art. 65, the tangential deviation t_{AB} of the point A from a tangent at B is found as follows:

$$t_{AB} = (\text{moment, about } A', \text{ of area } a_1/EI + \text{moment about } A',$$

$$\text{of area } A'GDB')$$

$$= \frac{1}{EI}\left(a_1\bar{x}_1 + \frac{1}{2}M_1l_1\frac{l_1}{3} + \frac{1}{2}M_2l_1\cdot\frac{2l_1}{3}\right)$$

$$= \frac{1}{EI}\left(a_1\bar{x}_1 + \frac{M_1l_1^2}{6} + \frac{M_2l_1^2}{3}\right)$$

Similarly, by taking moments about C' of areas of the moment diagrams for the next span, the tangential deviation t_{CB} is found.

$$t_{CB} = \frac{1}{EI}\left(a_2\bar{x}_2 + \frac{1}{2}M_3l_2\cdot\frac{l_2}{3} + \frac{1}{2}M_2\cdot l_2\frac{2l_2}{3}\right)$$

$$= \frac{1}{EI}\left(a_2\bar{x}_2 + \frac{M_2l_2^2}{3} + \frac{M_3l_2^2}{6}\right)$$

But, from similar triangles,

$$t_{AB}/l_1 = -t_{CB}/l_2$$

Hence,

$$\frac{a_1\bar{x}_1}{l_1} + \frac{M_1 l_1}{6} + \frac{M_2 l_1}{3} = -\left(\frac{a_2\bar{x}_2}{l_2} + \frac{M_3 l_2}{6} + \frac{M_2 l_2}{3}\right)$$

or

$$\frac{M_1 l_1}{6} + \frac{M_2(l_1 + l_2)}{3} + \frac{M_3 l_2}{6} = -\frac{a_1\bar{x}_1}{l_1} - \frac{a_2\bar{x}_2}{l_2}$$

Therefore,

$$\boldsymbol{M_1 l_1 + 2M_2(l_1 + l_2) + M_3 l_2} = -\frac{6a_1\bar{x}_1}{l_1} - \frac{6a_2\bar{x}_2}{l_2} \qquad (284)$$

If the beam in Fig. 378a is subjected to uniformly distributed loads w_1, w_2, etc., only, the right side of Eq. 284 is expressed directly in terms of the loads and span lengths as follows:

$$\boldsymbol{M_1 l_1 + 2M_2(l_1 + l_2) + M_3 l_2} = -\frac{w_1 l_1^3}{4} - \frac{w_2 l_2^3}{4} \qquad (285)$$

This equation expresses the theorem of three moments for a continuous beam resting on supports on the same level, and subjected to uniform loads that cause stresses that do not exceed the elastic limit of the material. If $w_1 = w_2$ and $l_1 = l_2$, Eq. 285 reduces to

$$\boldsymbol{M_1 + 4M_2 + M_3} = -\tfrac{1}{2}wl^2 \qquad (286)$$

The use of the three-moment theorem for the special case to which Eq. 286 applies is illustrated in the solution of the following problem.

Illustrative Problem

Problem 400. Let it be required to draw the shear and moment diagrams for a continuous beam of four spans, each of length l, when subjected to a load of w per unit length over the entire beam, and also to find the maximum bending stress (see Fig. 379a). The known quantities are: w, l, E, and I. The main steps in the solution are:

(a) By use of the theorem of three moments, find the negative bending moment over all supports.

(b) Find the reactions of the supports from the negative moments over the supports; all the external forces acting on the beam then will be known.

(c) Find the vertical shears at various sections, and draw the shear diagram.

(d) Find the bending moments at various sections, and draw the moment diagram.

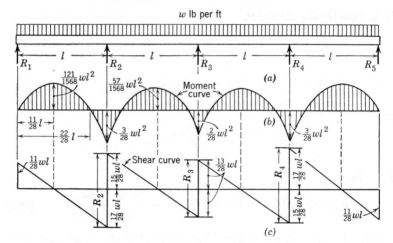

Fig. 379.   Moment and shear diagram for a continuous beam.

Solution.   (a) In accordance with the theorem of three moments, the following equations may be written:

$$M_1 + 4M_2 + M_3 = -\tfrac{1}{2}wl^2$$

$$M_2 + 4M_3 + M_4 = -\tfrac{1}{2}wl^2$$

$$M_3 + 4M_4 + M_5 = -\tfrac{1}{2}wl^2$$

Further, $M_1 = M_5 = 0$ since there is no restraint at the ends; and $M_2 = M_4$, from the condition of symmetry. The solution of these equations gives the following values:

$$M_1 = 0, \qquad M_2 = -\tfrac{3}{28}wl^2, \qquad M_3 = -\tfrac{2}{28}wl^2, \qquad M_4 = -\tfrac{3}{28}wl^2, \qquad M_5 = 0$$

(b) The bending moment at a section over the second support as found in the preceding is $-\tfrac{3}{28}wl^2$, but the bending moment at any section is the algebraic sum of the moments of the forces to the left of the section. Hence,

$$R_1 l - wl\frac{l}{2} = -\frac{3}{28}wl^2, \qquad \text{hence } R_1 = \frac{11}{28}wl$$

Similarly, the moment over the third support is found. Thus,

$$R_1 \cdot 2l + R_2 l - w \cdot 2l \cdot l = -\tfrac{2}{28}wl^2, \qquad \text{hence } R_2 = \tfrac{32}{28}wl$$

In a similar way, the value of R_3 is found to be $R_3 = \tfrac{26}{28}wl$, and, from symmetry, $R_4 = R_2$, and $R_5 = R_1$.

(c) The shear and moment diagrams are shown in Fig. 379b and c. The vertical shear at any section in the first span at the distance x from the left support is

$$V_x = R_1 - wx = \tfrac{11}{28}wl - wx$$

and hence the vertical shear is zero when $x = \tfrac{11}{28}l$; the maximum positive moment occurs at this section.

The shear just to the left of the second support is

$$V_{-2} = R_1 - wl = 1\tfrac{1}{28}wl - wl = -\tfrac{17}{28}wl$$

and the shear just to the right of the second support is

$$V_2 = R_1 + R_2 - wl = 1\tfrac{1}{28}wl + \tfrac{32}{28}wl - wl = +1\tfrac{5}{28}wl$$

Thus, the shear changes at the second support from $-\tfrac{17}{28}wl$ to $+1\tfrac{5}{28}wl$, owing to the reaction R_2; in other words, the reaction of a support is equal to the arithmetic sum of the shears at the two sides of the support.

The shears in other spans may be found by the same method as that used for the first span; the values are given in Fig. 379b.

Thus the reaction at any support may be found by solving for the shears on the two sides of the support and adding them rather than by the method used under (b).

(d) The bending moment at any section in the first span is

$$M'_x = R_1 x - \frac{wx^2}{2}$$

and, as previously noted, this is maximum when $x = 1\tfrac{1}{28}l$. Therefore, the maximum positive moment is

$$\text{Max. pos. moment} = \frac{11}{28}wl \cdot \frac{11}{28}l - \frac{w}{2}\left(\frac{11}{28}l\right)^2 = \frac{121}{1568}wl^2$$

which is less than the maximum negative moment $(\tfrac{3}{28}wl^2)$.

The inflection point occurs where $M'_x = 0$; thus,

$$M'_x = \frac{11}{28}wl \cdot x - \frac{wx^2}{2} = 0; \qquad \text{hence} \quad x = \frac{22}{28}l$$

The bending moment at any section in the second span is

$$M''_x = M_2 + V_2 x - \tfrac{1}{2}wx^2 = -\tfrac{3}{28}wl^2 + 1\tfrac{5}{28}wlx - \tfrac{1}{2}wx^2$$

The moment is maximum when $x = 1\tfrac{5}{28}l$, since this is the value that makes the shear in the second span equal to zero. The value of the maximum positive moment in this span is $\tfrac{57}{1568}wl^2$.

The greatest bending moment that the beam is subjected to is the negative moment at the second (or fourth) support, and hence the maximum stress in the beam is

$$\sigma = \frac{Mc}{I} = \frac{3}{28}wl^2 \cdot \frac{c}{I}$$

145. Values of moments and shears. In Fig. 380 are given the values of the coefficients from which the negative moments over the supports and the vertical shears at either side of each support may be found for continuous beams resting on supports on the same level, having equal spans l, and carrying a constant uniform load of w per unit length on each span.

The values directly above the supports are the moment coefficients: that is, the numbers by which $-wl^2$ must be multiplied in order to obtain the bending moments over the supports. Similarly, the numbers on either side of the supports are the shear coefficients: that is, the numbers by which wl must be multiplied to obtain the magnitude of the vertical shear for the section; the vertical shear is negative for the section to the left of each support and positive for the section to the right of each support. The reaction at each support is the arithmetic

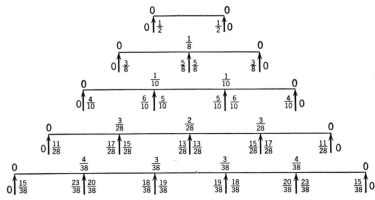

Fig. 380. Values of shear and moment coefficients of continuous beam of equal spans subjected to equal uniformly distributed loads on all spans.

sum of the vertical shears on the two sides of the support. The values given in Fig. 380 may be found by the methods discussed in Prob. 400.

Significance of Negative Moments. In continuous beams, the negative moments over the supports reduce the moments (and hence stresses) near the centers of the spans, and hence continuous beams in general are stronger and stiffer than similarly loaded simply supported beams of equal spans. On the other hand, the uneven settlement of supports may change the moments at the supports and throughout the beam from those found by the preceding analysis; further, the stiffer the beams, the greater is the change in the moments. Partly for this reason and partly because the loads on the various spans of continuous beams in structures may vary considerably from those assumed in the design, it frequently is assumed that, in uniformly loaded beams of four or more equal spans, all the spans (except the end spans) are subjected to the same maximum bending moment, a common value being $\frac{1}{12}wl^2$; the maximum moment in the end spans is somewhat greater ($\frac{1}{10}wl^2$ is frequently used). Compare these values with those given in Fig. 380 for beams having more than four spans, and note that the moments do not vary greatly over the inner supports. Two-span and three-span beams are stressed higher than beams of four or more spans, and for such beams the maximum moment in each span frequently is assumed to be $\frac{1}{10}wl^2$. However, the values used in any case may be based on the results of an analysis of the moments in continuous beams similar to that discussed in the preceding articles.

Problems

401. A continuous wooden beam consists of four equal spans, each 12 ft long, and is subjected to a uniform load of 200 lb per ft over its entire length. (a) Find the reaction of the second support. (b) If the beam has a rectangular cross section, the depth being one and one-half the width, what is the depth if the maximum fiber stress in the beam is 1000 lb per sq in.?

Ans. (a) $R_2 = 2740$ lb; (b) $h = 6.95$ in.

402. A 12-in. 40.8-lb steel I beam is used as a horizontal continuous beam over four spans. The lengths of the spans are 20, 12, 20, and 12 ft, respectively, from left to right. The loads are uniformly distributed over each span, the loads per foot of length on the four spans being 2000, 1600, 2000, and 1600 lb per ft, respectively. Compute the maximum bending stress in the beam.

Ans. $M_2 = -65,400$ lb-ft; $M_3 = -42,000$ lb-ft; $M_4 = -60,000$ lb-ft; $\sigma = 17,500$ lb per in.²

403. A continuous beam has three spans of 12 ft each. The first span is subjected to a uniformly distributed load of 2000 lb per ft. The other spans each have a 10,000-lb load at midspan. Compute the four reactions, assuming the elastic limit is not exceeded. *Ans.* $R_1 = 10,000$ lb; $R_2 = 19,650$ lb.

404. What should be the depth of a pine continuous beam having four equal spans of 10 ft, in order to resist a uniformly distributed load of 300 lb per ft over each span? Use a working stress of 1000 lb per sq in., and make the depth of the beam twice the width.

405. A continuous beam of two spans, 15 ft and 20 ft, carries a uniformly distributed load of 1500 lb per ft over the longer span and no load on the shorter span. Compute the maximum positive and negative bending moments and the reactions at the three supports. Assume that the elastic limit is not exceeded.

Ans. $M_2 = -42,800$ lb-ft; $M_{max} = 55,100$ lb-ft.

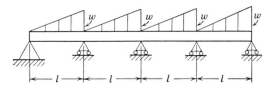

Fig. 381. Continuous beam with varying distributed load on each span.

406. A continuous beam consisting of four equal spans, each of length l, is loaded as shown in Fig. 381. Assume that the elastic limit of the material in the beam is not exceeded, and compute the bending moments over the two middle supports in terms of w and l. *Ans.* $M_2 = M_4 = -\frac{3}{56}wl^2$; $M_3 = -\frac{2}{56}wl^2$.

407. In Fig. 382, a continuous beam of two equal span lengths l is fixed at its left end. If the beam is subjected to a uniform load of w lb per ft over its entire length, compute the fixed-end bending moment and the bending moment over the middle support. Assume that the elastic limit is not exceeded. *Hint.* Write the three-moment equation for the two spans, and, for the additional equation needed, use Theorem II in Art. 65 to write the equation for t_{BA} which is equal to zero.

Ans. $M_1 = -\frac{1}{14}wl^2;\ M_2 = -\frac{3}{28}wl^2.$

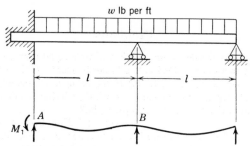

Fig. 382.   Continuous beam fixed at one end and simply supported at two other sections.

Chapter XVI

ELASTIC VIBRATION

OF LOAD-RESISTING MEMBERS

146. Introduction. A mechanical vibration as met in most engineering problems is a periodic motion which repeats itself in a definite time interval called the *period* of the vibration; each repetition of the motion is called a *cycle*, and the number of cycles per unit of time is called the frequency of vibration. Furthermore, the maximum displacement of any point in the body from its equilibrium position during a cycle (called the amplitude of the motion of the point) is usually small.

In Part I, the magnitude of the elastic deflection of a member caused by loads was considered. For example, in Chapter II, the angle of twist of a cylindrical shaft was found in terms of the twisting moment, dimensions of the shaft, and the stiffness of the material ($\theta = Tl/GJ$). Similarly, in Chapter IV, the elastic deflection of a beam was obtained in terms of the loads, the dimensions of the beam, and the modulus of elasticity of the material.

In some applications of load-resisting members, however, not only the magnitude of the deflection is desired, but also the frequency of the deflection, when the member is subjected to elastic vibration.

The prevention or reduction of vibration in machine parts and structural members is important in eliminating excessive wear, in reducing repeated stresses that are likely to cause a fatigue fracture

(Chap. IX), and in reducing objectionable noise. It is important, therefore, to consider, even though very briefly, the vibrational characteristics of some of the more common members used in structures and machines, such as cylindrical shafts subjected to torsion and various members subjected to bending.

147. Free vibrations. Consider the motion of a small rigid body of mass m and weight W (Fig. 383) suspended by an elastic weightless spring from a rigid support. The *spring constant* or *modulus of the spring* (that is, the force required to deflect the end of the spring a unit distance) is denoted by k, and the static deflection of the end of the spring due to the weight W is denoted by δ_{st}; hence, $k = W/\delta_{\text{st}}$. It is assumed that the body is free to move only along a vertical line, which is taken here as the x axis, x being regarded as positive when measured downward from the position of static equilibrium of the body. Let the body be given some initial displacement x_0 and then released, causing the body to oscillate or vibrate with a definite amplitude. The forces acting on the body when it has any displacement x are shown in Fig. 383, and the equation of motion $\Sigma F_x = ma_x$ applied to the body gives

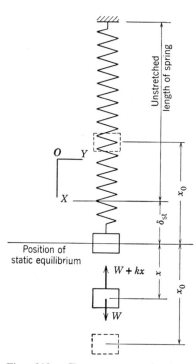

Fig. 383. Free or natural elastic vibration.

$$W - (W + kx) = ma_x \quad \text{or} \quad a_x = \frac{d^2x}{dt^2} = -\frac{k}{m}x \qquad (287)$$

in which a_x is the acceleration of the body. If we replace the constant k/m, for convenience, by p^2 and note that $W = k\delta_{\text{st}}$, the equation obtained is

$$p^2 = \frac{k}{m} = \frac{kg}{W} = \frac{g}{\delta_{\text{st}}} \qquad (288)$$

Hence, Eq. 287 may be written

$$\frac{d^2x}{dt^2} = -p^2x \qquad (289)$$

The motion described by Eq. 289 is a simple-harmonic motion (see any textbook on mechanics) and may be represented by a projection on the diameter of a circle of a point moving with constant angular velocity p on the circle. Thus the motion, represented by Eq. 289, is a periodic or oscillatory motion, and p usually is called the circular frequency. It is evident, therefore, that the time interval (period) T for each cycle of the motion is $2\pi/p$. Thus,

$$T = \frac{2\pi}{p} = 2\pi \sqrt{\frac{W}{kg}} = 2\pi \sqrt{\frac{\delta_{st}}{g}} \qquad (290)$$

The number of cycles per second f, called the *frequency*, is then

$$f = \frac{1}{T} = \frac{p}{2\pi} = \frac{1}{2\pi} \sqrt{\frac{kg}{W}} = \frac{1}{2\pi} \sqrt{\frac{g}{\delta_{st}}} \qquad (291)$$

If we substitute $g = 386$ in./sec^2 and express δ_{st} in inches, f may be expressed in cycles per second. Thus,

$$f = \frac{1}{2\pi} \sqrt{\frac{g}{\delta_{st}}} = \frac{3.127}{\sqrt{\delta_{st}}} \text{ cycles per second} \qquad (292)$$

Equations 290 and 291 show that the period and frequency of *free* vibration of the body depend only on the weight of the body and the stiffness of the spring, and are not affected by the initial conditions of the motion.

These equations will be found to be applicable to periodic motions of widely different arrangements of elastic members. In other words, Fig. 383 is a conventionalized diagram that can be used with small error to replace many actual motions of bodies that vibrate with small amplitudes.

It is important to observe that the preceding equations apply only to free vibrations: namely, to the periodic motion of a body acted on only by its weight and a force exerted by a spring (or system of springs) such that the force is proportional to the displacement of the body and acts always to restore the position of the body to its equilibrium position. Thus, the motion of the body described by the preceding equations does not occur in a resisting medium such as a liquid, which would produce a damped vibration rather than a free vibration. Nor is the motion a forced vibration in which an additional (periodic) force is applied to the body as it vibrates. In a forced vibration, if the period of the impressed force is the same as that of the free or natural period of vibration of the system, the theoretical amplitude of the vibration becomes exceedingly large. This condition is known as *resonance* and is, of course, a condition to be avoided in parts of machines and structures. It is sometimes important, therefore, to know the period or frequency of the free or natural elastic vibration of a member.

148. Free torsional vibration. As an application of Eq. 290 or 291, let it be required to find the period of the natural vibration of a cylindrical shaft to which is attached a rotor or disk D as indicated in

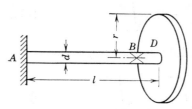

Fig. 384. The shaft is rigidly held at A, and the bearing B is assumed to be frictionless. If the disk is given an angular displacement θ and then is released, it will oscillate similar to a torsional pendulum under the influence of the torque exerted by the rod. The torque is proportional to the angular displace-

Fig. 384. Free torsional elastic vibration.

ment, provided that the elastic strength of the material is not exceeded, and is opposite in sense to θ. The equation of motion $\Sigma T_0 = I_0\alpha$, for the disk or rotor therefore becomes

$$-k\theta = I_0 \frac{d^2\theta}{dt^2} \quad \text{or} \quad \frac{d^2\theta}{dt^2} = -\frac{k}{I_0}\theta \tag{293}$$

where k is the torsional spring constant, or the torque T_0 required to produce a unit angle of twist of the rod or shaft to which the disk is attached, and I_0 is the moment of inertia of the disk about its geometric axis; the I of the shaft is assumed to be negligible. Equation 293 is the equation of motion for free torsional vibrations of many machine parts such as rotors or flywheels where the mass of the shaft is relatively small. Equation 293 has the same form as Eq. 287. The period of oscillation, therefore, is

$$T = \frac{2\pi}{p} = 2\pi \sqrt{\frac{I_0}{k}} \tag{294}$$

But in Art. 28 it was shown that the angle of twist θ for a cylindrical bar was given by the expression $\theta = Tl/GJ$. Therefore, since by definition $k = T/\theta$, the value of k becomes

$$k = \frac{T}{\theta} = \frac{GJ}{l} = \frac{G\pi d^4}{32l} \tag{295}$$

in which d is the diameter of the shaft and l is its length (Fig. 384). Furthermore, for a cylindrical homogeneous disk, $I_0 = Wr^2/2g$, in which W is the weight of the disk, r is its radius, and g is the acceleration due to gravity. Thus, Eq. 294 may be written

$$T = 2\pi \sqrt{\frac{16Wr^2l}{\pi g d^4 G}} \tag{296}$$

in which a consistent set of units, of course, must be used.

Two Bodies Connected by Shaft. Nodal Point. When two heavy masses such as the rotors of a large motor and generator are connected by a relatively small shaft, as shown in Fig. 385, torsional vibrations of the system may be produced by twisting the rotors in opposite directions and then releasing the applied twisting moments or torques. Since, after release, there are no external torques acting on the system, the principle of conservation of angular momentum may be applied. Thus, if I_1 and I_2 are the moments of inertia of the two rotors, and ω_1 and ω_2 are their angular velocities at any time, the principle of conservation of momentum is expressed by the equation:

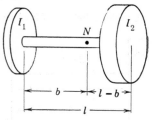

Fig. 385. Free torsion vibration of system having nodal point.

$$I_1\omega_1 + I_2\omega_2 = 0 \quad \text{or} \quad \omega_1 = -\omega_2\frac{I_2}{I_1} \tag{297}$$

Hence, the two bodies rotate in opposite directions during the vibration since their angular velocities are of opposite sign, and there must be a section N (called the nodal section) of the shaft that remains stationary. Thus, the motion of each body may be considered as that of a torsional pendulum (as in Fig. 384) of a shaft which is fixed at N, and the position of this nodal section can be determined since the periods of oscillation for the two parts of the system are equal. From Eq. 294, the period is

$$T = 2\pi\sqrt{I_1/k_1} = 2\pi\sqrt{I_2/k_2} \tag{298}$$

where k_1 and k_2 are the torsional spring constants of the two parts of the shaft as divided by the point N. Therefore $k_2/k_1 = I_2/I_1$, and, if the values of k from Eq. 295 are substituted, this equation becomes

$$\frac{b}{l - b} = \frac{I_2}{I_1}; \quad \text{hence} \quad b = \frac{I_2 l}{I_1 + I_2} \qquad (299)$$

By using this value of b for the length of the shaft in Eq. 295 and substituting the resulting value of k_1 in Eq. 298, we find the period of free torsional vibration for the system in Fig. 385 to be

$$T = 2\pi \sqrt{\frac{32 l I_1 I_2}{\pi d^4 G (I_1 + I_2)}} = 2\pi \sqrt{\frac{I_1 I_2 l}{J G (I_1 + I_2)}} \qquad (300)$$

Illustrative Problem

Problem 408. A Diesel engine, whose flywheel and other rotating parts are represented by A in Fig. 386, has a combined moment of inertia of 600 slug-ft². The engine drives a generator whose rotor, represented by B, has a moment of inertia of 100 slug-ft². The steel shaft connecting the engine to the generator is 4 in. in diameter and 5 ft long. The shearing modulus of elasticity of steel is $G = 12 \times 10^6$ lb/in.² Neglecting the mass of the shaft, calculate the natural frequency of torsional vibration of the system.

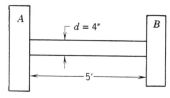

Fig. 386

Solution. The natural torsional frequency is

$$f = \frac{1}{T} = \frac{1}{2\pi} \sqrt{\frac{J G (I_A + I_B)}{I_A I_B l}}$$

in which $I_A = 600$, and $I_B = 100$ slug-ft².

$$J = \tfrac{1}{32} \pi d^4 = 8\pi \text{ in.}^4, \qquad G = 12 \times 10^6 \text{ lb per sq in.}$$

Thus,

$$f = \frac{1}{2\pi} \sqrt{\frac{8\pi \times 12,000,000 \times 700 \times 12}{600 \times 100 \times 60 \times (12)^2}} = 11.1 \text{ cycles per second}$$

Problems

409. In Prob. 408 let the shaft be made of an aluminum alloy (see Table 1). Calculate the frequency.   The weight of the shaft may be neglected.

Ans. $f = 6.25$ cycles per second.

410. If a forced vibration having a frequency of approximately 11 cycles per second is applied to the bodies in Prob. 408, the frequency of natural vibration of the bodies would need to be changed to prevent resonance.   (a) How much must the length l of the shaft be increased to cause a 20 per cent decrease in the natural frequency?   (b) How much must the diameter d of the shaft be decreased to cause a 20 per cent decrease in the natural frequency?   *Ans. (a) 33.8 in.; (b) 0.42 in.*

149. Free vibration of beam supporting a relatively large mass. In Fig. 387, a simple beam of constant cross section supports a body at the center of the span. The weight W of the body M is large

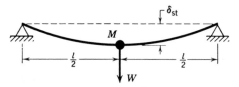

Fig. 387. Free vibration of simple beam carrying a concentrated mass at midpoint.

relative to the weight of the beam. Let it be required to determine the frequency of the natural or free vibration of the beam and body M.

According to Art. 67, the static elastic deflection of the center of the beam is $\delta_{st} = \dfrac{1}{48}\dfrac{Wl^3}{EI}$, and the frequency as found from Eq. 291 is

$$f = \frac{1}{2\pi}\sqrt{\frac{g}{\delta_{st}}} = \frac{1}{2\pi}\sqrt{\frac{48EIg}{Wl^3}} \tag{301}$$

in which EI frequently is called the stiffness factor for the beam. The correct expression including the mass of the beam is

$$f = \frac{1}{2\pi}\sqrt{\frac{48EIg}{(W + \frac{17}{35}wl)l^3}} \tag{302}$$

in which w is the weight per unit length of the beam. In obtaining Eq. 302 it is assumed that the elastic curve of the beam in the vibrational motion is the same as that of a beam subjected to a static concentrated load at the center of the span.

If, then, the weight of the beam is *not* negligible compared to W, only a small error will be introduced in obtaining the frequency of free vibration by neglecting the weight of the beam and assuming that one half of the weight of the beam is added to the weight W of the body M.

Equations 301 and 302 show that the natural frequency of the beam and body M (Fig. 387) can be made to vary by changing I or l for a beam of a given material or by using a material with a different modulus of elasticity.

Problems

411. Show that the period of free vibration of a cantilever beam which supports a body of weight W at the free end of the beam is

$$T = 2\pi \sqrt{\frac{Wl^3}{3EIg}}$$

if the weight of the beam is negligible compared to W. If the weight of the beam is *not* negligible, it can be shown that only a small error will be introduced in obtaining the period of vibration by neglecting the weight of the beam and assuming that one fourth of the weight of the beam is added to W. If the weight of the beam is $\frac{1}{2}W$, what error (in per cent) is introduced by neglecting the weight of the beam?   *Ans.*   Per cent error = 5.7.

412. In Fig. 387 let $l = 6$ ft and $W = 400$ lb. Assume that the beam is a cylindrical steel bar, the diameter d of which is such as to give a maximum static bending stress of 10,000 lb per sq in. Assume for steel that $E = 30 \times 10^6$ lb per sq in. and the weight per cubic inch is 0.28 lb. If the beam is subjected to a forced vibration having a frequency of 7.8 cycles per second, will the beam (and body M) probably develop resonance?   *Ans.*   Yes, $f = 7.84$ cycles per second.

413. If in Prob. 412 the diameter of the beam is increased 10 per cent, how much would the frequency of free vibration be increased?

150. Vibration reduction.

The engineering problem relating to vibration is frequently that of reducing a forced vibration, particularly of rotating bodies. There are several methods of reducing vibrations, based on the principles discussed in the preceding articles, the more important being:

1. Balancing to remove or reduce the exciting force.
2. Tuning to avoid resonance.
3. Damping, usually by introducing frictional forces.
4. Isolation, by introducing elastic supports.

Balancing. There are several widely used machines for determining the dynamic unbalance of rotating parts and the masses that must be added to produce balance, and hence to remove (or greatly reduce) the exciting force.

Tuning. In order that large amplitudes of vibration may be avoided, machines frequently are designed so that they do not operate at or near the critical speed, the critical speed of a rotating body being identical with its natural frequency of free vibration. This condition is called tuning. If the operating speed of a member is at or near the critical or resonant speed, even for a supposedly balanced member, a slight exciting force caused by deviations from assumed conditions may build up large amplitudes of motion. If a member is found to be operating near the resonant speed, it may be detuned (1) by changing the frequency of the exciting forces through (*a*) a change in the speed of rotation, or (*b*) a change in the number of forced impulses per revolution of the member, as, for example, a change in the number of jets in a turbine; or (2) by changing the natural frequency of the member by adjusting the relative stiffness and masses of the moving parts.

Damping. If the operating speeds of an apparatus or machine that is subjected to forced vibrations involve a wide range of speeds including the resonant speed, damping (caused by introducing frictional forces) frequently is useful in reducing the amplitudes that would occur near the resonant speed. Damping has only a small effect on amplitudes except near the resonant speed.

An automobile that must operate over a wide range of speeds and conditions of road is equipped with shock absorbers as friction dampers which limit the amplitude of resonant vibrations of the body of the car (spring weight) induced by road irregularities.

Isolation. When the exciting forces in a forced vibration of a body cannot be eliminated, it is necessary to resort to some method of isolating the vibration so that the periodic force reaction of the foundations or supporting frame is reduced. The usual method of isolation is to use some form of elastic suspension of the vibrating body. For example, if an automobile engine is mounted on springs of relatively low modulus, so that the operating speed of the engine is very much above the speed of natural vibration of the assembly of the engine and springs, damping is not needed since resonance does not occur. This method of avoiding resonance is called isolation of the vibration.

Appendix I

PROPERTIES OF AN AREA

151. Introduction. Various properties of an area are needed in the discussions of many of the topics considered in the foregoing chapters. It is assumed that the reader is familiar with some of the properties of areas needed, but, for convenience, the main properties of an area are treated briefly in this appendix. These properties are (1) first moment and centroid, (2) moment of inertia (or second moment) and radius of gyration, (3) product of inertia, and (4) principal axes and principal moments of inertia.

§ 1   First Moments and Centroids of Areas

152. Definitions. The moment of an area with respect to an axis is the algebraic sum of the moments of the elementary or differential parts of the area, the moment of each part being the product of the differential area and the perpendicular distance from the differential area to the axis. This moment is called the *first moment* to distinguish it from the moment of inertia (or second moment, see next section) of the area. The first moment of an area is sometimes also called the *statical moment* of the area.

Thus, if Q denotes the moment of an area a (Fig. 388), the foregoing

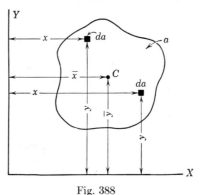

Fig. 388

definition may be expressed mathematically as follows:

$$Q_x = \int y \, da \quad \text{and} \quad Q_y = \int x \, da \tag{303}$$

Dimension and Sign. The dimension of a moment of an area is L^3 in which L denotes length. Therefore, if the inch (or foot) is chosen as the unit of length, Q may be expressed as inches cubed (or feet cubed). The sign of a moment of an area may be either positive or negative, and the value of the moment may be equal to zero.

Problems

By use of Eq. 303, determine the first moments of the areas specified below with respect to the axes specified:

414. A rectangular area of base b and altitude h with respect to an axis coincident with the base.

415. A right-triangular area of base b and altitude h with respect to an axis coincident with the base. *Ans.* $\frac{1}{6}bh^2$.

416. A semicircular area of radius r with respect to the diameter. *Ans.* $\frac{2}{3}r^3$.

153. Centroids found by integration. The *centroid* of an area is a point whose distance (called a centroidal distance) from any axis times the total area is equal to the moment of the area with respect to that axis. Hence, the coordinates $\bar{x}$ and $\bar{y}$ of the centroid C of an area a (Fig. 388) may be found from the equations

$$a\bar{x} = \int x \, da \quad \text{and} \quad a\bar{y} = \int y \, da \tag{304}$$

Expressed in another way, the centroid of an area is that point at which the whole area may be conceived to be concentrated and have the same moment with respect to any axis as has the actual (distributed) area.

If an area is symmetrical with respect to an axis, the centroid of the area lies on the axis of symmetry. This statement is evident from the fact that the moments of the areas on the opposite sides of the axis are numerically equal but of opposite sign. If an area is symmetrical with respect to each of two axes, the centroid of the area is the point of intersection of the two axes of symmetry.

In determining the centroid of an area by the method of integration, from Eq. 304, it is possible to select the differential area in various ways and to express the element in terms of either Cartesian or polar coordinates. The resulting integral may be a single or a double integral, depending on the way the element is selected. The integral, of course, is a definite integral, the limits of integration depending on the boundary curve of the area. In any case the element of area must be chosen so that

1. All points of the element are the same distance from the line about which moments are taken; otherwise, the distance from the line to the element will be indefinite, or

2. The centroid of the element is known, in which case the moment of the element about the moment axis is the product of the element and the distance of its centroid from the axis or plane.

The centroids of some of the common areas will be found in the following illustrative problems:

Illustrative Problems

Find, by the method of integration, the centroids of the following areas with respect to the axes indicated:

Problem 417. *Area of a Triangle.* In accordance with the first of the preceding rules, the elements of area will be taken as strips parallel to the base of the triangle (Fig. 389); the triangle is chosen as a right-angle triangle for convenience only. Since each element is bisected by the median drawn from the vertex opposite the base, the centroid of each element, and hence of the area, lies on this median. If x denotes the width of the strip, the area of the strip is $da = x\,dy$. Thus,

$$a\bar{y} = \int xy\,dy$$

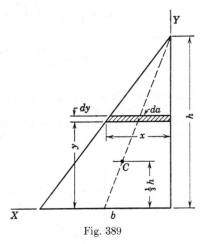

Fig. 389

From similar triangles, the relation between x and y is

$$\frac{x}{h - y} = \frac{b}{h} \quad \text{or} \quad x = \frac{b}{h}(h - y)$$

Hence,

$$a\bar{y} = \frac{b}{h}\int_0^h (h - y)y\,dy = \frac{1}{6}bh^2$$

Therefore,

$$\bar{y} = \frac{\frac{1}{6}bh^2}{\frac{1}{2}bh} = \frac{1}{3}h$$

The centroid of a triangular area, then, is on the median line at a distance perpendicular to the base of one third of the altitude from the base.

Problem 418. *Sector of a Circle. First Method.* The element of area will be selected in accordance with the first of the preceding rules, as indicated in Fig.

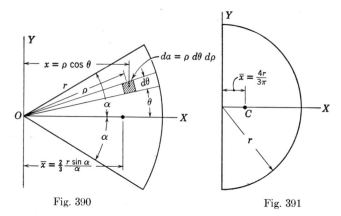

Fig. 390   Fig. 391

390. Since the area is symmetrical with respect to the x axis, the centroid lies on this axis, and hence $\bar{y} = 0$. The value of $\bar{x}$ then may be found from the equation

$$a\bar{x} = \int x \, da = \int_0^r \int_{-\alpha}^{+\alpha} \rho \cos\theta \, \rho \, d\rho \, d\theta = \frac{2}{3} r^3 \sin\alpha$$

Therefore,

$$\bar{x} = \frac{\frac{2}{3} r^3 \sin\alpha}{a} = \frac{\frac{2}{3} r^3 \sin\alpha}{r^2 \alpha} = \frac{2}{3} \frac{r \sin\alpha}{\alpha}$$

If $\alpha = 90° = \pi/2$ radians, that is, if the sector is a semicircular area, $\bar{x} = 4r/3\pi$, as indicated in Fig. 391.

Second Method. In accordance with the second of the preceding rules, the element of area will be selected as a triangle, as indicated in Fig. 392. The area of

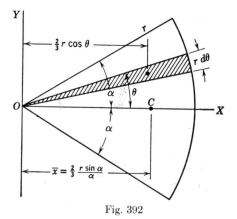

Fig. 392

the (cross hatched) triangle is $\frac{1}{2} r^2 \, d\theta$, and the distance of its centroid from the y axis is $\frac{2}{3} r \cos\theta$. Hence, the moment of the triangular area with respect to the y

axis is $\frac{1}{3}r^3 \cos\theta \, d\theta$, and $\bar{x}$ is obtained from the equation

$$a\bar{x} = \int_{-\alpha}^{+\alpha} \frac{1}{3} r^3 \cos\theta \, d\theta = \frac{2}{3} r^3 \sin\alpha$$

Therefore,

$$\bar{x} = \frac{\frac{2}{3} r^3 \sin\alpha}{r^2 \alpha} = \frac{2}{3} \frac{r \sin\alpha}{\alpha}$$

Problem 419. *Parabolic Segment.* Let the segment be bounded by the x axis, the line $x = b$, and the parabola $y = hx^2/b^2$, as shown in Fig. 393. A strip par-

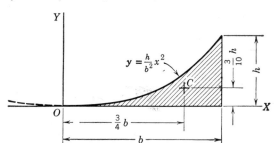

Fig. 393

allel to the y axis will be selected as the element of area, the area of the strip being expressed by $y \, dx$. The area of the segment, then, is

$$a = \int da = \int_0^b y \, dx = \frac{h}{b^2} \int_0^b x^2 \, dx = \frac{h}{b^2} \left[\frac{1}{3} x^3 \right]_0^b = \frac{1}{3} bh$$

To find $\bar{x}$,

$$a\bar{x} = \int x \, da = \int_0^b xy \, dx = \frac{h}{b^2} \int_0^b x^3 \, dx = \frac{1}{4} hb^2$$

Therefore,

$$\bar{x} = \frac{\frac{1}{4}hb^2}{a} = \frac{\frac{1}{4}hb^2}{\frac{1}{3}bh} = \frac{3}{4} b$$

To find $\bar{y}$, the same elementary strip will be selected, but, since each point of the element is not the same distance from the x axis, its moment must be expressed as the product of the area of the strip and its centroidal distance $y/2$ from the x axis. Thus,

$$a\bar{y} = \int_0^b \frac{1}{2} y \cdot y \, dx = \frac{1}{2} \frac{h^2}{b^4} \int_0^b x^4 \, dx = \frac{1}{10} h^2 b$$

$$\bar{y} = \frac{\frac{1}{10}h^2b}{a} = \frac{\frac{1}{10}h^2b}{\frac{1}{3}bh} = \frac{3}{10} h$$

Problems

420. Show that the coordinates of the centroid C of the shaded **area in Fig. 394** are as given in the figure.

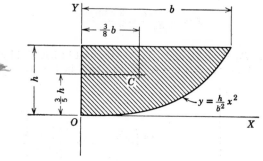

Fig. 394

421. In Fig. 395, the curves from O through A are represented by the equation $y = (h/b^n)x^n$. Show that, for any value of n, the coordinates of the centroid of

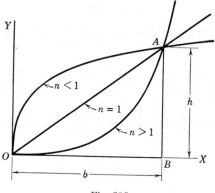

Fig. 395

the area contained between OB, AB and the appropriate curve OA for the given value of n are $\bar{x} = \dfrac{n+1}{n+2}\, b$ and $\bar{y} = \dfrac{1}{2}\dfrac{n+1}{2n+1}\, h$.

154. Centroids of composite areas.

As noted in Art. 152, if the centroid of an area is known, the moment with respect to an axis is found most easily by multiplying the area by the distance of the centroid from the axis. Thus, if a given area can be divided into parts, the centroids of which are known, the moment of the whole area may be found, without integrating, by obtaining the algebraic sum of the moments of the parts into which the area is divided, the moment of each part being the product of that part and the distance of its centroid from the line. Thus, for example, if a'_1, a'_2, a'_3, etc., denote the parts into which an area a is divided, and x'_0, x''_0, x'''_0, etc., denote the x coordinates of the centroids of the respective parts, then

$$(a'_1 + a'_2 + a'_3 + \cdots)\bar{x} = a'_1 x'_0 + a'_2 x''_0 + a'_3 x'''_0 \qquad (305)$$

or

$$a\bar{x} = \Sigma(a'x_0)$$

Similarly,

$$a\bar{y} = \Sigma(a'y_0)$$

Illustrative Problem

Problem 422. Locate the centroid of the T section shown in Fig. 396.

Solution. If axes be selected as indicated, it is evident from symmetry that $\bar{x}$ = 0. By dividing the given area into areas a'_1 and a'_2, and by taking moments

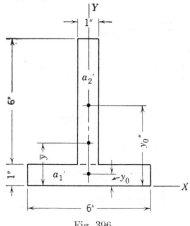

Fig. 396

about the bottom edge of the area, $\bar{y}$ may be found as follows:

$$a\bar{y} = \Sigma(a'y_0), \qquad \bar{y} = \frac{6 \times \frac{1}{2} + 6 \times 4}{6 + 6} = 2.25 \text{ in.}$$

Problems

423. Locate the centroid of the angle section shown in Fig. 411.

424. Locate the centroid of the area shown in Fig. 397; this is a so-called thin-

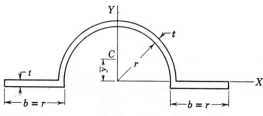

Fig. 397

walled section similar to those employed in airplane construction in which t is small compared to r.

Ans. $\bar{y} = \dfrac{2(r^2 + rt + t^2/3) - tr}{(r + t/2)\,\pi + 2r}$, or, if t is small and is neglected $\bar{y} = \dfrac{2r}{2 + \pi}$.

425. Find the coordinates of the centroid C in Fig. 398.

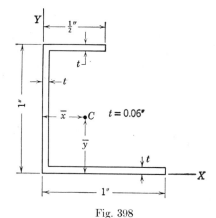

Fig. 398

426. From a square area 6 in. on a side, an isosceles triangle is cut out whose base coincides with one side of the square. If the centroid of the remaining area is at the vertex of the triangle, what is the altitude of the triangle?

Ans. $h = 3.8$ in.

427. A triangular corner whose area is 25 sq in. is cut from a square 10 in. on a side. What are the dimensions of the triangle if the centroid of the remaining area is 4 in. from one side of the square?   *Ans.* $8\frac{1}{3}$ in. by 6 in.

§ 2   Second Moment or Moment of Inertia of an Area

155. Moment of inertia of an area defined. In the analysis of many engineering problems as, for example, in determining the stresses in a beam or a shaft, expressions of the form $\int x^2\, da$ frequently are met, in which da represents an element of an area a, and x is the distance of the element from some axis in, or perpendicular to, the plane of the area, the limits of integration being such that each element of the area is included in the integration. An expression of this form is called the *second moment* of the area or the *moment of inertia* of the area with respect to the given axis.

The moment of inertia of an area with respect to an axis in, or perpendicular to, the plane of the area, then, may be defined as the sum of the products obtained by multiplying each element of the area by the square of its distance from the given axis.

The term moment of inertia is somewhat misleading, since inertia is a property of physical bodies only, and hence an area does not possess inertia. For this reason the term, second moment of an area, is to be preferred, particularly when the expressions of the form here discussed are being contrasted with expressions that were defined as first moments of areas in the preceding section. It may be noted that each term $x^2\, da$ in the summation can be written in the form $x(x\, da)$ and hence represents the moment of the moment of an element of area, that is, the second moment of the element. The term moment of inertia, however, is very widely used, primarily because the expression is of the same form as an expression that is defined as the moment of inertia of a body.

The moment of inertia of an area with respect to an axis will be denoted by I for an axis in the plane of the area and by J for an axis perpendicular to the plane of the area. The particular axis (or direction of the axis) about which the moment of inertia is taken will be denoted by subscripts. Thus, the mo-

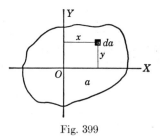

Fig. 399

ments of inertia of the area (Fig. 399) with respect to the x and y axes are expressed as follows:

$$I_x = \int y^2\, da \quad \text{and} \quad I_y = \int x^2\, da \tag{306}$$

Dimension and Sign. Since the moment of inertia of an area is the sum of a number of terms, each of which is the product of an area and the square of a distance, the moment of inertia of an area is expressed as a length to the fourth power (L^4). If, then, the inch (or foot) be taken as the unit of length, the moment of inertia will be expressed as inches (or feet) to the fourth power (written in.^{4} or ft^4). Furthermore, the sign of each of the products $x^2\,da$ is always positive, since x^2 is always positive, whether x is positive or negative, and da is essentially positive. Therefore the moment of inertia, or second moment, of an area can never be equal to zero and is always positive. In this respect it differs from the first moment of an area, which may be positive, negative, or zero, depending on the position of the moment axis.

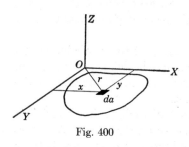

Fig. 400

156. Polar moment of inertia. The moment of inertia of an area with respect to a line perpendicular to the plane of the area is called the *polar moment of inertia* of the area and, as noted in Art. 155, will be denoted by J. Thus the polar moment of inertia, with respect to the z axis, of an area in the xy plane (Fig. 400) may be expressed as follows:

$$J_z = \int r^2\,da$$

$$= \int (x^2 + y^2)\,da$$

$$= \int x^2\,da + \int y^2\,da$$

Therefore,

$$J_z = I_y + I_x \tag{307}$$

Hence, the following proposition may be stated:

The polar moment of inertia of an area with respect to any axis is equal to the sum of the moments of inertia of the area with respect to any two rectangular axes in the plane of the area that intersect on the given polar axis.

157. Radius of gyration. Since the moment of inertia of an area is four dimensions of length, it may be expressed as the product of the total area a and the square of a distance k. Thus,

$$I_x = \int y^2 \, da = ak_x{}^2, \qquad J_z = \int r^2 \, da = ak_z{}^2 \qquad (308)$$

The distance k is called the *radius of gyration* of the area with respect to the given axis, the subscript denoting the axis with respect to which the moment of inertia is taken. The radius of gyration of an area with respect to a line, then, may be defined as a distance such that, if the area were conceived to be concentrated at this distance from the given line, the moment of inertia would be the same as the moment of inertia of the actual or distributed area with respect to the same line.

From the equation $I_y = \int x^2 \, da = ak_y{}^2$, it may be noted that $k_y{}^2$, the square of the radius of gyration with respect to the y axis, is the mean of the squares of the distances, from the y axis, of the equal elements of area into which the given area may be divided, and that it is *not* the square of the mean of these distances. The mean distance $\bar{x}$ of the elements of area from the y axis is the centroidal distance as discussed in the preceding chapter. Hence $a\bar{x}^2$ does *not* represent the moment of inertia of an area with respect to the y axis.

158. Parallel-axis theorem. If the moment of inertia of an area with respect to a centroidal axis in the plane of the area is known, the moment of inertia with respect to any parallel axis in the plane may be determined, without integrating, by means of a proposition which may be established as follows: In Fig. 401, let YY be any axis through the centroid C of an area, and let $Y'Y'$ be any axis parallel to YY and at a distance d therefrom. Further, let the moment of inertia of the area with respect to the axis YY be denoted by $\bar{I}$ and the moment of inertia with respect to $Y'Y'$ by I'. By definition, then,

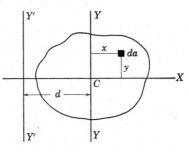

Fig. 401

$$I' = \int (x + d)^2 \, da = \int x^2 \, da + 2d \int x \, da + d^2 \int da$$

and since $\int x \, da = a\bar{x} = 0$, we find

$$I' = \bar{I} + ad^2 \qquad (309)$$

Hence, the following proposition may be stated:

> The moment of inertia of an area with respect to any axis in the plane of the area is equal to the moment of inertia of the area with respect to a parallel centroidal axis, plus the product of the area and the square of the distance between the two axes. This proposition is called the parallel-axis theorem.

A corresponding relation exists between the radii of gyration of the area with respect to two parallel axes, one of which passes through the centroid of the area. For, by replacing I' by ak^2 and $\bar{I}$ by $a\bar{k}^2$, the preceding equation becomes

$$ak^2 = a\bar{k}^2 + ad^2$$

Hence,

$$k^2 = \bar{k}^2 + d^2 \tag{310}$$

where k denotes the radius of gyration of the area with respect to any axis in the plane of the area, and $\bar{k}$ denotes the radius of gyration of the area with respect to a parallel centroidal axis.

Similarly, for polar moments of inertia and radii of gyration it can be shown that

$$J = \bar{J} + ad^2 \quad \text{and} \quad k^2 = \bar{k}^2 + d^2 \tag{311}$$

where $\bar{J}$ and $\bar{k}$ denote the polar moment of inertia and radius of gyration, respectively, of the area with respect to the polar centroidal axis, and J and k denote the polar moment of inertia and radius of gyration, respectively, of the area with respect to an axis parallel to the centroidal axis and at a distance d therefrom.

159. Moments of inertia found by integration. In determining the moment of inertia of a plane area with respect to a line, it is possible to select the element of area in various ways and to express the area of the element in terms of either Cartesian or polar coordinates. Furthermore the integral may be either a single or double integral, depending on the way in which the element of area is selected; the limits of integration are determined, of course, from the boundary curve of the area. In any case, however, the elementary area must be taken so that

1. All points in the element are equally distant from the axis with respect to which the moment of inertia is to be found; otherwise the distance x in the expression $x^2\,da$ would be indefinite. Or, so that

2. The moment of inertia of the element, with respect to the axis about which the moment of inertia of the whole area is to be found, is

known, the moment of inertia of the area then being found by summing up the moments of inertia of the elements. Or, so that

3. The centroid of the element is known and also the moment of inertia of the element with respect to an axis which passes through the centroid of the element and is parallel to the given axis; the moment of inertia of the element then may be expressed by means of the parallel-axis theorem.

The moments of inertia of some of the simple areas are found in the following illustrative problems.

Illustrative Problems

Problem 428.   Determine the moment of inertia of a rectangular area, in terms of its base b and altitude h, with respect to (a) a centroidal axis parallel to the base, (b) an axis coinciding with the base.

Solution.   (a) *Centroidal Axis.*   The element of area will be selected in accordance with rule 1, previously stated, as indicated in Fig. 402. The moment of in-

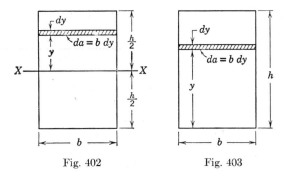

Fig. 402   Fig. 403

ertia of the rectangular area with respect to the centroidal axis, then, is

$$I_x = \int y^2 \, da = \int_{-h/2}^{+h/2} y^2 b \, dy = \frac{1}{12} b h^3$$

(b) *Axis Coinciding with the Base.*   *First Method.*   The element of area will be selected as indicated in Fig. 403. The moment of inertia of the rectangle with respect to the base, then, is

$$I_b = \int y^2 \, da = \int_0^h y^2 b \, dy = \frac{1}{3} b h^3$$

Second Method.   Since the moment of inertia of the rectangle with respect to a centroidal axis is $\frac{1}{12} b h^3$, the moment of inertia with respect to the base may be found from the parallel-axis theorem (Art. 158). Thus,

$$I_b = I_x + a \left(\frac{h}{2}\right)^2 = \frac{1}{12} b h^3 + b h \times \frac{h^2}{4} = \frac{1}{3} b h^3$$

Problem 429. Determine the moment of inertia of a triangular area, in terms of its base b and altitude h, with respect to (a) an axis coinciding with its base, (b) a centroidal axis parallel to the base.

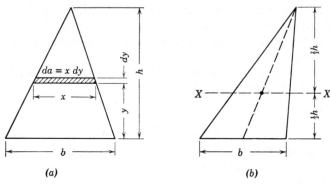

(a)   (b)

Fig. 404

Solution. (a) *Axis Coinciding with the Base.* The elementary area is selected as shown in Fig. 404a. The moment of inertia of the area of the triangle with respect to the base, then, is

$$I_b = \int y^2 \, da = \int y^2 x \, dy$$

But, from similar triangles,

$$\frac{x}{b} = \frac{h-y}{h} \quad \text{or} \quad x = \frac{b}{h}(h-y)$$

Therefore,

$$I_b = \frac{b}{h} \int_0^h y^2(h-y) \, dy = \frac{1}{12} bh^3$$

(b) *Centroidal Axis Parallel to the Base.* The centroidal axis parallel to the base (axis XX) is shown in Fig. 404b (see Prob. 417). If the parallel-axis theorem is used, the moment of inertia of the triangular area with respect to the centroidal axis is

$$\bar{I}_x = I_b - a(\tfrac{1}{3}h)^2 = \tfrac{1}{12}bh^3 - \tfrac{1}{2}bh \times \tfrac{1}{9}h^2 = \tfrac{1}{36}bh^3$$

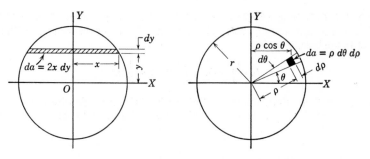

Fig. 405   Fig. 406

Problem 430. Determine the moment of inertia of the area of a circle, in terms of its radius r, with respect to an axis coinciding with the diameter, using (a) Cartesian coordinates; (b) polar coordinates.

Solution. (a) *Cartesian Coordinates.* The element of area is selected as shown in Fig. 405. The moment of inertia of the circular area with respect to the diameter, then, is

$$I_x = \int y^2 \, da = \int y^2 2x \, dy = 2 \int_{-r}^{+r} y^2 \sqrt{r^2 - y^2} \, dy = \frac{1}{4}\pi r^4 = \frac{1}{64}\pi d^4$$

(b) *Polar Coordinates.* The element of area is selected as shown in Fig. 406. Hence,

$$I_x = \int y^2 \, da = \int_0^r \int_0^{2\pi} \rho^3 \sin^2 \theta \, d\rho \, d\theta$$

$$= \frac{r^4}{4} \int_0^{2\pi} \sin^2 \theta \, d\theta = \frac{r^4}{4} \times \pi = \frac{1}{4}\pi r^4 = \frac{1}{64}\pi d^4$$

Problem 431. Determine the polar moment of inertia of the area of a circle of radius r with respect to a centroidal axis, by (a) integration, (b) the use of the theorem of Art. 156.

Solution. (a) *By Integration.* If the element of area as indicated in Fig. 407 is selected, the polar moment of inertia of the circular area is

$$J_z = \int \rho^2 \, da = \int_0^r \rho^2 2\pi\rho \, d\rho = \frac{1}{2}\pi r^4 = \frac{1}{32}\pi d^4$$

(b) *By Use of Theorem of Art. 156.* Since I_x and I_y are each equal to $\frac{1}{4}\pi r^4$ (Prob. 430), the polar moment of inertia of the area of the circle is

$$J_z = I_x + I_y = \tfrac{1}{4}\pi r^4 + \tfrac{1}{4}\pi r^4 = \tfrac{1}{2}\pi r^4$$

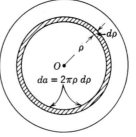

Fig. 407

Note that, for a hollow circular area a for which r_2 is the outer radius and r_1 is the inner radius, we have

$$J_z = \tfrac{1}{2}\pi r_2^4 - \tfrac{1}{2}\pi r_1^4 = \tfrac{1}{2}\pi(r_2^2 - r_1^2)(r_2^2 + r_1^2) = \tfrac{1}{2}a(r_2^2 + r_1^2)$$

Problems

432. By use of Eq. 306, determine the moment of inertia of a semicircular area with respect to the base of the semicircle, in terms of r, the radius of the semicircle.

433. Determine the moment of inertia of the area of a circle, with respect to an axis tangent to the circle, in terms of r, the radius of the circle. Make use of the results obtained in Prob. 430 and the parallel-axis theorem.

434. Determine, by use of Eq. 307, the polar moment of inertia of the area of a rectangle of base b and altitude h with respect to the centroidal axis.

Ans. $J = \tfrac{1}{12}bh(b^2 + h^2)$.

435. Find the moment of inertia and radius of gyration of a circular area 16 in. in diameter, with respect to a diameter.

436. Determine, by use of Eq. 306, the moments of inertia of the area of an ellipse, the principal axes of which are $2b$ and $2h$, with respect to the principal axes. The equation of the ellipse is $x^2/b^2 + y^2/h^2 = 1$.   *Ans.* $I_b = \tfrac{1}{4}\pi bh^3$; $I_h = \tfrac{1}{4}\pi hb^3$.

437. The base of a triangle is 8 in., and its altitude is 10 in. Find the moment of inertia and radius of gyration of the area of the triangle with respect to the base.

438. Find the polar moment of inertia and radius of gyration of the area of a square, each side of which is 15 in., with respect to an axis through one corner of the square. *Ans.* $k = 12.3$ in.

439. Find the polar moment of inertia, with respect to a centroidal axis, of the area of an isosceles triangle having a base b and altitude h.

$$Ans. \quad J = \tfrac{1}{12}bh(\tfrac{1}{4}b^2 + \tfrac{1}{3}h^2).$$

160. Moments of inertia of composite areas.

When a composite area can be divided into a number of simple areas, such as triangles, rectangles, and circles, for which the moments of inertia are known, the moment of inertia of the entire area may be obtained as the sum of the moments of inertia of the several areas. Likewise, the moment of inertia of the part of an area that remains after one or more simple areas are removed may be found by subtracting, from the moment of inertia of the given area, the sum of the moments of inertia of the several parts removed.

Illustrative Problems

Problem 440. Locate the horizontal centroidal axis XX of the T section shown in Fig. 408, and find the moment of inertia of the area with respect to this centroidal axis.

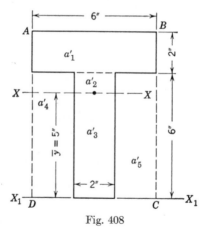

Fig. 408

Solution. First Method. The distance $\bar{y}$ of the centroid of the area from the axis X_1X_1 may be found from the equation

$$a\bar{y} = \Sigma(a'y_0)$$

Thus,

$$\bar{y} = \frac{12 \times 7 + 12 \times 3}{12 + 12} = 5 \text{ in.}$$

The moment of inertia with respect to the XX axis is the sum of the moments of inertia of the three parts, a'_1, a'_2, and a'_3, with respect to that axis; thus,

$$I_x = \tfrac{1}{12} \times 6 \times (2)^3 + 12 \times (2)^2 + \tfrac{1}{3} \times 2 \times (1)^3 + \tfrac{1}{3} \times 2 \times (5)^3$$

$$= 4 + 48 + 0.67 + 83.33 = 136 \text{ in.}^4$$

Second Method. The moment of inertia of the T section also may be determined as follows: First find the moment of inertia of the T section with respect to the axis X_1X_1 by subtracting the moments of inertia of the parts a'_4 and a'_5 from the moment of inertia of the rectangular area $ABCD$, and then find $\bar{I}_x$ for the T section by use of the parallel-axis theorem. Thus, the moment of inertia I_x of the T section with respect to the X_1X_1 axis is

$$I_x = \tfrac{1}{3} \times 6 \times (8)^3 - 2 \times \tfrac{1}{3} \times 2 \times (6)^3 = 736 \text{ in.}^4;$$

and

$$\bar{I}_x = I_x - ad^2 = 736 - 24 \times (5)^2 = 136 \text{ in.}^4$$

Problem 441. Find the moment of inertia of the channel section shown in Fig. 409 with respect to the line XX. Find also the moment of inertia with respect to the parallel centroidal axis.

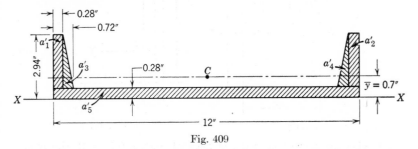

Fig. 409

Solution. The area may be divided into triangles and rectangles as shown in Fig. 409. The values used in the solution may be put in tabular form, as shown in the following, where a' denotes the area of any part, y_0 the distance of the centroid of the part from the line XX, I_0 the moment of inertia of the part with respect to its own centroidal axis parallel to XX, and I'_x the moment of inertia of the part with respect to the axis XX.

Part	a'	y_0	$a'y_0$	I_0	$a'y_0^2$	$I'_x = I_0 + ay_0^2$
a'_1	0.745	1.61	1.20	0.44	1.93	2.37
a'_2	0.745	1.61	1.20	0.44	1.93	2.37
a'_3	0.585	1.17	0.68	0.23	0.80	1.03
a'_4	0.585	1.17	0.68	0.23	0.80	1.03
a'_5	3.360	0.14	0.47	0.02	0.07	0.09
	6.02 in.^{2}		4.23 in.^{3}			6.89 in.^{4}

Thus the moment of inertia I_x of the area with respect to the XX axis is

$$I_x = \Sigma I'_x = 6.89 \text{ in.}^4$$

Further, the total area is $a = \Sigma a' = 6.02$ in.^{2}, and the moment of the area with respect to the XX axis is $\Sigma(a'y_0) = 4.23$ in.^{3} Hence, the distance $\bar{y}$ of the centroid of the area from the XX axis is

$$\bar{y} = \frac{\Sigma(a'y_0)}{a} = \frac{4.23}{6.02} = 0.70 \text{ in.}$$

Therefore, the moment of inertia with respect to a line through the centroid and parallel to XX is given by the equation:

$$\bar{I}_x = I_x - ad^2 = 6.89 - 6.02 \times (0.70)^2 = 3.94 \text{ in.}^4$$

Problems

442. A wooden column is built up of two 2-in.-by-8-in. and two 2-in.-by-10-in. planks as shown in Fig. 410. Find the moment of inertia of the cross section with respect to the centroidal axis XX.   *Ans.* $I_x = 1496$ in.^{4}

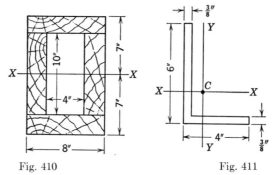

Fig. 410   Fig. 411

443. Find the moment of inertia of the angle section (Fig. 411) with respect to each of the centroidal axes parallel to the two legs of the angle.

444. In Fig. 412 is shown the cross section of a column made of a 10-in. 35-lb steel I section to which two steel plates, each $\frac{5}{8}$ in. by 11 in., are attached by rivets (not shown). Calculate the moments of inertia of the whole area about the X and Y axes. A steelmaker's handbook gives the following values for the I section alone: area $a_2 = 10.29$ in.^{2}, $I_x = 146.4$ in.^{4}, $I_y = 8.5$ in.^{4} Total area $= a = a_1 + a_2 = 13.74 + 10.29 = 24.03$ in.^{2} Also calculate the radius of gyration with respect to each axis.   *Ans.* $I_x = 536$ in.^{4}; $I_y = 147.1$ in.^{4}

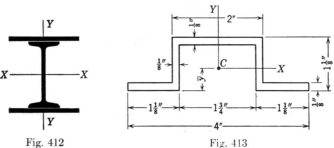

Fig. 412   Fig. 413

445. The cross section of a member used in airplane construction is shown in Fig. 413. Calculate the moment of inertia of the area with respect to the X axis passing through the centroid C.   *Ans.* $\bar{y} = 0.54$ in.; $\bar{I}_x = 0.15$ in.[4]

446. The cross section of a member used in airplane construction is shown in Fig. 414a. The member is built up of a thin metal sheet of thickness $t = 0.02$ in. bent into a semicircular shape. Stiffening flanges consisting of 1-in.-by-1-in.-by-

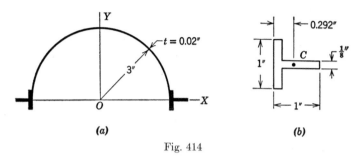

(a)   **(b)**

Fig. 414

$\frac{1}{8}$-in. aluminum T sections are riveted or welded to the shape. Calculate the moment of inertia of the whole area about the axis OY. An aluminum maker's handbook gives the following values for the T section alone (Fig. 414b): area = 0.267 in.[2], centroidal distance = 0.292 in., $\bar{I}_v = 0.023$ in.[4]

447. In Fig. 415 is shown the cross section of a standard $3\frac{1}{4}$-in.-by-5-in. Z bar (fillets are neglected). Find the moments of inertia of the section with respe t to the centroidal axes XX and YY.

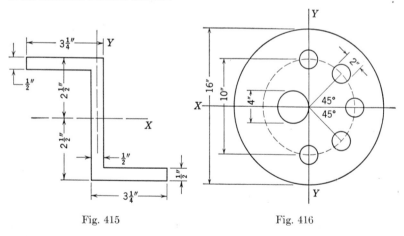

Fig. 415   Fig. 416

448. In Fig. 416 is represented a 16-in. circular plate in which there are drilled five 2-in. holes and one 4-in. hole, as shown. Find the moment of inertia of the area of the holes with respect to the XX axis and also with respect to the YY axis.
            Ans. $I_x = 252$ in.[4]

161. Approximate method. It is sometimes necessary to determine the moment of inertia of an area that has a boundary curve which cannot be defined by a mathematical equation. An approximate value of the moment of inertia of such an area may be found by the following method. For convenience, however, a simple area will be selected so that the approximate value of the moment of inertia as determined by

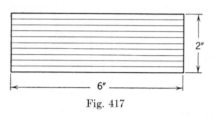

Fig. 417

this method may be compared with the exact value. Thus, let the moment of inertia of the area of a rectangle, with respect to an axis coinciding with its base, be found. The area may be divided into any convenient number of equal narrow strips

parallel to the base, as shown in Fig. 417; the narrower the strips, the more closely will the result agree with the exact result. Let the area be divided into ten such strips each 0.2 in. in width. The moment of inertia of the rectangular area is equal to the sum of the moments of inertia of the strips. The moment of inertia of any particular strip with respect to the base of the rectangle is

$$\tfrac{1}{12} \times 6 \times (\tfrac{1}{5})^3 + 6 \times \tfrac{1}{5} \times y^2$$

where y is the distance of the center of the particular strip from the base. The first term is small and may be omitted without serious error. The moment of inertia of each strip then is approximately equal to the product of the area of the strip and the square of the distance of its center from the base. Hence, the moment of inertia of the rectangle is

$$I = \tfrac{6}{5}(0.1^2 + 0.3^2 + 0.5^2 + 0.7^2 + 0.9^2 + 1.1^2 + 1.3^2$$

$$+ 1.5^2 + 1.7^2 + 1.9^2)$$

$$= \tfrac{6}{5} \times 13.3 = 15.96 \text{ in.}^4$$

According to Prob. 428, the exact value is

$$I = \tfrac{1}{3}bh^3 = \tfrac{1}{3} \times 6 \times 2^3 = 16 \text{ in.}^4$$

§ 3 Product of Inertia

162. Product of inertia defined. If the moments of inertia of an area with respect to any two rectangular axes are known, the moment of inertia with respect to any other axis passing through the point of intersection of the two axes frequently may be obtained most easily in terms of the moments of inertia of the area with respect to the two rectangular axes and an expression of the form $\int xy\,da$, in which da is an element of the given area and x and y are the coordinates of the element with respect to the two rectangular axes. This expression is called the *product of inertia* of the area with respect to the axes and is denoted by I_{xy}. Hence, the product of inertia of an area with respect to any two rectangular axes may be defined as the sum of the products obtained by multiplying each element of area by the product of the two coordinates of the element with respect to the two rectangular axes. That is,

$$I_{xy} = \int xy\,da \qquad (312)$$

The product of inertia of an area, like the moment of inertia of an area, is of four dimensions in length and, therefore, is expressed as inches (or feet, etc.) to the fourth power (in.^{4}, ft^4, etc.). Unlike the moment of inertia, however, the product of inertia of an area is not always positive, but may be negative or may be zero, since either x or y may be negative and hence their product may be negative, and the sum of the products may be equal to zero.

Axes of Symmetry. The product of inertia of an area with respect to two rectangular axes is zero if either one of the axes is an axis of symmetry. This follows from the fact that, for each product $xy\,da$ for an element on one side of the axis of symmetry, there is an equal product of opposite sign for the corresponding element on the other side of the axis, and hence the expression $\int xy\,da$ equals zero.

Illustrative Problems

Problem 449. Find the product of inertia of the area of the triangle, shown in Fig. 418, with respect to the x and y axes.

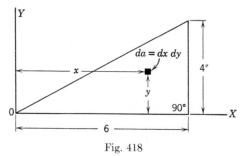

Fig. 418

Solution. The limiting value of y for any value of x is $y = \frac{2}{3}x$. Hence,

$$I_{xy} = \int xy \, da = \int_0^6 \int_0^{\frac{2}{3}x} xy \, dx \, dy$$

$$= \frac{2}{9} \int_0^6 x^3 \, dx = 72 \text{ in.}^4$$

Problem 450. Find the product of inertia of the area of the quadrant of a circular area (Fig. 419) with respect to the x and y axes, in terms of its radius r.

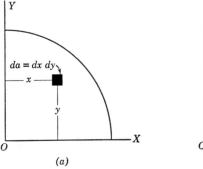

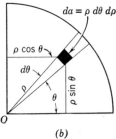

$$(a) \qquad\qquad (b)$$

Fig. 419

First Method. Let the elementary area be selected as shown in Fig. 419a and expressed in terms of rectangular coordinates; then,

$$I_{xy} = \int_0^r \int_0^{\sqrt{r^2 - x^2}} xy \, dx \, dy = \int_0^r x \left[\frac{y^2}{2} \right]_0^{\sqrt{r^2 - x^2}} dx$$

$$= \int_0^r x \cdot \frac{r^2 - x^2}{2} \, dx = \frac{1}{2} \int_0^r (r^2 x - x^3) \, dx = \frac{1}{2} \left[\frac{r^2 x}{2} - \frac{x^4}{4} \right]_0^r = \frac{1}{8} r^4$$

Second Method. Let the elementary area be selected as shown in Fig. 419b and be expressed in terms of polar coordinates; then,

$$I_{xy} = \int xy \, da = \int_0^r \int_0^{\pi/2} \rho \cos\theta \cdot \rho \sin\theta \cdot \rho \, d\rho \, d\theta$$

$$= \int_0^r \int_0^{\pi/2} \rho^3 \, d\rho \cdot \frac{1}{2} \sin 2\theta \, d\theta = \frac{1}{2} \frac{r^4}{4} \int_0^{\pi/2} \sin 2\theta \, d\theta$$

$$= \frac{r^4}{8} \left[-\cos 2\theta \cdot \frac{1}{2} \right]_0^{\theta = \pi/2} = -\frac{r^4}{16} (-2) = \frac{1}{8} r^4$$

Problems

451. Find, by use of Eq. 312, the product of inertia of the area of a rectangle having a base b and an altitude h, with respect to two adjacent sides.

Ans. $\pm \frac{1}{4} b^2 h^2$.

452. Find the product of inertia in terms of b and h of a right-angle triangle (Fig. 420) with respect to the x and y axes shown passing through the centroid C. If b and h have the values shown in Fig. 420, what is the value of I_{xy}?

Ans. $I_{xy} = -\frac{1}{72}b^2h^2$; $I_{xy} = -32$ in.[4]

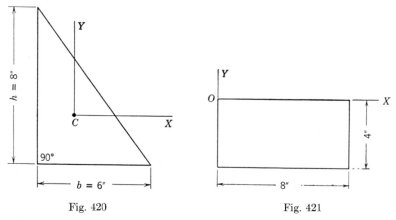

Fig. 420   Fig. 421

453. Find the product of inertia of the rectangular area with respect to the x and y axes as shown in Fig. 421.   *Ans.* $I_{xy} = -256$ in.[4]

454. Find the product of inertia, with respect to the coordinate axes, of the area bounded by the parabola $y^2 = hx$, the line $x = b$, and the x axis.   *Ans.* $\frac{1}{6}hb^3$.

163. Parallel-axis theorem for products of inertia. When the product of inertia of an area is known for any pair of rectangular axes passing through the centroid of the area, the product of inertia of the

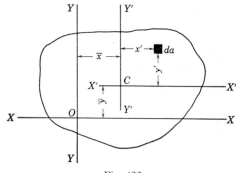

Fig. 422

area with respect to any parallel set of axes may be determined without integrating. Thus, in Fig. 422, $X'X'$ and $Y'Y'$ are axes through the centroid C of the area; XX and YY are parallel axes passing through the point O. The coordinates of C with respect to XX and YY are denoted by $\bar{x}$ and $\bar{y}$. If the product of inertia of the area with respect to XX and YY be denoted by I_{xy} and the product of inertia with respect to $X'X'$ and $Y'Y'$ be denoted by $\bar{I}_{xy}$, then, by definition,

$$I_{xy} = \int (x' + \bar{x})(y' + \bar{y}) \, da$$

$$= \int x'y' \, da + \bar{x}\bar{y} \int da + \bar{y} \int x' \, da + \bar{x} \int y' \, da$$

Since each of the last two integrals is the first moment of the area with respect to a centroidal axis, each integral is equal to zero. The equation then becomes

$$\boldsymbol{I_{xy} = \bar{I}_{xy} + a\bar{x}\bar{y}} \tag{313}$$

which is called the parallel axis theorem for products of inertia of areas.

That is, the product of inertia of any area with respect to any pair of rectangular axes in its plane is equal to the product of inertia of the area with respect to a pair of parallel centroidal axes plus the product of the area and the coordinates of the centroid of the area with respect to the given pair of axes.

Illustrative Problem

Problem 455. Find, by use of the parallel-axis theorem, the product of inertia of the area shown in Fig. 423 with respect to the x and y axes.

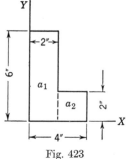

Fig. 423

Solution. The area may be divided into rectangles a_1 and a_2 as shown. Using the formula $I_{xy} = \bar{I}_{xy} + a \cdot \bar{x}\bar{y}$, we have, for the area a_1,

$$I_{xy} = 0 + 12 \times 1 \times 3 = 36 \text{ in.}^4$$

and, for area a_2,

$$I_{xy} = 0 + 4 \times 3 \times 1 = 12 \text{ in.}^4$$

Hence, for the entire area,

$$I_{xy} = 36 + 12 = 48 \text{ in.}^4$$

Problems

456. Find the product of inertia of the area $a = a_1 + a_2$, shown in Fig. 424, with respect to the x and y axes.   *Ans.* $I_{xy} = 792$ in.^{4}

457. Locate the centroid C of the angle section shown in Fig. 425, and determine the product of inertia with respect to centroidal axes parallel to the two legs of the angle.

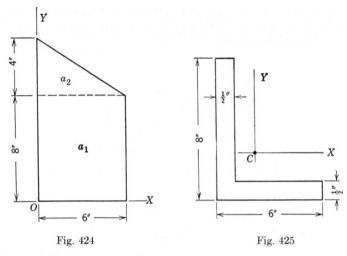

Fig. 424   Fig. 425

458. Find the product of inertia of the area shown in Fig. 426 with respect to the coordinate axes indicated.   *Ans.* $I_{xy} = 21.3$ in.^{4}

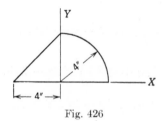

Fig. 426

459. Calculate the product of inertia of the area shown in Fig. 427 with respect to the axes indicated.

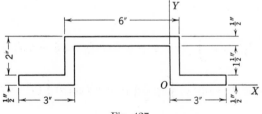

Fig. 427

164. Relation between moments of inertia and products of inertia with respect to two sets of rectangular axes through the same point in the area. Let I_x, I_y, I_{xy} denote the moments of inertia and product of inertia of the area in Fig. 428 with respect to the axes OX and OY. Let it be required to find the moments of inertia

I'_x and I'_y, and the product of inertia I'_{xy}, with respect to the axes OX' and OY' which are inclined an angle θ with the axes OX and OY.

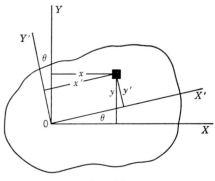

Fig. 428

The moment of inertia of the area in Fig. 428 with respect to the axis OX' is expressed by the equation

$$I'_x = \int y'^2 \, da = \int (y \cos \theta - x \sin \theta)^2 \, da$$

$$= \cos^2 \theta \int y^2 \, da + \sin^2 \theta \int x^2 \, da - 2 \sin \theta \cos \theta \int xy \, da$$

$$= I_x \cos^2 \theta + I_y \sin^2 \theta - 2I_{xy} \sin \theta \cos \theta \tag{314}$$

In a similar manner, the following equation may be derived:

$$I'_y = I_x \sin^2 \theta + I_y \cos^2 \theta + 2I_{xy} \sin \theta \cos \theta \tag{315}$$

Likewise,

$$I'_{xy} = \int x'y' \, da = \int (x \cos \theta + y \sin \theta)(y \cos \theta - x \sin \theta) \, da$$

$$= (\cos^2 \theta - \sin^2 \theta) \int xy \, da + (\cos \theta \sin \theta) \int (y^2 - x^2) \, da$$

$$= I_{xy} \cos 2\theta + \tfrac{1}{2}(I_x - I_y) \sin 2\theta \tag{316}$$

Thus, from Eqs. 314, 315, and 316, the moments of inertia and product of inertia of an area with respect to any set of rectangular axes may be found, without integrating, in terms of the moments of inertia and product of inertia with respect to a given set of rectangular axes passing through the same origin.

By adding Eqs. 314 and 315, the following important equation is found:

$$I'_x + I'_y = I_x + I_y \qquad (317)$$

That is, the sum of the moments of inertia of an area with respect to all pairs of rectangular axes having a common point of intersection is constant. It should be noted also that each side of Eq. 317 is equal to the polar moment of inertia of the area with respect to an axis intersecting the area at the common point.

Axes for Which the Product of Inertia Is Zero. It may be shown that, through any point in an area, one set of rectangular axes may be drawn for which the product of inertia is zero. Thus, in Eq. 316, if I'_{xy} is made equal to zero, we obtain the equation

$$\tan 2\theta = -\frac{I_{xy}}{\frac{1}{2}(I_x - I_y)} \qquad (318)$$

and hence, when θ (Fig. 428) has a value given by this equation, the product of inertia with respect to the OX' and OY' axes is zero; in the next article it is shown that the axes for which the product of inertia is zero are principal axes.

165. Principal axes. In the analysis of many engineering problems, the moment of inertia of an area must be found with respect to a certain axis called a principal axis. A principal axis of inertia of an area, for a given point in the area, is an axis about which the moment of inertia of the area is either greater or less than for any other axis passing through the given point. It will be proved in this article that, through any point in an area, two rectangular axes can be drawn for which the moments of inertia of the area are greater and less, respectively, than for any other axes passing through the point. There are then two principal axes of inertia of an area for any point in the area. Further, it will be shown that axes for which the product of inertia is zero are principal axes. And, since the product of inertia of an area is zero for axes of symmetry, it follows that axes of symmetry are principal axes. The foregoing statements may be demonstrated as follows:

The direction of the principal axes may be determined from Eq. 314 of Art. 164 which may be written in the form

$$I'_x = I_x \frac{1 + \cos 2\theta}{2} + I_y \frac{1 - \cos 2\theta}{2} - I_{xy} \sin 2\theta$$

$$= \frac{I_x + I_y}{2} + \frac{I_x - I_y}{2} \cos 2\theta - I_{xy} \sin 2\theta \qquad (319)$$

The value of θ that will make I'_x have a maximum or a minimum value may be found by equating to zero the first derivative of I'_x with respect to θ. Thus,

$$\frac{dI'_x}{d\theta} = \sin 2\theta(I_y - I_x) - 2I_{xy}\cos 2\theta = 0$$

$$\tan 2\theta = \frac{2I_{xy}}{I_y - I_x} \tag{320}$$

which is the same as Eq. 318. From this equation two values of 2θ are obtained which differ by 180°, the corresponding values of θ differing by 90°. For one value of θ, the value of I'_x will be a maximum, and, for the other, a minimum. If $I_{xy} = 0$ (which will always be the case if either the x or y axis is an axis of symmetry), the value of θ is zero, and hence axes of symmetry are principal axes.

Illustrative Problem

Problem 460. Find the moments of inertia of the angle section shown in Fig. 429 with respect to principal axes passing through the centroid.

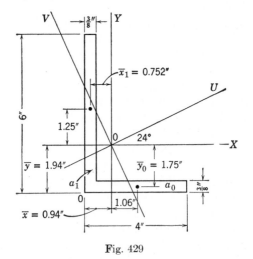

Fig. 429

Solution. The steps in the solution will be made as follows:

1. The centroid of the area will be located; that is, $\bar{x}$ and $\bar{y}$ will be found.

2. The moments of inertia and the product of inertia ($\bar{I}_x$ and $\bar{I}_y$, and $\bar{I}_{xy}$) with respect to the centroidal x and y axes then will be found by the methods discussed in Art. 160.

3. The directions of the principal axes then will be found by use of the equations of Art. 165.

4. The moment of inertia with respect to each of the principal axes, U and V, then will be found by means of Eqs. 314 and 315.

$$\bar{x} = \frac{4 \times \frac{3}{8} \times 2 + 5\frac{5}{8} \times \frac{3}{8} \times \frac{3}{16}}{4 \times \frac{3}{8} + 5\frac{5}{8} \times \frac{3}{8}} = \frac{3.396}{3.61} = 0.94 \text{ in.}$$

$$\bar{y} = \frac{4 \times \frac{3}{8} \times \frac{3}{16} + 5\frac{5}{8} \times \frac{3}{8} \times 3\frac{3}{16}}{4 \times \frac{3}{8} + 5\frac{5}{8} \times \frac{3}{8}} = \frac{7.01}{3.61} = 1.94 \text{ in.}$$

$$\bar{I}_x = \frac{1}{12} \times \frac{3}{8} \times (5\frac{5}{8})^3 + 5\frac{5}{8} \times \frac{3}{8} \times (1\frac{1}{4})^2 + \frac{1}{12} \times 4 \times (\frac{3}{8})^3 + 4 \times \frac{3}{8} \times (1\frac{3}{4})^2$$

$$= 5.57 + 3.30 + 0.02 + 4.59 = 13.48 \text{ in.}^4$$

$$\bar{I}_y = \frac{1}{12} \times 5\frac{5}{8} \times (\frac{3}{8})^3 + 5\frac{5}{8} \times \frac{3}{8} \times (\frac{3}{4})^2 + \frac{1}{12} \times \frac{3}{8} \times 4^3 + 4 \times \frac{3}{8} \times (1\frac{1}{16})^2$$

$$= 0.02 + 1.19 + 2.00 + 1.69 = 4.90 \text{ in.}^4$$

The value of $\bar{I}_{xy}$ may be found by means of Eq. 313. Thus,

$$\bar{I}_{xy} = \bar{I}_{0xy} + a_0 \bar{x}_0 \bar{y}_0 + \bar{I}_{1xy} + a_1 \bar{x}_1 \bar{y}_1$$

$$= 4 \times \frac{3}{8} \times 1.06 \times (-1.75) + 5.62 \times \frac{3}{8} \times 1.25 \times (-0.752)$$

$$= -4.76 \text{ in.}^4$$

The directions of the principal axes are found from Eq. 320. Thus,

$$\tan 2\theta = \frac{2 \times (-4.76)}{4.90 - 13.48} = 1.11$$

$$2\theta = 48° \quad \text{or} \quad 228°, \qquad \theta = 24° \quad \text{or} \quad 114°$$

From Eq. 314, the moment of inertia with respect to the axis making an angle of 24° with OX (denoted by OU) is

$$I_u = 13.48 \cos^2 24° + 4.90 \sin^2 24° - 2(-4.76) \sin 24° \cos 24°$$

$$= 11.23 + 0.81 + 3.53 = 15.59 \text{ in.}^4$$

Using $\theta = 114°$ and denoting the corresponding axis by OV, we have

$$I_v = 13.48 \cos^2 114° + 4.90 \sin^2 114° - 2(-4.76) \sin 114° \cos 114°$$

$$= 2.23 + 4.08 - 3.53 = 2.78 \text{ in.}^4$$

Problems

461. Figure 430 represents the cross section of a standard 10-in. 25-lb steel I beam. $\bar{I}_x = 122.1$ in.^{4}, $\bar{I}_y = 6.89$ in.^{4}, and $a = 7.38$ in.^{2} Find the moment of inertia and radius of gyration of the section with respect to a line through the centroid making an angle of 30° with the x axis. *Ans.* $I = 93.3$ in.^{4}

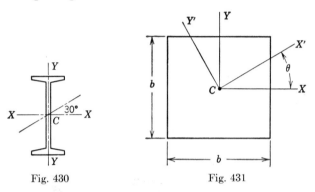

Fig. 430

Fig. 431

462. Show, by use of Eq. 314, that the moment of inertia of the area of a square is constant ($I'_x = I_x$ in Fig. 431) for all axes in the plane of the area that pass through the center C, and hence that every such axis is a principal axis.

463. In the Z section shown in Fig. 432, $\bar{I}_x = 25.32$ in.^{4} and $\bar{I}_y = 9.11$ in.^{4} Find the principal moments of inertia. *Ans.* 3.10 in.^{4}; 31.3 in.^{4}

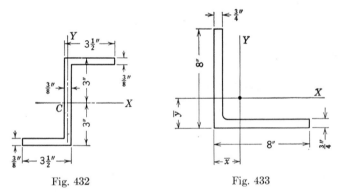

Fig. 432

Fig. 433

464. In the angle section shown in Fig. 433, $a = 11.44$ sq in., $\bar{x} = \bar{y} = 2.28$ in., $\bar{I}_x = \bar{I}_y = 69.7$ in.^{4} Locate the principal axes of inertia, and calculate the principal moments of inertia. Also determine the minimum radius of gyration.
Ans. $I_{\max} = 111.2$ in.^{4}, $I_{\min} = 28.2$ in.^{4}, $k_{\min} = 1.57$ in.

166. Graphical solution. Let the moments of inertia I_x and I_y and the product of inertia I_{xy} of an area a with respect to a given set of rectangular axes OX and OY in the area be known (Fig. 434a); and let it be required to find the moments of inertia I'_x and I'_y, and the product of inertia I'_{xy}, with respect to another set of rectangular axes OX' and OY', passing through the same point in the area, in terms of the known values I_x, I_y, I_{xy}, and the angle θ between the axes OX and OX'.

Equations 314, 315, and 316 give the algebraic expressions for I'_x, I'_y, and I'_{xy}, and it will now be shown that the equations may be solved graphically as follows by use of the Mohr-Land Construction (Fig. 434).

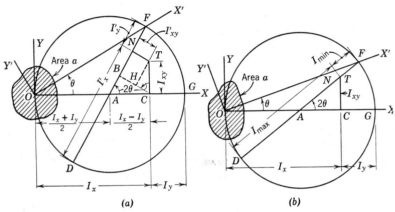

Fig. 434

Mohr-Land Construction. Figure 434a is also frequently called the *dyadic circle*. It is constructed as follows:

1. On OX lay off $OC = I_x$ and $CG = I_y$; $I_x > I_y$.
2. Lay off $CT = I_{xy}$ parallel to OY ($+$ upward, $-$ downward).
3. On OG as a diameter, draw a circle; A is the center.
4. Draw OX', making the given angle θ with OX, cutting the circle at F.
5. Draw the diameter FD, and draw TN perpendicular to FD. Then $DN = I'_x$, $NF = I'_y$, and $NT = I'_{xy}$.

Proof. Draw $CB \perp$ to DF; $TH \perp$ to CB. The first part of our proof concerns I'_x. From Fig. 434a, we have

$$I'_x = DN = DA + AB + BN \tag{321}$$

To prove that Eq. 321 is true, we show that the quantities DA, AB, and BN are equal, respectively, to the corresponding terms in the right side of Eq. 319. Taking DA first, we note in Fig. 434a that

$$DA = OA = \frac{I_x + I_y}{2}$$

which is the first term on the right side of Eq. 319. Taking AB next, we see from triangle ABC that

$$AB = AC \cos 2\theta = \frac{I_x - I_y}{2} \cos 2\theta$$

which is the second term on the right side of Eq. 319. Lastly, from triangle HTC, we note that

$$BN = HT = CT \sin 2\theta = I_{xy} \sin 2\theta$$

which is the last (third) term on the right side of Eq. 319. Therefore, by the substitution of these three quantities, respectively, for DA, AB and BN in Eq. 321, we find that this equation becomes

$$I'_x = \frac{I_x + I_y}{2} + \frac{I_x - I_y}{2} \cos 2\theta + I_{xy} \sin 2\theta$$

which is the same as Eq. 319; this proves that DN in Fig. 434a does represent the value of I'_x.

Starting in a similar manner, from Fig. 434a we find that

$$I'_y = NF = AF - AB - BN \tag{322}$$

Since $AF = OA = (I_x + I_y)/2$, and, since the quantities representing AB and BN have already been determined, we find, by the substitution of these quantities in Eq. 322, that

$$I'_y = \frac{I_x + I_y}{2} - \frac{I_x - I_y}{2} \cos 2\theta - I_{xy} \sin 2\theta$$

which is the same as Eq. 315.

Finally, from Fig. 434a, we find that

$$I'_{xy} = NT = CB - CH$$

But $CB = (I_x - I_y)/2 \sin 2\theta$ and $CH = I_{xy} \cos 2\theta$. Therefore,

$$I'_{xy} = \frac{I_x - I_y}{2} \sin 2\theta - I_{xy} \cos 2\theta$$

which is identical with Eq. 316.

Principal Axes. Draw a diameter DF through T (Fig. 434b), thus making $I'_{xy} = 0$ (see Art. 165). Then $DN = I_{\max}$ and $NF = I_{\min}$ are the principal moments of inertia, and OX' and OY' in Fig. 434b are the directions of the principal axes of inertia of the area a with respect to the point O.

Appendix II

PROPERTIES OF ROLLED-STEEL SECTIONS

Note. The tables given here are not complete. They are intended to illustrate the type of material that may be found in handbooks and are included in this book for convenience in solving problems. Similar tables for aluminum-alloy structural sections are found in *Structural Handbook of Aluminum Company of America.*

TABLE A

PROPERTIES

OF

CHANNELS

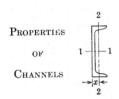

Depth of Channel	Weight per Foot	Area of Section	Width of Flange	Thickness of Web	Axis 1-1			Axis 2-2			
					I	r	I/c	I	r	I/c	x
In.	Lb.	In.²	In.	In.	In.⁴	In.	In.³	In.⁴	In.	In.³	In.
15	55.0	16.11	3.814	0.814	429.0	5.16	57.2	12.1	0.87	4.1	0.82
15	45.0	13.17	3.618	0.618	373.9	5.33	49.8	10.3	0.88	3.6	0.79
15	33.9	9.90	3.400	0.400	312.6	5.62	41.7	8.2	0.91	3.2	0.79
12	40.0	11.73	3.415	0.755	196.5	4.09	32.8	6.6	0.75	2.5	0.72
12	20.7	6.03	2.940	0.280	128.1	4.61	21.4	3.9	0.81	1.7	0.70
10	35.0	10.27	3.180	0.820	115.2	3.34	23.0	4.6	0.67	1.9	0.69
10	15.3	4.47	2.600	0.240	66.9	3.87	13.4	2.3	0.72	1.2	0.64
9	25.0	7.33	2.812	0.612	70.5	3.10	15.7	3.0	0.64	1.4	0.61
9	13.4	3.89	2.430	0.230	47.3	3.49	10.5	1.8	0.67	0.97	0.61
8	21.25	6.23	2.619	0.579	47.6	2.77	11.9	2.2	0.60	1.1	0.59
8	11.5	3.36	2.260	0.220	32.3	3.10	8.1	1.3	0.63	0.79	0.58
7	19.75	5.79	2.509	0.629	33.1	2.39	9.4	1.8	0.56	0.96	0.58
7	9.8	2.85	2.090	0.210	21.1	2.72	6.0	0.98	0.59	0.63	0.55
6	15.5	4.54	2.279	0.559	19.5	2.07	6.5	1.3	0.53	0.73	0.55
6	8.2	2.39	1.920	0.200	13.0	2.34	4.3	0.70	0.54	0.50	0.52
5	11.5	3.36	2.032	0.472	10.4	1.76	4.1	0.82	0.49	0.54	0.51
5	6.7	1.95	1.750	0.190	7.4	1.95	3.0	0.48	0.50	0.38	0.49
4	7.25	2.12	1.720	0.320	4.5	1.47	2.3	0.44	0.46	0.35	0.46
4	5.4	1.56	1.580	0.180	3.8	1.56	1.9	0.32	0.45	0.29	0.46
3	6.0	1.75	1.596	0.356	2.1	1.08	1.4	0.31	0.42	0.27	0.46
3	4.1	1.19	1.410	0.170	1.6	1.17	1.1	0.20	0.41	0.21	0.44

TABLE B

PROPERTIES

OF

I BEAMS

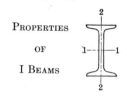

Depth of Beam	Weight per Foot	Area of Section	Width of Flange	Thickness of Web	Axis 1–1			Axis 2–2		
					I	r	I/c	I	r	I/c
In.	Lb.	In.²	In.	In.	In.⁴	In.	In.³	In.⁴	In.	In.³
27	90.0	26.34	9.000	0.524	2958.3	10.60	219.1	75.3	1.69	16.7
24	120.0	35.13	8.048	0.798	3010.8	9.26	250.9	84.9	1.56	21.1
24	79.9	23.33	7.000	0.500	2087.2	9.46	173.9	42.9	1.36	12.2
24	74.2	21.70	9.000	0.476	1950.1	9.48	162.5	61.2	1.68	13.6
21	60.4	17.68	8.250	0.428	1235.5	8.36	117.7	43.5	1.57	10.6
20	100.0	29.20	7.273	0.873	1648.3	7.51	164.8	52.4	1.34	14.4
20	65.4	19.08	6.250	0.500	1169.5	7.83	116.9	27.9	1.21	8.9
18	90.0	26.29	7.236	0.796	1256.5	6.91	139.6	51.9	1.40	14.3
18	54.7	15.94	6.000	0.460	795.5	7.07	88.4	21.2	1.15	7.1
18	48.2	14.09	7.500	0.380	737.1	7.23	81.9	30.0	1.46	8.0
15	75.0	21.85	6.278	0.868	687.2	5.61	91.6	30.6	1.18	9.8
15	42.9	12.49	5.500	0.410	441.8	5.95	58.9	14.6	1.08	5.3
15	37.3	10.91	6.750	0.332	405.5	6.10	54.1	19.9	1.35	5.9
12	55.0	16.04	5.600	0.810	319.3	4.46	53.2	17.3	1.04	6.2
12	40.8	11.84	5.250	0.460	268.9	4.77	44.8	13.8	1.08	5.3
12	31.8	9.26	5.000	0.350	215.8	4.83	36.0	9.5	1.01	3.8
12	27.9	8.15	6.000	0.284	199.4	4.95	33.2	12.6	1.24	4.2
10	40.0	11.69	5.091	0.741	158.0	3.68	31.6	9.4	0.90	3.7
10	30.0	8.75	4.797	0.447	133.5	3.91	26.7	7.6	0.93	3.2
10	25.4	7.38	4.660	0.310	122.1	4.07	24.4	6.9	0.97	3.0
10	22.4	6.54	5.500	0.252	113.6	4.17	22.7	9.0	1.17	3.3
9	35.0	10.22	4.764	0.724	111.3	3.30	24.7	7.3	0.84	3.0
9	30.0	8.76	4.601	0.561	101.4	3.40	22.5	6.4	0.85	2.8
9	21.8	6.32	4.330	0.290	84.9	3.67	18.9	5.2	0.90	2.4
8	25.5	7.43	4.262	0.532	68.1	3.03	17.0	4.7	0.80	2.2
8	18.4	5.34	4.000	0.270	56.9	3.26	14.2	3.8	0.84	1.9
7	20.0	5.83	3.860	0.450	41.9	2.68	12.0	3.1	0.74	1.6
7	15.3	4.43	3.660	0.250	36.2	2.86	10.4	2.7	0.78	1.5
6	17.25	5.02	3.565	0.465	26.0	2.28	8.7	2.3	0.68	1.3
6	12.5	3.61	3.330	0.230	21.8	2.46	7.3	1.8	0.72	1.1
5	10.0	2.87	3.000	0.210	12.1	2.05	4.8	1.2	0.65	0.82
4	10.5	3.05	2.870	0.400	7.1	1.52	3.5	1.0	0.57	0.70
3	7.5	2.17	2.509	0.349	2.9	1.15	1.9	0.59	0.52	0.47
3	5.7	1.64	2.330	0.170	2.5	1.23	1.7	0.46	0.53	0.40

TABLE C

PROPERTIES

OF EQUAL

ANGLES

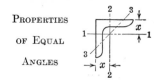

Size	Weight per Foot	Area of Section	Axis 1–1 and Axis 2–2				Axis 3–3*
			I	r	I/c	x	r
Inches	Lb.	In.²	In.⁴	In.	In.³	In.	In.
8 ×8 ×1⅛	56.9	16.73	98.0	2.42	17.5	2.41	1.55
8 ×8 × ½	26.4	7.75	48.6	2.51	8.4	2.19	1.58
6 ×6 ×1	37.4	11.00	35.5	1.80	8.6	1.86	1.16
6 ×6 × ⅜	14.9	4.36	15.4	1.88	3.5	1.64	1.19
5 ×5 ×1	30.6	9.00	19.6	1.48	5.8	1.61	0.96
5 ×5 × ⅜	12.3	3.61	8.7	1.56	2.4	1.39	0.99
4 ×4 ×¹³⁄₁₆	19.9	5.84	8.1	1.18	3.0	1.29	0.77
4 ×4 × ¼	6.6	1.94	3.0	1.25	1.0	1.09	0.79
3½×3½×¹³⁄₁₆	17.1	5.03	5.3	1.02	2.3	1.17	0.67
3½×3½× ¼	5.8	1.69	2.0	1.09	0.79	0.97	0.69
3 ×3 × ⅝	11.5	3.36	2.6	0.88	1.3	0.98	0.57
3 ×3 × ½	9.4	2.75	2.2	0.90	1.1	0.93	0.58
3 ×3 × ⅜	7.2	2.11	1.8	0.91	0.83	0.89	0.58
3 ×3 × ¼	4.9	1.44	1.2	0.93	0.58	0.84	0.59
2½×2½× ½	7.7	2.25	1.2	0.74	0.73	0.81	0.47
2½×2½× ⅛	2.08	0.61	0.38	0.79	0.20	0.67	0.50
2 ×2 × ⁷⁄₁₆	5.3	1.56	0.54	0.59	0.40	0.66	0.39
2 ×2 × ⅛	1.65	0.48	0.19	0.63	0.13	0.55	0.40
1½×1½× ⅜	3.35	0.98	0.19	0.44	0.19	0.51	0.29
1½×1½× ⅛	1.23	0.36	0.08	0.46	0.07	0.42	0.30
1 ×1 × ¼	1.49	0.44	0.04	0.29	0.06	0.34	0.19
1 ×1 × ⅛	0.80	0.23	0.02	0.31	0.03	0.30	0.19

* Axis 3–3 is the principal axis about which the radius of gyration is least.

$I = a r^2$

TABLE D

Properties

OF

Unequal Angles

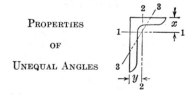

Size	Weight per Foot	Area of Section	Axis 1-1				Axis 2-2				Axis 3-3*
			I	r	I/c	x	I	r	I/c	y	r
Inches	Lb.	In.²	In.⁴	In.	In.³	In.	In.⁴	In.	In.³	In.	In.
8 ×6 ×1	44.2	13.00	80.8	2.49	15.1	2.65	38.8	1.73	8.9	1.65	1.28
8 ×6 × 7/16	20.2	5.93	39.2	2.57	7.1	2.45	19.3	1.80	4.2	1.45	1.30
8 ×3½×1	35.7	10.50	66.2	2.51	13.7	3.17	7.8	0.86	3.0	0.92	0.73
8 ×3½× 7/16	16.5	4.84	32.5	2.59	6.4	2.95	4.1	0.92	1.5	0.70	0.74
7 ×3½×1	32.3	9.50	45.4	2.19	10.6	2.70	7.5	0.89	3.0	0.96	0.74
7 ×3½× 3/8	13.0	3.80	19.6	2.27	4.3	2.48	3.5	0.96	1.3	0.73	0.76
6 ×4 ×1	30.6	9.00	30.8	1.85	8.0	2.17	10.8	1.09	3.8	1.17	0.85
6 ×4 × 3/8	12.3	3.61	13.5	1.93	3.3	1.94	4.9	1.17	1.6	0.94	0.88
6 ×3½×1	28.9	8.50	29.2	1.85	7.8	2.26	7.2	0.92	2.9	1.01	0.74
6 ×3½× 5/16	9.8	2.87	10.9	1.95	2.7	2.01	2.9	1.00	1.0	0.76	0.77
5 ×4 × 7/8	24.2	7.11	16.4	1.52	5.0	1.71	9.2	1.14	3.3	1.21	0.84
5 ×4 × 3/8	11.0	3.23	8.1	1.59	2.3	1.53	4.7	1.20	1.6	1.03	0.86
5 ×3½× 7/8	22.7	6.67	15.7	1.53	4.9	1.79	6.2	0.96	2.5	1.04	0.75
5 ×3½× 5/16	8.7	2.56	6.6	1.61	1.9	1.59	2.7	1.03	1.0	0.84	0.76
5 ×3½× ½	13.6	4.00	10.0	1.58	3.0	1.66	4.0	1.01	1.6	0.91	0.75
5 ×3 ×13/16	19.9	5.84	14.0	1.55	4.5	1.86	3.7	0.80	1.7	0.86	0.64
5 ×3 × 5/16	8.2	2.40	6.3	1.61	1.9	1.68	1.8	0.85	0.75	0.68	0.66
4½×3 ×13/16	18.5	5.43	10.3	1.38	3.6	1.65	3.6	0.81	1.7	0.90	0.64
4½×3 × 5/16	7.7	2.25	4.7	1.44	1.5	1.47	1.7	0.87	0.75	0.72	0.66
4 ×3½×13/16	18.5	5.43	7.8	1.19	2.9	1.36	5.5	1.01	2.3	1.11	0.72
4 ×3½× 5/16	7.7	2.25	3.6	1.26	1.3	1.18	2.6	1.07	1.0	0.93	0.73
4 ×3 ×13/16	17.1	5.03	7.3	1.21	2.9	1.44	3.5	0.83	1.7	0.94	0.64
4 ×3 × ¼	5.8	1.69	2.8	1.28	1.0	1.24	1.4	0.89	0.60	0.74	0.65
3½×3 ×13/16	15.8	4.62	5.0	1.04	2.2	1.23	3.3	0.85	1.7	0.98	0.62
3½×3 × ¼	5.4	1.56	1.9	1.11	0.78	1.04	1.3	0.91	0.58	0.79	0.63
3 ×2½× 9/16	9.5	2.78	2.3	0.91	1.2	1.02	1.4	0.72	0.82	0.77	0.52
3 ×2½× ¼	4.5	1.31	1.2	0.95	0.56	0.91	0.74	0.75	0.40	0.66	0.53
3 ×2 × ½	7.7	2.25	1.9	0.92	1.0	1.08	0.67	0.55	0.47	0.58	0.43
3 ×2 × ¼	4.1	1.19	1.1	0.95	0.54	0.99	0.39	0.57	0.25	0.49	0.43
2½×2 × ½	6.8	2.00	1.1	0.75	0.70	0.88	0.64	0.56	0.46	0.63	0.42
2½×2 × ⅛	1.86	0.55	0.35	0.80	0.20	0.74	0.20	0.61	0.13	0.49	0.43
2 ×1½× 3/8	3.99	1.17	0.43	0.61	0.34	0.71	0.21	0.42	0.20	0.46	0.32
2 ×1½× ⅛	1.44	0.42	0.17	0.64	0.13	0.62	0.09	0.45	0.08	0.37	0.33

* Axis 3-3 is the principal axis about which the radius of gyration is least.

Index

455